VOLUME 2

NONLINEAR AND
MULTIVARIATE THEORY

# The Approximation
# of Functions

This book is in the

**ADDISON-WESLEY SERIES IN**

**COMPUTER SCIENCE AND INFORMATION PROCESSING**

---

*Consulting Editors*

RICHARD S. VARGA AND MICHAEL A. HARRISON

VOLUME 2

NONLINEAR AND
MULTIVARIATE THEORY

# The Approximation
# of Functions

*by*

**JOHN R. RICE**

*Purdue University*

ADDISON-WESLEY PUBLISHING COMPANY

READING, MASSACHUSETTS . MENLO PARK, CALIFORNIA
LONDON · DON MILLS, ONTARIO

# Preface

This second volume continues the main theme of the first, namely the study of approximation of a function $f(x)$ by an approximating function $F(A, x)$ with a finite number of parameters $A = (a_1, a_2, \ldots, a_n)$. The central problem is to determine those parameters $A^*$ so that $F(A^*, x)$ approximates $f(x)$ best in some sense. The analysis of this problem requires us to consider the existence, uniqueness and characteristic properties of best approximations. The solution of this problem requires us to consider computational methods. These are the four main topics of this volume.

As usual with monographs at this level, the specific topics selected reflect the author's interest and personal preference. The first volume is entitled "Linear Theory" and this implies, correctly, that most of this second volume is concerned with nonlinear problems. There is one chapter on multivariate approximation problems which is essentially a linear theory.

The first chapter contains a study of varisolvent approximating functions. This is a general class of nonlinear approximating functions for which one can develop a "Tchebycheff type" theory of approximation. A number of specific nonlinear approximating functions, e.g. rationals and exponentials, belong to this class. The main points of the theory (in particular uniqueness and alternation theorems) are developed quickly in the first part of the chapter. The remainder of the chapter is concerned with a detailed analysis which shows that these are the "only" approximating functions for which there is a Tchebycheff type theory, e.g. an alternation theorem.

The next three chapters consider three specific classes of nonlinear approximating functions. In Chapter 8 we consider $F(A, x)$ of the form $\sum a_i \gamma(t_i, x)$ where the $\{a_i, t_i\}$ are parameters. The specific choice of $\gamma(t, x) = e^{tx}$ leads to exponential approximation. Other interesting cases arise by taking $\gamma(t, x) = x^t$ or $(1 + xt)^{-1}$ or $(x - t)_+^n$. The exponential approximation problem is particularly intractable in computation and the discussion of computational methods is rudimentary. A successful attack on this problem is one of the more challenging problems in computational methods of approximation.

Rational approximation is by far the best understood nonlinear approximation problem. This is partly due to the fact that it is more tractable (a number of results can be obtained by linear methods) and partly because it has received the most attention. The theory of both polynomial and "generalized" rational approximation is presented in detail. A wide variety of

v

computational methods has been proposed for rational approximation. The most widely used (and probably the best) methods are variations of the Remes algorithm. A general development of this algorithm is given which allows one to obtain (by making various assumptions and approximations) many of these variations (both old and new). Three other methods of particular interest are also discussed.

Approximation by piecewise-polynomial spline functions is presented in Chapter 10. Splines are of recent origin and there are still gaps in this theory. However, spline functions are extremely versatile in applications and, in addition, have some important theoretical properties. Some of these properties are developed in a section on "optimal approximation of linear functionals." The final section of this chapter discusses computational methods based on the work of Carl de Boor for both linear and nonlinear spline approximation.

An examination of the results on these preceding specific nonlinear approximating functions shows that much of the linear theory does not carry over. It is natural to ask whether this is a general property of nonlinear approximation. This leads to the study of abstract nonlinear approximation in Chapter 11. This theory is essentially geometric in nature and is set entirely in finite dimensional spaces. Even in these spaces, there are considerable difficulties and a number of open questions. A good deal of the chapter is devoted to a study of uniqueness and the conclusion is reached that nonlinearity of $F(A, x)$ entails (in "nice" spaces) a lack of a general uniqueness theorem for best approximations.

Multivariate approximation tends to be simple in theory and difficult in practice. For example, the theory of $L_2$-approximation here is identical with the univariate theory. Part of the practical difficulty comes from the inevitable increase in the "size" of the problems and part comes from the inability to handle complicated shapes of regions. It is pointed out how tensor products can be exploited for rectangular regions in several variables. One of the most successful techniques for applications is to embed the problem into one where tensor products can be used. The bulk of the chapter considers the uniqueness (or lack of it) for Tchebycheff approximation. Once this difficulty can be handled, then one can develop both theory and computational methods.

The final chapter considers in depth the relationship between interpolation and best approximation. The basic work in this area is due to T. S. Motzkin and J. L. Walsh and they have obtained some striking results. Many of their results have been extended to certain nonlinear problems by the author and these are given also. The final section presents the Lawson algorithm for the computation of $L_\infty$-approximations by means of a sequence of weighted $L_2$-approximations. This algorithm has considerable promise for several problems for which Tchebycheff approximation is, so far, intractable.

I would like to express my gratitude to the General Motors Research Laboratories for encouraging this work. Two of these chapters were originally drafted in 1963 while I was there. I would also like to express my gratitude to the Air Force Office of Scientific Research which partially supported me during the academic year 1965–66 under contract AF(639)–1616. During this time the final three chapters (10, 11 and 12) were drafted and the others were revised. I also express my thanks to Carl de Boor, William Cody and John Hoff who read parts of the manuscript and offered valuable suggestions.

*West Lafayette, Indiana*
*October 1968*

J.R.R.

*To my parents*
*Margaret L. and John C. K. Rice*

# Contents

# 7

# Varisolvent Functions

## 7-1 INTRODUCTION

It is natural in all science to endeavor to push back the frontiers of the unknown. A very natural frontier in approximation theory (as in many other branches of mathematics) is the passage from the linear theory to a nonlinear theory. This passage has been a difficult barrier in approximation theory (again as in many other branches of mathematics). At the time of this writing the most significant advance beyond the linear theory has occurred in the theory of Tchebycheff approximation (though more efficient methods of nonlinear descent may soon invalidate this statement). A later chapter presents the first tentative form of an abstract theory of nonlinear approximation.

The first important step toward a nonlinear theory was made independently by Motzkin (1949) and Tornheim (1950). Though part of the theory of Tchebycheff approximation by rational functions is classical, the classical results are obtained by methods essentially of the linear theory. The equivalent concepts of unisolvent functions and $n$-parameter families are discussed in Section 3–7. Unfortunately, this theory has not been useful in practice because the usual nonlinear approximating functions are not unisolvent. Furthermore, it has been shown (Rice, 1960) that unisolvent functions are the only approximating functions satisfying a certain closure hypothesis to which the elegant linear theory may be extended. Thus, any theory of nonlinear Tchebycheff approximation which includes some common approximating functions must sacrifice some part of the linear theory.

A more useful nonlinear theory must include some of the elementary nonlinear approximating functions. Hence in order to obtain a clue as to the direction to proceed, it is natural to examine closely some known examples. For rational approximations the number of alternations to characterize a best approximation is variable. From Theorem 3–9 it is seen that this number varies only as a function of the parameters, and is completely independent of the function $f(x)$ being approximated, or the interval upon which the approximation is to be made. This suggests defining a *degree* (dependent only on the parameters) of an abstract approximating function so that the following statement is valid: $F(A^*, x)$ *is a best approximation*

1

to $f(x)$ *if and only if* $F(A^*, x) - f(x)$ *alternates at least* $m(A^*)$ *times where* $m(A^*)$ *is the degree of* $F$ *at* $A^*$. This statement is valid for rational approximations, and one can easily convince oneself that it is valid for approximation by $ab^x + c$. With these two examples accounted for, one feels that this is the clue needed for a more useful nonlinear theory.

A careful examination of rational functions and $ab^x + c$ shows that the validity of the above statement follows from two properties of the functions. Both of these are natural extensions of the properties of unisolvent functions. The first of these is Property Z, where the number of allowable zeros *varies* with the parameters. The second is a solvence property that is defined only locally (i.e. in a neighborhood of a given approximating function) rather than globally as is the case for unisolvent functions. Furthermore, the number of points at which one can "solve" *varies* with the parameters, and this number is the same number as for Property Z. One may now abstractly define a *varisolvent approximating function* as any approximating function with these two properties. The details of this are presented in the next section.

With the knowledge that there are at least two desirable examples of varisolvent functions, one may proceed to develop the various aspects of the theory of approximation by varisolvent functions. This is done in Sections 7–3 through 7–5.

It is of great interest to know whether varisolvent functions are the only functions that have a *degree* which gives a characteristic number of alternations of best approximation. If there were other functions with this degree one would want to include them in the theory also. This question corresponds to the problems studied in Chapter 3 (Vol. 1) on the limits of a Tchebycheff type theory. In Sections 7–6 through 7–9 the limits of this varisolvent type theory are discussed in detail. The main conclusions are as follows:

(a) if $F(A, x)$ is only assumed to be a continuous function, then the set of approximating functions which allow a varisolvent type theory are all those functions with a certain Property $A$. Property $A$ is quite complicated.

(b) if one assumes in addition that the set

$$\{F(A, x) \mid \max |F(A, x)| \leq M\}$$

is compact and arcwise connected, then it is shown that only varisolvent approximating functions allow a varisolvent type theory (Rice, 1960).

(c) the only approximating functions which allow a theory analogous to the linear theory are the *locally unisolvent* functions (Rice, 1964C).

The final section of the chapter contains a list of some known and conjectured varisolvent functions and a discussion of some of the difficulties associated with these approximating functions. Approximation with a Tchebycheff norm is considered throughout this chapter and we write $\|f - g\|$ for

$$\max_{x \in [0, 1]} |f(x) - g(x)|$$

whenever there is no chance of ambiguity.

## 7–2 VARISOLVENT FUNCTIONS

The real function $F(A, x)$ is defined for $x \in [0, 1]$ and $A \in P$ where $P$ is the parameter space. $F$ is continuous in the sense that given $A_0 \in P$, $x_0 \in [0, 1]$ and $\epsilon > 0$, then there is a $\delta > 0$ such that for $A \in P$, $x \in [0, 1]$, $\|A_0 - A\| + |x_0 - x| < \delta$ then we have

$$|F(A_0, x_0) - F(A, x)| < \epsilon.$$

There are two essential properties of unisolvent functions which need to be generalized so as to have variable degree. These are solvence, Definition 3–5, and Property Z, Definition 3–4. Property Z has a very simple generalization as follows:

**Definition 7–1.** *F has Property Z of degree m at $A^* \in P$ if for $A \neq A^*$, $F(A^*, x) - F(A, x)$ has at most $m - 1$ zeros for $x \in [0, 1]$.*

Property Z is a global property in the sense that $F(A^*, x)$ is compared with all of the elements represented in $P$. The definition of solvence for unisolvent functions is also a global property. An examination of the examples of the previous section shows that there is no global solving ability present. Thus any abstract definition to generalize solvence must be local in nature if we are to include these examples in our theory. In particular an examination of these examples shows that we can solve in the neighborhood of a particular function $F(A^*, x)$ and at a certain number of $x$ values. The number of $x$ values and the size of the neighborhood are seen to depend on the particular function $F(A^*, x)$.

This leads naturally to the following generalization of solvence:

**Definition 7–2.** *F is locally solvent of degree m at $A^* \in P$ if given a set $\{x_j \mid 0 \leq x_1 < x_2 < \cdots < x_m \leq 1\}$ and $\epsilon > 0$, then there is a $\delta(A^*, \epsilon, x_1, \ldots, x_m) > 0$ such that $|Y_j - F(A^*, x_j)| < \delta$ implies that there exists a solution $A \in P$ to the system*

$$F(A, x_j) = Y_j, \qquad j = 1, 2, \ldots, m$$

*with*

$$\| F(A, x) - F(A^*, x)\| < \epsilon.$$

A *varisolvent function* is a function $F$ which possesses both of these properties (with the same degree) for each $A \in P$. Thus $F$ has Property $Z$ of degree $m$ at $A^*$, and $F$ is solvent of degree $m$ at $A^*$. The *degree of $F$ at $A^*$* is the common degree of Property $Z$ and local solvence and is denoted throughout this chapter by $m(A^*)$. It is assumed that $m(A)$ is *uniformly bounded* in $P$.

In the remainder of this section we consider some properties of varisolvent functions which are not specifically related to approximation theory, but are rather properties which would enter into any type of analysis involving varisolvent functions. The first of these properties involves zeros. In Definition 7–1 the term zero has its most elementary meaning, without regard to multiplicity. For a continuous function one can very easily define zeros of multiplicities 1 and 2. A zero $x_0$ is said to be a simple zero (of multiplicity 1) if $f(x)$ changes sign at $x_0$ and a double zero (of multiplicity 2) if $f(x)$ does not change sign at $x_0$. Zeros of higher multiplicity are not considered in this chapter. The following lemma shows that Definition 7–1 is valid when multiplicity is taken into account.

**Lemma 7–1.** *Let $F$ be varisolvent of degree $m(A^*)$ at $A^* \in P$. Then the sum of the multiplicities of the zeros of $F(A^*, x) - F(A, x)$ cannot exceed $m(A^*) - 1$.*

*Proof.* Let $\{x_j \mid j = 1, 2, \dots, k\}$ be the set of zeros of $F(A^*, x) - F(A, x)$. The degree of $F$ at $A$ is then at least $k + 1$. Assume, for concreteness, that $x_1$ is a double zero and $F(A, x) - F(A^*, x) > 0$ near $x_1$. Since the degree of $F$ is at least $k + 1$ at $A$, there is for any $\epsilon > 0$ an $A_1 \in P$ such that

$$F(A_1, x_j) = F(A, x_j), \qquad j = 2, \dots, k$$

$$F(A_1, x_1) < F(A, x_1)$$

$$\| F(A_1, x) - F(A, x) \| < \epsilon$$

For $\epsilon$ sufficiently small it is clear that

    (a)   every double zero of $F(A, x) - F(A^*, x)$ is either a double zero of $F(A_1, x) - F(A^*, x)$ or has been replaced by two simple zeros;

    (b)   every simple zero of $F(A, x) - F(A^*, x)$ is a simple zero of $F(A_1, x) - F(A^*, x)$ and

    (c)   $F(A_1, x) - F(A^*, x)$ has two simple zeros near $x_1$.

Hence the number of simple zeros of $F(A_1, x) - F(A^*, x)$ is at least one more than the number of simple zeros of $F(A, x) - F(A^*, x)$. This process may be continued to obtain $A_n \in P$ such that $F(A_n, x) - F(A^*, x)$ has at least as many simple zeros as $F(A, x) - F(A^*, x)$ has zeros, counting multiplicity. This concludes the proof.

When speaking of varisolvent functions, one can associate with each function $F(A, x)$ the point $A$ in $P$. Since $P$ may be visualized as being in

$E_n$, one is tempted to tacitly apply the topology of $E_n$ to the set

$$\{F(A, x) \mid A \in P\}.$$

For many examples, however, this topology is completely unsuitable. When one considers the approximating function

$$E(a, b, c, d, x) = \begin{cases} ab^x + c; \ |a| < \infty, |c| < \infty; \ 0 < b < \infty \text{ with } b \neq 1 \\ c + dx; \ b = 1, |c| < \infty, |d| < \infty, \end{cases}$$

it is very difficult to define any sort of topology on $E_4$ which induces a meaningful topology for the set $\{E(A, x)\}$. The conclusion to be drawn from this discussion is that the topology must be defined on the set $\{E(A, x)\}$ itself. This topology is induced on the parameter set $P$ by the simple convention that $A_1$ is close to $A_2$ if $F(A_1, x)$ is close to $F(A_2, x)$. For the purposes of this chapter the natural topology to use for $\{F(A, x) | A \in P\}$ is to define the open $\epsilon$-sphere about $F(A^*, x)$ as the set:

$$\{F(A, x) \mid \| F(A, x) - F(A^*, x)\| < \epsilon\}. \tag{7-2.1}$$

This definition of the topology is extended naturally to $P$ by defining the open $\epsilon$-sphere about $A^*$ as the set

$$\{A \mid \| F(A, x) - F(A^*, x)\| < \epsilon\}. \tag{7-2.2}$$

The next theorem shows an interesting topological property of the set $P$. This property follows directly from Definitions 7-1 and 7-2, though for particular examples of varisolvent functions the property can be established more directly.

**Theorem 7-1.** *Let $F$ be a varisolvent function.*

*Define* $\qquad\qquad P_k = \{A \mid A \in P, m(A) \geq k\}.$

*Then $P_k$ is an open set.*

*Proof.* Let $A^* \in P_k$ be given. Since the degree of solvence of $F$ at $A^*$ is at least $k$, there is an $A_1 \in P$ such that $F(A^*, x) - F(A_1, x)$ has $k - 1$ (at least) simple zeros in the interior of $[0, 1]$. Let

$$\{x_j \mid j = 1, 2, \ldots, k - 1, x_j < x_{j+1}\}$$

be the set of these zeros, and set $x_0 = 0$, $x_k = 1$. Let

$$\delta = \min_{j} \ \max_{x \in [x_j, x_{j+1}]} \ |F(A^*, x) - F(A_1, x)|, \qquad j = 0, 1, 2, \ldots, k - 1.$$

Now if for any $A \in P$ we have $\| F(A, x) - F(A^*, x)\| < \delta$, then $F(A, x) - F(A_1, x)$ has at least $k - 1$ zeros. This implies that the degree of $A$ is at least $k$, and thus the set $P_k$ contains the open $\epsilon$-sphere

$$\{A \mid \| F(A, x) - F(A^*, x) \| < \delta\}$$

about $A^*$. This concludes the proof.

The situation often arises in analysis where one has an infinite collection of objects, and one would like to assert that the collection has an accumulation point. The simplest result of this nature asserts that an infinite bounded sequence of real numbers contains a convergent subsequence. The following theorem from the theory of real variables allows a similar conclusion to be drawn about sequences of varisolvent functions.

**Theorem 7–2.** *Let $\{f_\alpha(x)\}$ be a uniformly bounded infinite set of functions continuous on $[0, 1]$ with Property Z of fixed degree. Then $\{f_\alpha(x)\}$ contains a pointwise convergent subsequence.*

This theorem was first established by Rice (1960). The technique of proof is not one of approximation theory, but the theorem is essential in the study of the limits of a Tchebycheff type theory for varisolvent functions. The proof may be omitted without interrupting the continuity of this chapter.

The proof is by induction. The first two lemmas establish the theorem for Property Z of degrees 1 and 2. The third lemma considers a special situation where the induction is from $k$ to $k + 2$. In the final phase of the proof the induction is from $k$ to $k + 1$.

Throughout the proof when a sequence of functions is chosen whose function values converge at a particular point, it is always chosen so that the convergence is monotonic at that point.

**Lemma 7–2.** *Let $\{f_\alpha(x)\}$ be a uniformly bounded infinite set of functions continuous in $[0, 1]$ which are mutually nonintersecting. Then $\{f_\alpha(x)\}$ contains a pointwise convergent sequence.*

*Proof.* Consider $\{f_\alpha(0)\}$ which is a bounded set of real numbers and hence contains a convergent monotonic sequence $\{f_k(0) \mid k = 1, 2, \ldots\}$. Since $\{f_k(0)\}$ is monotonic so is $\{f_k(x)\}$ monotonic for every $x \in [0, 1]$. Since $\{f_k(x)\}$ is bounded it follows that $\{f_k(x)\}$ is convergent for every $x \in [0, 1]$.

**Lemma 7–3.** *Let $\{f_\alpha(x)\}$ be a uniformly bounded infinite set of functions continuous on $[0, 1]$ with Property Z of degree 2. Then $\{f_\alpha(x)\}$ contains a pointwise convergent sequence.*

*Proof.* For simplicity the sequences $f_{1l}(x), f_{2l}(x), \ldots$ and $g_{1l}(x), g_{2l}(x), \ldots$ are denoted by $F_l$ and $G_l$, and their limits at $x$ are denoted by $F_l(x)$ and $G_l(x)$ if these limits exist. If $F_l, G_l$ are monotonic at $x$, $F_l \subset G_l$ will be used to indicate that $F_l$ is a subsequence of $G_l$ with the order preserved.

Choose a sequence $F_0$ from $\{f_\alpha(x)\}$ such that $F_0$ converges monotonically at 0 and 1. If $F_0$ is increasing at both 0 and 1 or decreasing at both points then the functions of $\{f_{k0}(x)\}$ must be mutually nonintersecting, and Lemma 7–2 states that $F_0$ is a pointwise convergent sequence.

If $F_0$ converges in opposite directions at 0 and 1, then choose $F_1 \subset F_0$ such that $F_1(\frac{1}{2})$ exists. The direction of convergence of $F_1$ at $x = \frac{1}{2}$ must agree with the direction of convergence of $F_1$ at either 0 or 1. Hence a subsequence $G_1 \subset F_1$ may be chosen which is pointwise convergent in an interval of length $\frac{1}{2}$ as in Lemma 7–2.

Choose $F_2 \subset G_1$ so that $F_2$ converges at the midpoint of the remaining interval. Again the direction of convergence of $F_2$ at the midpoint must agree with the direction of convergence at one of the endpoints. As in Lemma 7–2 there is a subsequence $G_2 \subset F_2$ which is pointwise convergent except in an interval of length $\frac{1}{4}$.

In this way an infinite number of subsequences $G_1 \supset G_2 \supset \cdots \supset G_l \supset \cdots$ may be found where $G_l$ is pointwise convergent except possibly in an interval of length $2^{-l}$. The diagonal sequence of this sequence of sequences may be formed and it converges at all points of $[0, 1]$ with possibly one exception. In case the diagonal sequence fails to converge at one point then a further subsequence is chosen that converges there also.

**Lemma 7–4.** *Let $\{f_\alpha(x)\}$ be a uniformly bounded infinite set of functions continuous on $[0, 1]$ with Property Z of degree $n$ and such that for every $x \in [0, 1]$, every monotonic infinite sequence from $\{f_\alpha(x)\}$ is monotonic decreasing. Then $\{f_\alpha(x)\}$ contains a pointwise convergent sequence.*

*Proof.* The proof is by induction on the degree of Property $Z$. The lemma has been established for $k = 1$ and $k = 2$. It will be shown that if the lemma is true for Property $Z$ of degree $k$, then it is true for Property $Z$ of degree $k + 2$.

Select a sequence $F_0$ from $\{f_\alpha(x)\}$ which converges at $x = 0, \frac{1}{2}, 1$. $F_0$ is monotonically decreasing at these points. The assertion is now made that $F_0$ either has a subsequence which is convergent in $[0, \frac{1}{2}]$ or one which is convergent in $[\frac{1}{2}, 1]$.

Assume that there is no convergent subsequence in $[\frac{1}{2}, 1]$. Then there is an $x_1 \in [\frac{1}{2}, 1]$ such that $F_0(x_1)$ does not exist. Choose subsequences $F_1 \subset F_0$, $G_1 \subset F_0$ such that $F_1(x_1) < G_1(x_1)$. For some $k_1, f_{k_11}(x_1) < G_1(x_1)$, and therefore there is a subsequence $H_1 \subset G_1$ such that every function of $H_1$ intersects $f_{k_11}(x)$ in $(\frac{1}{2}, x_1)$ and $(x_1, 1)$.

$H_1$ does not converge in $[\frac{1}{2}, 1]$ and hence there is an $x_2$, say in $[x_1, 1]$, such that $H_1(x_2)$ does not exist. Choose $F_2 \subset H_1$, $G_2 \subset H_1$ such that $F_2(x_2) < G_2(x_2)$. Again for some $k_2$, $f_{k_22}(x_2) < G_2(x_2)$ and hence there is a subsequence $H_2 \subset G_2$ such that every function of $H_2$ intersects $f_{k_22}(x)$ in $(x_1, x_2)$ and $(x_2, 1)$.

In this way an infinite sequence $F_0^* = \{f_{k_l l}(x)|l = 1, 2, \ldots; f_{k_l l}(x) \in F_0\}$ is obtained such that every member of this sequence intersects every other member at least twice in $[\frac{1}{2}, 1]$. Therefore in $[0, \frac{1}{2}]$ $F_0^*$ has Property $Z$ of degree $n - 2$. The induction hypothesis is applied in $[0, \frac{1}{2}]$ to obtain a pointwise convergent subsequence $G_0^* \subset F_0^*$.

It has thus been shown that there is a sequence $G_0^*$ from $\{f_\alpha(x)\}$ which converges in an interval of length $\frac{1}{2}$. The entire construction is now repeated to obtain $G_1^* \subset G_0^*$ which converges in half of the remaining interval. Continuing in this way a sequence of sequences $G_0^* \supset G_1^* \supset \cdots$ is obtained which converge except in intervals of length $\frac{1}{2}, \frac{1}{4}, \ldots$. The diagonal process is used as in Lemma 7–3 to obtain a subsequence which is pointwise convergent in $[0, 1]$.

It is clear that this lemma is also true when "decreasing" is replaced by "increasing."

*Proof of Theorem* 7–2. The proof is by induction. The induction hypothesis is that the theorem is true for Property $Z$ of degree $k$. For $k = 1$ the theorem follows from Lemma 7–2.

It is assumed that $\{f_\alpha(x)\}$ has Property $Z$ of degree $k + 1$. If there is a subset of $\{f_\alpha(x)\}$ satisfying the assumptions of Lemma 7–4, the proof is complete. If there is no such subset, then there is a sequence $F_0$ from $\{f_\alpha(x)\}$ which has opposite directions of convergence at two points, $x_1$ and $x_2$. Let $A$ be the set of points in $[0, 1]$ such that all subsequences of $F_0$ are monotonic at these points. Since $A$ contains $x_1$ and $x_2$, it is nonvoid. If $A \neq [0, 1]$ then $x_3$ may be chosen in $A$ and $x_4$ not in $A$ such that $|x_3 - x_4|$ is arbitrarily small. If $A = [0, 1]$ then $A$ may be divided into two nonvoid sets; one with all increasing subsequences and one with all decreasing subsequences. Then $x_3$ may be chosen in the first set and $x_4$ in the second so that $|x_3 - x_4|$ is arbitrarily small. In either case there is a subsequence $F_1 \subset F_0$ and points $x_3, x_4 \in [0, 1]$ such that $F_1$ has opposite directions of convergence at $x_3$ and $x_4$ and $[x_3, x_4]$ has length less than $\frac{1}{2}$ (for concreteness we assume $x_3 < x_4$).

Since every member of $F_1$ intersects every other member of $F_1$ at least once in $[x_3, x_4]$, then in each of the intervals $[0, x_3]$ and $[x_4, 1]$, $F_1$ has Property $Z$ of degree $k$. By the induction hypothesis there is a subsequence $F_2 \subset F_1$ which converges pointwise in these intervals.

If $F_2$ satisfies the assumptions of Lemma 7–4 in $[x_3, x_4]$ the proof is complete. If not, a repetition of the above argument shows that there is a subsequence $F_3 \subset F_2$ which converges outside of $[x_5, x_6]$ where the length of $[x_5, x_6]$ is less than $\frac{1}{4}$.

This process is repeated to obtain an infinite number of sequences $F_1 \supset F_2 \supset \cdots \supset F_l \supset \cdots$ where $F_l$ is pointwise convergent except in an interval of length less than $2^{-l}$. The diagonal sequence may be taken as in

Lemma 7–3 to obtain a pointwise convergent sequence in $[0, 1]$. This concludes the proof.

## 7–3  EXISTENCE OF BEST APPROXIMATIONS

One of the fundamental questions in the approximation problem is the question of existence of best approximations. Up to this chapter this question has usually been rather simple. For linear approximating functions (see Chapter 1) there are classical methods for establishing the existence of best approximations. For unisolvent approximations, the assumption of a global solvence (see Chapter 3) is sufficient to establish the existence of best approximations. The only real difficulty (so far) is for rational functions.

The assumption that $F$ is a varisolvent function is *not* sufficient to establish the existence of best approximations. Thus the existence of best approximations (if present) must follow from some additional property of the particular approximating function. Since the existence of best approximations is such a desirable property, one normally extends the definition of the approximating function to ensure this property. Theorem 7–2 indicates how this should be done. The problem is to ensure the existence of $F(A^*, x)$ so that, in the Tchebycheff norm,

$$\| F(A^*, x) - f(x) \| = \inf_{A \, \in \, P} \| F(A, x) - f(x) \|. \tag{7–3.1}$$

There is always a sequence $\{ F(A_n, x) \}$ such that

$$\lim_{n \to \infty} \| F(A_n, x) - f(x) \| = \inf_{A \, \in \, P} \| F(A, x) - f(x) \|.$$

It is clear that the sequence $\{ F(A_n, x) \}$ is uniformly bounded, and hence it follows from Theorem 7–2 that $\{ F(A_n, x) \}$ contains a pointwise convergent subsequence. Hence if the set

$$\{ F(A, x) \mid A \in P \} \tag{7–3.2}$$

is compact under pointwise convergence, then one can establish the existence of best approximations for every continuous $f(x)$.

## 7–4  BASIC THEOREMS

In this section the basic theorems concerning the uniqueness and characterization of best approximations are established. The first theorem gives a characterization of best approximations. Once this result is established, it is shown that best approximations are unique by the same argument as used for linear approximating functions. In this section $X$ denotes any compact subset of $[0, 1]$, with the condition that on $X$, $f(x) \not\equiv F(A_0, x)$ for any $A_0 \in P$.

**Theorem 7–3.** *Let $F$ be a varisolvent function with degree $m(A^*)$ at $A^* \in P$. Then $F(A^*, x)$ is a best approximation to $f(x)$ on $X$ if and only if $f(x) - F(A^*, x)$ alternates at least $m(A^*)$ times on $X$.*

*Proof.* Assume that $F(A^*, x) - f(x)$ alternates $m(A^*)$ times. It is now shown that the assumption that there is an $A \in P$ such that

$$\max_{x \in X} |F(A, x) - f(x)| < \max_{x \in X} |F(A^*, x) - f(x)| \qquad (7\text{--}4.1)$$

leads to a contradiction. Let $\{x_j \mid j = 1, 2, \ldots, m(A^*) + 1, x_j < x_{j+1}\}$ be a set in $X$ upon which $F(A^*, x) - f(x)$ alternates $m(A^*)$ times. Examine the values

$$F(A, x_j) - F(A^*, x_j) = F(A, x_j) - f(x_j) - F(A^*, x_j) + f(x_j),$$
$$j = 1, 2, \ldots, m(A^*) + 1.$$

Inequality (7–4.1) implies that

$$\mathrm{sgn}\,[F(A, x_j) - F(A^*, x_j)] = -\,\mathrm{sgn}\,[F(A, x_{j+1}) - F(A^*, x_{j+1})].$$

Hence $F(A, x) - F(A^*, x)$ has at least $m(A^*)$ zeros which is a contradiction. Note that this argument is the exact parallel to the one used for linear approximating functions, Theorem 3–1. The proof of the "only if" portion of the theorem requires a somewhat revised argument.

Assume that $F(A^*, x) - f(x)$ alternates exactly $k$ times, $k < m(A^*)$. It is shown that there is a function $F(A, x)$ such that (7–4.1) is valid. The following construction is illustrated in Fig. 7–1.

If $\max_{x \in X} |F(A^*, x) - f(x)|$ is not assumed at both $x = 0$ and $x = 1$, then one of the intervals $[0, \delta]$, $[1 - \delta, 1]$, say $[0, \delta]$ for concreteness, is chosen with $\delta$ determined so that for some $\epsilon_0 > 0$

$$|F(A^*, x) - f(x)| < \max_{x \in X} |F(A^*, x) - f(x)| - \epsilon_0, \qquad x \in [0, \delta].$$

Let

$$0 = x_0 < x_{m(A^*)-k} < x_{m(A^*)-k+1} < \cdots < x_{m(A^*)} = 1$$

divide $X$ into $k + 1$ subsets so that

(a)  $F(A^*, x_j) - f(x_j) = 0, \qquad j = m(A^*) - k, \ldots, m(A^*) - 1,$

(b)  $F(A^*, x) - f(x)$ alternates exactly once on any two adjacent subsets, but does not alternate on any one subset.

Chose $m(A^*) - k - 1$ distinct points, $\{x_j \mid j = 1, 2, \ldots, m(A^*) - k - 1, x_j < x_{j+1}\}$, in $[0, \delta]$. Let

$$\alpha_j = \max_{x \in [x_j, x_{j+1}]} \big(F(A^*, x) - f(x)\big) - \min_{x \in [x_j, x_{j+1}]} \big(F(A^*, x) - f(x)\big)$$
$$n_j = \max_{x \in X} |F(A^*, x) - f(x)| - \alpha_j/2$$

for $j = m(A^*) - k - 1, m(A^*) - k, \ldots, m(A^*) - 1$.

Take

$$\epsilon = \min_{j} (\eta_j, \epsilon_0/2)$$

and let $x'$ denote a point in $X$ where $\max_{x \in X} |F(A^*, x) - f(x)|$ is attained.

Since $F$ is solvent at $A^*$, there is an $A \in P$ such that

$$F(A, x_j) - F(A^*, x_j) = 0, \qquad j = 1, 2, \ldots, m(A^*) - 1, \quad (7\text{-}4.2)$$

$$|F(A, x') - f(x')| < |F(A^*, x') - f(x')| \text{ and} \quad (7\text{-}4.3)$$

$$\|F(A, x) - F(A^*, x)\| < \epsilon. \quad (7\text{-}4.4)$$

From (7-4.2) it follows that $F(A, x) - F(A^*, x)$ has no more zeros in $[0, 1]$. From (7-4.3) it follows that $F(A, x)$ is uniformly closer to $f(x)$ than $F(A^*, x)$ at the points where $\max_{x \in X} |F(A^*, x) - f(x)|$ is attained. Inequality (7-4.4) implies

$$\max_{x \in [0, \delta]} |F(A, x) - f(x)| < \max_{x \in X} |F(A^*, x) - f(x)|.$$

Therefore $F(A, x)$ is a better approximation to $f(x)$ than $F(A^*, x)$.

If $\max_{x \in X} |F(A^*, x) - f(x)|$ is assumed at both $x = 0$ and $x = 1$, let the interval $[0, \delta]$ be replaced by $[x_{m(A^*)-k} - \delta, x_{m(A^*)-k}]$ where $\{x_j \mid j = 0, m(A^*) - k, \ldots, m(A^*)\}$, $\delta$, $\epsilon_0$, $\alpha_j$, $n_j$ and $\epsilon$ are defined in a manner analogous to the preceding construction.

For $m(A^*) - k - 1$ even, choose $m(A^*) - k - 1$ points

$$\{x_j \mid x_{m(A^*)-k} - \delta \leq x_1 < x_2 < \cdots < x_{m(A^*)-k-1} < x_{m(A^*)-k}\}$$

and determine $A \in P$ so that

$$|F(A, 0) - f(0)| < |F(A^*, 0) - f(0)|, \quad (7\text{-}4.5)$$

$$|F(A, 1) - f(1)| < |F(A^*, 1) - f(1)|, \quad (7\text{-}4.6)$$

$$\|F(A, x) - F(A^*, x)\| < \epsilon, \quad (7\text{-}4.7)$$

$$F(A, x_j) - F(A^*, x_j) = 0, \qquad j = 1, 2, \ldots, m(A^*) - 1.$$

The function $F(A, x)$ is a better approximation to $f(x)$ than $F(A^*, x)$.

For $m(A^*) - k - 2$ even choose $m(A^*) - k - 1$ points

$$\{x_j \mid x_{m(A^*)-k} - \delta < x_2 < x_3 < \cdots < x_{m(A^*)-k-1} < x_{m(A^*)-k}\}$$

and determine $A \in P$ so that (7-4.5), (7-4.6) and (7-4.7) hold and

$$F(A, x_j) - F(A^*, x_j) = 0, \qquad j = 2, \ldots, m(A^*) - 1. \quad (7\text{-}4.8)$$

If $F(A, x) - F(A^*, x)$ has a zero in addition to those given in (7-4.8), then (7-4.5) and (7-4.6) imply that this is a double zero. This is not possible because by Lemma 7-1 $F(A, x) - F(A^*, x)$ cannot have more than $m(A^*) - 1$

zeros counting multiplicities. Thus $F(A, x)$ is a better approximation to $f(x)$ than $F(A^*, x)$. This concludes the proof.

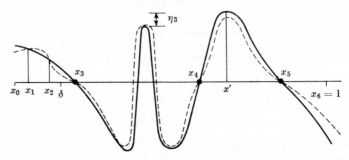

FIG. 7–1. The construction of Theorem 7–3 for $m(A^*) = 6$, $k = 3$. $F(A^*, x)$ is shown in solid line, $F(A, x)$ in dashed line.

**Theorem 7–4.** *The best approximation to a continuous function is unique if $F(A, x)$ is varisolvent.*

*Proof.* The argument is exactly parallel to that used for linear approximating functions in Theorem 3–3. If one assumes that $f(x)$ possesses two distinct approximations $F(A_1, x)$ and $F(A_2, x)$, then (see Fig. 3–7) $F(A_1, x) - F(A_2, x)$ has at least $k = \min[m(A_1), m(A_2)]$ zeros counting multiplicity. This contradicts Lemma 7–1.

The theorem of de la Vallée Poussin that gives lower and upper bounds on the deviation of the best approximation may also be generalized to varisolvent functions. Again the proof is the exact parallel of that given for linear approximating functions.

**Corollary.** *If the difference $F(A_0, x) - f(x) = \phi(x)$ assumes the values*

$$\phi_i = \phi(x_i), \qquad x_i < x_{i+1},$$

*at $m(A_0) + 1$ points in $X$ with $\mathrm{sgn}\,[\phi_i\phi_{i+1}] = -1$, then*

$$\min_i |\phi_i| \leq \inf_A \max_{x \in X} |F(A, x) - f(x)| \leq \max_{x \in X} |F(A_0, x) - f(x)|. \qquad (7\text{–}4.9)$$

## 7–5 APPROXIMATION ON SUBSETS

One of the major methods (the method of ascent) for the computation of best approximations depends on the so-called "subset theorem", see Section 6–8. For linear approximating functions this method depends on Theorem 3–5. A similar theorem may be established for varisolvent functions, which provides a foundation for the definition of a method of ascent algorithm for varisolvent functions.

**Theorem 7–5.** *Let $F(A, x)$ be a varisolvent function, and let $F(A^*, x)$ be the best approximation to $f(x)$ on $X$. Then there is a subset $X_0$ of $m(A^*) + 1$ points of $X$ such that $F(A^*, x)$ is the best approximation to $f(x)$ on $X_0$. Furthermore $X_0$ is a subset which maximizes the deviation of the best approximation to $f(x)$ among all subsets of $m(A^*) + 1$ points.*

*Proof.* The proof follows the same line of reasoning as the proof of Theorem 3–5 for linear approximating functions.

From Theorem 7–3 it follows that $F(A^*, x) - f(x)$ alternates $m(A^*)$ times on $X$. Hence there is a subset $X_0$ of $m(A^*) + 1$ points upon which $F(A^*, x) - f(x)$ alternates $m(A^*)$ times. By Theorem 7–3 $F(A^*, x)$ is the best approximation to $f(x)$ on $X_0$.

On the other hand the deviation of the best approximation on any subset of $X$ cannot be larger than

$$\max_{x \in X} |F(A^*, x) - f(x)| = \max_{x \in X_0} |F(A^*, x) - f(x)|.$$

This concludes the proof.

In order to determine the best approximation to $f(x)$ on a given subset $X_0$ of $m(A^*) + 1$ points, it is sufficient (and usually necessary) to solve the system of nonlinear equations:

$$F(A^*, x_j) - f(x_j) = (-1)^j d, \qquad j = 1, 2, \ldots, m(A^*) + 1. \quad (7\text{–}5.1)$$

The difficulty of solving the system (7–5.1) depends on the nature of $F(A, x)$. In most cases it is not possible to solve the system directly, and an iterative method may be used. Another difficulty in the determination of the best approximation on a given set of points is that one does not have any *a priori* knowledge of the degree $m(A^*)$ of the best approximation.

The exact computation of the best approximation on [0, 1] (or any set containing an infinite number of points) is in general impossible. However, one can exactly (at least within the accuracy that one can solve (7–5.1)) determine the best approximation on a finite point set. This observation follows from Theorem 7–5. One of the classical methods of estimating the best approximation on [0, 1] is the de la Vallée Poussin algorithm. For linear approximating functions, this algorithm is known to converge (see Chapter 3) and some results are available on the rate of convergence. It should be noted that this is usually an inefficient computational approach.

The situation is somewhat more complicated for varisolvent functions. To discuss the algorithm in detail let

$$X = \{x_i \mid i = 1, 2, \ldots\}$$

be dense in [0, 1] and set

$$X_m = \{x_i \mid i = 1, 2, \ldots, m\}.$$

Further assume the existence of best approximations $F(A^*, x)$ and $F(A_m, x)$ to $f(x)$ on $X$ and $X_m$, respectively. Let

$$\rho^* = \| F(A^*, x) - f(x) \|, \qquad \rho_m = \max_{x \in X_m} | F(A_m, x) - f(x) |.$$

There are two questions posed with the de la Vallée Poussin algorithm. They are

(a)  Does $\lim\limits_{m \to \infty} \rho_m = \rho^*$ ?

(b)  Does $\lim\limits_{m \to \infty} F(A_m, x) = F(A^*, x)$ ?

For linear approximating functions, the assumption of linearity is enough to show that an affirmative answer to (a) implies an affirmative answer to (b). For varisolvent functions, however, these two questions are independent; and there are simple examples where the answer to the first question is yes and the second answer is no. In actual practice one is usually much more concerned with the first question than the second.

In order to investigate the properties of $F$ required to answer (a) in the affirmative, let us consider the following situation: choose points $y_0$ and $y_m$ such that

$$| F(A_m, y_0) - f(y_0) | = \| F(A_m, x) - f(x) \|$$

$$| y_0 - y_m | = \min_{x_i \in X_m} | y_0 - x_i |, \qquad y_m \in X_m.$$

It is always true that $\rho^* \geq \rho_m$ since $X_m$ is a subset of $X$. On the other hand

$$\rho^* \leq \| F(A_m, x) - f(x) \| = | F(A_m, y_0) - f(y_0) |$$

$$\leq | F(A_m, y_0) - F(A_m, y_m) | + | F(A_m, y_m) - f(y_m) | + | f(y_m) - f(y_0) |.$$

Now the term $| f(y_m) - f(y_0) |$ tends to zero as $m$ tends to infinity since $X$ is dense in $[0, 1]$ and $f(x)$ is continuous on $[0, 1]$, i.e. uniformly continuous. Further we have

$$| F(A_m, y_m) - f(y_m) | \leq \rho_m$$

and hence

$$\rho^* \leq | F(A_m, y_0) - F(A_m, y_m) | + \rho_m + o(1)$$

where $o(1)$ denotes a term which tends to zero as $m$ tends to infinity. In order to know that $\rho_m \to \rho^*$ it is sufficient to know that the term

$$| F(A_m, y_0) - F(A_m, y_m) |$$

tends to zero as $m$ tends to infinity. This result may be stated as follows:

**Theorem 7-6.** *A sufficient condition for the de la Vallée Poussin algorithm to converge in the sense that*

$$\lim_{m \to \infty} \rho_m = \rho^*$$

*is that*

$$\lim_{m \to \infty} |F(A_m, y_0) - F(A_m, y_m)| = 0. \qquad (7\text{-}5.2)$$

There are several assumptions on $F$ that one can make which imply (7-5.2). The most obvious is to assume that the set $\{F(A_m, x)\}$ forms an equicontinuous set of functions. However, some common varisolvent functions do not satisfy this assumption. To illustrate the difficulties involved in an analysis of this algorithm, it is not known whether the sequence $\{F(A_m, x)\}$ is necessarily uniformly bounded on the interval $[0, 1]$. For specific examples, this, and much more, may be established using additional properties relating to the closure of the set $\{F(A, x)\}$ under pointwise convergence.

## 7-6   THE LIMITS OF A TCHEBYCHEFF TYPE THEORY— CHARACTERIZATION

In Sections 3–9 through 3–11 a detailed study was made of the implication of the validity of certain theorems on the nature of the approximating functions. The oldest example of such a theorem is Haar's theorem which states that if best approximations by a linear approximating function

$$L(A, x) = \sum_{i=1}^{n} a_i \phi_i(x)$$

are unique for every continuous function $f(x)$, then the set $\{\phi_i(x)\}$ is a Tchebycheff set, and conversely. In Chapter 3 the difficulties of considering characterization alone were mentioned. The purpose of this section is to consider this problem for varisolvent functions. These results are due to Rice (1960).

In order to state the problem precisely we have

**Definition 7-3.** *$F$ has Property $S$ of degree $m(A^*)$ at $A^*$ if for every continuous $f(x)$, the alternation $m(A^*)$ times of $F(A^*, x) - f(x)$ is sufficient for $F(A^*, x)$ to be a best approximation to $f(x)$.*

**Definition 7-4.** *$F$ has Property $N$ of degree $m(A^*)$ at $A^*$ if for every continuous $f(x)$, the alternation $m(A^*)$ times of $F(A^*, x) - f(x)$ is necessary for $F(A^*, x)$ to be a best approximation to $f(x)$.*

**Definition 7-5.** *$F$ has Property $NS$ of degree $m(A^*)$ at $A^*$ if $F$ has both Property $N$ and Property $S$ of degree $m(A^*)$ at $A^*$.*

If a function $F$ has Property $NS$, then best approximations by $F$ are characterized in exactly the same way as best approximations by a varisolvent function. The precise statement of the problem to be considered in this section is:

PROBLEM. *Let $\mathscr{A}$ be a set of basic assumptions on $F$. Determine a Property $\mathscr{H}$ for $F$ which is both necessary and sufficient for $F$ to have Property $NS$.*

The first set of assumptions considered for this problem is that $F(A, x)$ be a continuous function of $A$ and $x$. This is the simplest possible assumption and one of great interest. Unfortunately the resulting Property $\mathscr{H}$ is rather cumbersome and not at all elegant. Thus the problem is also considered with a second assumption, namely that $\{F(A, x)\}$ is closed under pointwise convergence. These assumptions are stated precisely as follows:

ASSUMPTION $\mathscr{A}1$. *$F(A, x)$ is continuous in the sense that given $\epsilon > 0$, $A_0 \in P$ and $x_0 \in [0, 1]$ there is a $\delta > 0$ such that $A \in P$, $x \in [0, 1]$*

$$\|A_0 - A\| + |x_0 - x| < \delta \qquad (7\text{-}6.1)$$

*implies*

$$|F(A_0, x_0) - F(A, x)| < \epsilon.$$

*It is further assumed that if $A_0 \neq A_1$, then $F(A_0, x) \neq F(A_1, x)$ for some $x \in [0, 1]$.*

The expression $\|A_0 - A\|$ is written with a norm sign in (7-6.1) to emphasize that the norm on the parameter space $P$ is derived from the uniform norm on the set $\{F(A, x)\}$. See equations (7-2.1) and (7-2.2). The range $R$ of $F$ is defined to be the set

$$R = \{(x, F(A, x)) \mid x \in [0, 1], A \in P\} \qquad (7\text{-}6.2)$$

in the $xy$-plane.

ASSUMPTION $\mathscr{A}2$. *Assumption $\mathscr{A}1$ is included and in addition $P$ is arcwise connected and $F$ is closed under pointwise convergence, i.e.*

$$\lim_{m \to \infty} F(A_m, x) = G(x), \qquad x \in [0, 1]$$

*with $|F(A_m, x)| < M$ implies that there is an $A_0 \in P$ such that*

$$G(x) = F(A_0, x).$$

If $F$ satisfies Assumption $\mathscr{A}2$, then $F$ is said to be *closed*.

In the analysis of this problem it is assumed that the degree of a property has a finite upper bound for all $A \in P$.

## 7–7  THE PROBLEM WITH ASSUMPTION $\mathscr{A}1$

The Property $\mathscr{H}$ equivalent to Property $NS$ under Assumption $\mathscr{A}1$ is the combination of Property $Z$, Definition 7–1 and Property $A$.

**Definition 7–6.** *F has Property A if for every* $A^* \in P$ *there is a degree* $m(A^*)$ *such that given an integer* $k < m(A^*)$, *a set*

$$\{x_j \mid 0 = x_0 < x_1 < \cdots < x_{k+1} = 1\}$$

*and* $\epsilon$ *with*

$$0 < \epsilon < \tfrac{1}{2} \min_j (x_{j+1} - x_j), \qquad j = 0, 1, 2, \ldots, k \qquad (7\text{–}7.1)$$

*then there exist* $A_1, A_2 \in P$ *such that*

(a)   $\| F(A^*, x) - F(A_1, x) \| < \epsilon$
        $\| F(A^*, x) - F(A_2, x) \| < \epsilon$          (7–7.2)

(b)   $F(A^*, x) - F(A_1, x)$ *and* $F(A^*, x) - F(A_2, x)$ *change sign between* $x_j - \epsilon$ *and* $x_j + \epsilon$ *and have no zeros outside* $[x_j - \epsilon, x_j + \epsilon]$, $j = 1$, $2, \ldots, k$. *Further*

$$F(A_1, 0) < F(A^*, 0) < F(A_2, 0). \qquad (7\text{–}7.3)$$

In order to digest this definition somewhat consider Figure 7–2. For $k = 0$, property $A$ implies that there are members of the set $\{F(A, x)\}$ which are arbitrarily close to $F(A^*, x)$ but uniformly above or below $F(A^*, x)$. For $k > 0$, there are members of $\{F(A, x)\}$ close to $F(A^*, x)$ which intersect $F(A^*, x)$ in the neighborhood $[x_j - \epsilon, x_j + \epsilon]$ of the given point $x_j$ an odd number of times. Essentially Property $A$ says that given $F(A^*, x)$ one can "weave" another $F(A, x)$ through it as one pleases with up to $m(A^*)$ weaves. This weaving property is exactly what is used to establish the necessity of $m(A^*)$ alternations of $F(A^*, -x)$ $f(x)$ for a best approximation, i.e. Property $N$. The nontrivial and more important fact is that the converse is true.

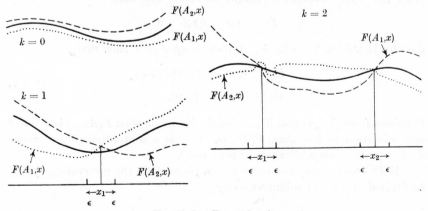

FIG. 7–2.  Property $A$.

It was pointed out in Chapter 3 that Property $Z$ is all that is required to establish Property $S$. The first theorem on the problem states that the combination of Property $Z$ and Property $A$ is equivalent to Property $NS$. It is important to note that one does not establish the equivalence of Property $N$ with Property $A$ separately, or the equivalence of Property $Z$ with Property $S$.

**Theorem 7–7.** *With Assumption $\mathscr{A}1$ $F$ has Property $NS$ of degree $m(A^*)$ if and only if $F$ has Property $A$ and Property $Z$ of degree $m(A^*)$.*

The proof of Theorem 7–7 follows from the following four lemmas which state, respectively

$$\text{Property } A \quad \Rightarrow \text{ Property } N$$
$$\text{Property } Z \quad \Rightarrow \text{ Property } S$$
$$\text{Property } NS \Rightarrow \text{ Property } Z$$
$$\text{Property } NS \Rightarrow \text{ Property } A.$$

Assumption $\mathscr{A}1$ is included in the hypothesis of each of these lemmas without explicit mention.

**Lemma 7–5.** *If $F$ has Property $A$ of degree $m(A^*)$ at $A^*$, then $F$ has Property $N$ of degree $m(A^*)$ at $A^*$.*

*Proof.* The proof of this lemma follows the same general lines as the second part of the proof of Theorem 7–3 where it was established that varisolvent functions have Property $N$.

Assume that $F$ has Property $A$ of degree $m(A^*)$ but does not have Property $N$ of degree $m(A^*)$. This implies that for some $f(x)$, $F(A^*, x)$ is a best approximation to $f(x)$ but $F(A^*, x) - f(x)$ does not alternate $m(A^*)$ times. If $F(A^*, x) - f(x)$ does not alternate at all, let $x_0$ be a point where $|F(A^*, x) - f(x)|$ assumes its maximum value. Say that

$$F(A^*, x_0) - f(x_0) > 0,$$

then by Definition 7–6 with $k = 0$ there is an $A_1 \in P$ such that

$$\| F(A^*, x) - F(A_1, x) \| < \epsilon$$
$$F(A^*, 0) > F(A_1, 0). \tag{7–7.4}$$

It follows from (7–7.4) that if $\epsilon$ is sufficiently small, then $F(A_1, x)$ is a better approximation to $f(x)$ than $F(A^*, x)$. This is a contradiction, and hence $F(A^*, x) - f(x)$ must alternate at least once.

If $F(A^*, x) - f(x)$ alternates $k < n$ times, then the interval $[0, 1]$ may be divided into $k + 1$ subintervals by

$$0 = x_0 < x_1 < \cdots < x_{k+1} = 1$$

so that

$$F(A^*, x_j) - f(x_j) = 0, \qquad j = 1, 2, \ldots, k \qquad (7\text{-}7.5)$$

and so that $F(A^*, x) - f(x)$ alternates exactly once on any two adjacent subintervals, but does not alternate on any one subinterval. Let

$$\alpha_j = \max\,[F(A^*, x) - f(x)] - \min\,[F(A^*, x) - f(x)]$$

with the maximum and minimum taken over $[x_j, x_{j+1}]$, $j = 0, 1, 2, \ldots, k$;

$$\eta_j = \| F(A^*, x) - f(x) \| - \frac{\alpha_j}{2} \qquad (7\text{-}7.6)$$
$$\epsilon' = \tfrac{1}{4} \min_j |x_{j+1} - x_j|.$$

About each point $x_j$, $j = 1, 2, \ldots, k$ there is an interval $[x_j - \epsilon_j, x_j + \epsilon_j]$ such that in this interval

$$|F(A^*, x) - f(x)| < \tfrac{1}{4} \| F(A^*, x) - f(x) \|.$$

Set

$$\epsilon = \min\,\left( \epsilon', \epsilon_1, \ldots, \epsilon_k, \eta_0, \eta_1, \ldots, \eta_k, \tfrac{1}{4} \| F(A^*, x) - f(x) \| \right)$$

and determine $A_1, A_2 \in P$ so that (a) and (b) of Property $A$ are satisfied with this choice of $A^*$, $\{x_j\}$ and $\epsilon$. Further choose one of $A_1$ and $A_2$, say $A_1$ for concreteness, so that

$$|F(A^*, x) - f(x)| > |F(A_1, x) - f(x)|, \qquad x \in [0, x_1 - \epsilon]. \quad (7\text{-}7.7)$$

By the definition of $A_1$ from property $A$ it follows that (7-7.7) holds for all $x$ outside the intervals $[x_j - \epsilon, x_j + \epsilon]$. It follows from (7-7.6) and (7-7.2) that in the intervals $[x_j - \epsilon, x_j + \epsilon]$

$$|F(A_1, x) - f(x)| \leq \tfrac{1}{2} \| F(A^*, x) - f(x) \|.$$

Thus $F(A_1, x)$ is a better approximation to $f(x)$ than $F(A^*, x)$ which contradicts the original assumption on $F(A^*, x)$. This proves the lemma.

Note that at no time was the fact considered that $m(A^*)$ may vary as a function of $A^*$.

**Lemma 7–6.** *If $F$ has Property $Z$ of degree $m(A^*)$ at $A^*$, then $F$ has Property $S$ of degree $m(A^*)$ at $A^*$.*

*Proof.* The proof of this lemma follows the exact same lines as the proof of the first part of Theorem 7–3 where it was shown that varisolvent functions have Property $S$. The argument is not repeated here.

**Lemma 7–7.** *If $F$ has Property $NS$ of degree $m(A^*)$ at $A^*$, then $F$ has Property $Z$ of degree $m(A^*)$ at $A^*$.*

2

*Proof.* Assume that there is an $A \in P$ such that $F(A, x) - F(A^*, x)$ has $m(A^*)$ or more zeros. Define

$$M(x) = \tfrac{1}{2}[F(A, x) + F(A^*, x)]$$

$$\eta = \tfrac{1}{2}\| F(A, x) - F(A^*, x)\|$$

and let

$$\{x_i | 0 \le x_1 < x_2 < \cdots < x_{m+1} \le 1\}$$

be $m = m(A^*)$ points where $F(A^*, x) - F(A, x) = 0$ along with one point where $F(A, x) \ne F(A^*, x)$, say $F(A^*, x_2) > F(A, x_2)$ for concreteness. Set

$$\delta = \tfrac{1}{4} \min (x_1, x_2 - x_1, \ldots, 1 - x_{m+1})$$

with $x_1$ or $1 - x_{m+1}$ omitted if they are zero. A function $f_1(x)$ continuous on $[0, 1]$ is defined as follows (see Fig. 7.3)

$$f_1(x) = \begin{cases} M(x) & x \in [x_j + \delta, x_{j+1} - \delta], \\ & \qquad j = 1, 2, \ldots, m \\ M(x) & x \in [0, x_1 - \delta], \quad x_1 > 0 \\ M(x) & x \in [x_{n+1} + \delta, 1], \quad x_{n+1} < 1 \\ F(A^*, x_j) + (-1)^{j+1}\left(\dfrac{3\eta}{2}\right) & x = x_j, \quad j = 1, 2, \ldots, m + 1 \end{cases}$$

In the remaining intervals $f_1(x)$ is defined so as to be continuous and so that

$$|F(A^*, x) - f_1(x)| < 3\eta/2$$
$$|F(A, x) - f_1(x)| < 3\eta/2.$$

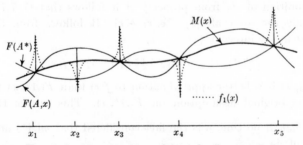

FIG. 7–3.   Construction of $f_1(x)$ for Lemma 7–7.

Note that $F(A^*, x) - f_1(x)$ alternates exactly $m$ times while $F(A, x) - f_1(x)$ alternates exactly $m - 2$ times.

Another function $f_2(x)$ may be constructed by the same procedure so that $F(A^*, x) - f_2(x)$ and $F(A, x) - f_2(x)$ alternate exactly $m - 2$ and $m$ times, respectively. Now

$$\| F(A^*, x) - f_1(x)\| = \| F(A, x) - f_1(x)\| = 3\eta/2, \qquad (7\text{-}7.8)$$

$$\| F(A^*, x) - f_2(x)\| = \| F(A, x) - f_2(x)\| = 3\eta/2. \qquad (7\text{-}7.9)$$

Since $F$ has Property $S$ of degree $m(A^*)$ at $A^*$, it follows that $F(A^*, x)$ is a best approximation to $f_1(x)$. From (7–7.8) it follows that $F(A, x)$ is also a best approximation to $f_1(x)$. Since $F(A, x) - f_1(x)$ alternates $m - 2$ times, the degree $m(A)$ at $A$ is at most $m - 2$. Therefore, $F(A, x)$ is a best approximation to $f_2(x)$ since $F(A, x) - f_2(x)$ alternates $m > m(A)$ times. From (7–7.9) it follows that $F(A^*, x)$ is also a best approximation to $f_2(x)$. But $F(A^*, x) - f_2(x)$ alternates exactly $m - 2$ times which contradicts the fact that $F$ has Property $N$ of degree $m$ at $A^*$. Thus the original assumption is false, and the lemma is established.

**Lemma 7–8.** *If $F$ has Property $NS$ of degree $m(A^*)$ at $A^*$, then $F$ has Property $A$ of degree $m(A^*)$ at $A^*$.*

*Proof.* For the construction given in this proof see Fig. 7–4.

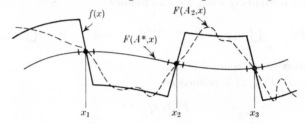

$$f(x) \qquad F(A_2, x)$$
$$F(A^*, x)$$
$$x_1 \qquad\qquad x_2 \qquad\qquad x_3$$

FIG. 7–4.  The construction of $f(x)$ for Lemma 7–8.

Let $A^* \in P$, $k < m(A^*)$, $\epsilon > 0$ and $\{x_j \mid 0 = x_0 < x_1 < \cdots < x_{k+1} = 1\}$ be given with (7–7.1). A construction establishing the existence of $A_2$ of Definition 7–6 is described. The existence of $A_1$ follows by a similar construction. A function $f(x)$ is defined as follows: $f(x)$ is continuous in $[0, 1]$; $f(x) - F(A^*, x)$ is linear in the interval $[x_j - \epsilon, x_j + \epsilon]$, $j = 1, 2, \ldots, k$ and

$$f(x) = F(A^*, x) + (-1)^{j+1}\epsilon/3$$

for

$$x \in [x_j + \epsilon, x_{j+1} - \epsilon], \qquad j = 1, 2, \ldots, k; \ x \in [0, x_1 - \epsilon], \ x \in [x_k + \epsilon, 1].$$

Since $F(A^*, x) - f(x)$ alternates exactly $k$ times, $F(A^*, x)$ is not a best approximation to $f(x)$. Hence there is an $A_2 \in P$ such that $F(A_2, x)$ is a better approximation to $f(x)$ than $F(A^*, x)$. This implies that $F(A_2, x) - F(A^*, x)$ has no zeros outside the interval $[x_j - \epsilon, x_j + \epsilon]$, $j = 1, 2, \ldots, k$ and alternates in sign from $x_j - \epsilon$ to $x_j + \epsilon$. Furthermore

$$\| F(A^*, x) - F(A_2, x) \| < 2\epsilon/3.$$

Hence $F(A_2, x)$ satisfies (a) and (b) of Property $A$, and this concludes the proof.

It has already been remarked that every varisolvent function has Property $A$. Two examples are given of functions which have Property $A$ and which are not varisolvent.

EXAMPLE 1.
$$P = \{a \mid a \text{ is rational}\}$$
$$F(A, x) = a$$

EXAMPLE 2. Let the number $p$ be of the form $c/2^n$ where $c$ is odd. Then the index $j(p)$ of $p$ is defined to be $n$. The multiplication of a set $P$ of real numbers by a constant $a$ is defined by

$$aP = \{ap \mid p \in P\}$$

and $p_0 + aP$ means $\{p_0 + ap \mid p \in P\}$.

Let

$$P_1 = \{\pm 2^{-j} \mid j = 1, 2, \ldots\} \cup \{0\}.$$

$P_k$ is defined recursively from $P_{k-1}$ as follows

$$P_k = \bigcup_{p \in P_{k-1}} \{p + P_1/(2^{2+j(p)})\} \quad \text{and} \quad P = \bigcup_{k=1}^{\infty} P_k.$$

$P$ is a nowhere dense countable set.

For $a \in P$, $F(A, x)$ is defined as

$$F(A, x) = a.$$

One may verify that $F$ has Property $A$ and Property $Z$ and hence property $NS$.

Note that in both of these examples there are continuous functions which have no best approximation.

## 7–8 THE PROBLEM WITH ASSUMPTION $\mathscr{A}2$

The Assumption $\mathscr{A}1$ allows $F$ to have some pathological characteristics, and hence the Property $A$ found in the preceding section is somewhat complicated. In order to restrict the pathological character of $F$, there are two new assumptions in assumption $\mathscr{A}2$. The first of these is that the parameter space $P$ be arcwise connected. While this is not a strong assumption on $P$ it does imply that the range $R$ of $F$ is a particularly simple region.

The main theorem in this section asserts that under Assumption $\mathscr{A}2$ then Property $NS$ is equivalent to varisolvence. In order to be able to establish solvence, it is essential that one be able to assert that a convergent sequence from $\{F(A, x)\}$ has a limit in $\{F(A, x)\}$. This is exactly the second assumption, i.e. closure under pointwise convergence.

If $P$ is an arcwise connected set (recall again that the topology of $P$, and hence the definition of arcwise connected, is derived from the topology of $\{F(A, x)\}$), then the range $R$ is as follows: Let

$$L(x) = \{(x, F(A, x)) \mid A \in P\}.$$

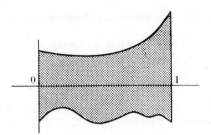

Fig. 7–5.  The range $R$ of $F$.

This is a subset of the $(x, F)$-plane lying on a line. Since $F$ is continuous and $P$ is connected, $L(x)$ is a line segment and

$$R = \bigcup_{x \in [0, 1]} L(x).$$

Let $L_0(x)$ be the interior of $L(x)$ and set

$$R_0 = \bigcup_{x \in [0, 1]} L_0(x).$$

Assumption $\mathcal{A}1$ is included in the hypothesis of the following lemma.

**Lemma 7–9.** *If $P$ is arcwise connected and if $F$ has Property NS of some degree at every point of $P$, then given $A^* \in P$ there is an $\epsilon > 0$ such that for all $x \in [0, 1]$*

$$(x, F(A^*, x) \pm \epsilon) \in R_0. \tag{7–8.1}$$

*Proof.* Since $F$ has Property *NS* of some degree, it follows from Lemma 7–8 that $F$ has Property $A$ of corresponding degree. In the definition of Property $A$ set $k = 0$. Then there are $A_1, A_2 \in P$ such that

$$F(A_1, x) < F(A^*, x) < F(A_2, x), \ x \in [0, 1].$$

Set

$$\epsilon_1 = \min_{x \in [0, 1]} \left| F(A_1, x) - F(A^*, x) \right| > 0,$$

$$\epsilon_2 = \min_{x \in [0, 1]} \left| F(A_2, x) - F(A^*, x) \right| > 0,$$

$$\epsilon = \tfrac{1}{2} \min (\epsilon_1, \epsilon_2).$$

This $\epsilon > 0$ satisfies (7–8.1).

The main theorem of this section is

**Theorem 7–8.** *With Assumption $\mathcal{A}2$ $F$ has Property NS of degree $m(A^*)$ for every $A^* \in P$ if and only if $F$ is varisolvent of degree $m(A^*)$ at $A^* \in P$.*

*Proof.* The proof of this theorem is broken into three parts

$$\text{Varisolvence} \Rightarrow \text{Property } NS$$
$$\text{Property } NS \Rightarrow \text{Property } Z$$
$$\text{Property } NS \Rightarrow \text{solvence}$$

The first part is demonstrated by Theorem 7–3, and the second part is demonstrated by Lemma 7–7 which applies here without modification. Hence the entire effort consists of establishing the third part.

The proof of the third part is broken into three lemmas. The first of these shows that Property $NS$ and closure imply that $F$ has Property $A$ modified so that $F(A_1, x)$ and $F(A_2, x)$ (see Definition 7–6) agree with $F(A^*, x)$ at exactly the given points rather than in the neighborhood of the given points. The assumption of closure and Theorem 7–2 are essential for the proof of this lemma and the second one. The second lemma establishes solvence in a very special situation, and the third lemma gives a rather complex constructive proof of the fact that Property $NS$ implies solvence. Assumption $\mathscr{A}2$ is included in the hypothesis of each lemma without mention.

**Lemma 7–10.** *Let $F$ have Property $NS$ of degree $m(A^*)$ for every point $A^* \in P$. Then given an $A^* \in P$, $\epsilon > 0$, $k < m(A^*)$ and a set*

$$\{x_j \,|\, 0 \le x_1 < x_2 < \cdots < x_{k+1} \le 1\},$$

*there exist $A_1$, $A_2 \in P$ such that*

(a)    $\|F(A^*, x) - F(A_1, x)\| < \epsilon$

       $\|F(A^*, x) - F(A_2, x)\| < \epsilon$

(b)    $F(A^*, x) - F(A_1, x)$  *and*  $F(A^*, x) - F(A_2, x)$  *have a simple zero at each $x_j$ and have no other simple zeros.*

(c)    $F(A_2, x) < F(A^*, x) < F(A_1, x)$ *for some $x \in [0, 1]$.*

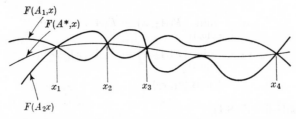

Fig. 7–6.   The functions $F(A_1, x)$, $F(A_2, x)$ constructed in Lemma 7–10.

*Proof.* The construction is given for $F(A_1, x)$; a similar construction is valid for $F(A_2, x)$. By Lemma 7–9 it is possible to choose $\epsilon > 0$ small enough for (7–8.1) to be valid for all $x$ and $|F(A, x)| < M$. It is assumed that $\epsilon$ is so chosen. Let $n_0$ be an integer such that

$$1/n_0 < \tfrac{1}{4} \min (x_1, x_2 - x_1, \ldots, x_k - x_{k-1}, 1 - x_k)$$

where $x_1$ and $1 - x_k$ are omitted if they are zero.

A sequence of continuous functions

$$\{f_n(x)|n = n_0, n_0 + 1, \ldots\}$$

is defined as follows (see Fig. 7–7): $f_n(x)$ is continuous in $[0, 1]$;

$$f_n(x) = F(A^*, x) + (-1)^j \epsilon/3 \qquad (7\text{–}8.2)$$

for

$$x \in [x_j + 1/n, x_{j+1} - 1/n],$$
$$x \in [0, x_1 - 1/n] \text{ if } x_1 \neq 0,$$
$$x \in [x_k + 1/n, 1] \text{ if } x_k \neq 1;$$

$f_n(x) - F(A^*, x)$ is linear in each of the remaining intervals.

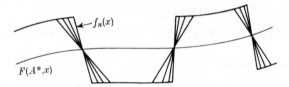

FIG. 7–7.   The definition of $f_n(x)$.

$F(A^*, x)$ is not a best approximation to any $f_n(x)$, since $F(A^*, x) - f_n(x)$ alternates at most $k$ times. It is now shown that there is a $B_n \in P$ such that $F(B_n, x)$ is a best approximation to $f_n(x)$. This is the point where the assumption of closure under pointwise convergence and Theorem 7–2 are used.

Consider a sequence $\{F(B_{np}, x)|p = 1, 2, \ldots\}$ for which

$$\lim_{p \to \infty} \| F(B_{np}, x) - f_n(x)\| = \inf_{A \in P} \| F(A, x) - f_n(x)\|.$$

The set $\{F(B_{np}, x)\}$ is uniformly bounded since

$$\| F(B_{np}, x) - P(A^*, x)\| \leq 2\epsilon/3 \qquad (7\text{–}8.3)$$

for $n$ sufficiently large. This set has Property $Z$ by Lemma 7–7. Theorem 7–2 may be applied to extract a convergent subsequence of $\{F(B_{np}, x)\}$. The Assumption $\mathscr{A}2$ implies that this subsequence has a limit in $P$, i.e.,

$$\lim_{p \to \infty} F(B_{np}, x) = F(B_n, x),$$

which is a best approximation to $f_n(x)$.

In the same way the sequence $\{F(B_n, x)\}$ has a limit $F(A_1, x)$. It is now verified that this limit satisfies the conclusions of the lemma. It follows from the construction of $f_n(x)$ and (7–8.3) that

$$0 \leq [F(A_2, x) - F(A^*, x)](-1)^j \leq (-1)^j \epsilon$$

for

$$x \in [x_j, x_{j+1}],$$

$$x \in [0, x_1] \text{ if } x_1 \neq 0,$$

$$x \in [x_k, 1] \text{ if } x_k \neq 1.$$

If $A_1 \neq A^*$ then $F(A_1, x) - F(A^*, x)$ has a simple zero at each $x_j$. Note that $F(A_1, x) - F(A^*, x)$ cannot be zero on an interval.

It remains to be shown that $A_1 \neq A^*$. Note that $F(B_n, x) - f_n(x)$ alternates at least $k + 1$ times, for the degree of $F$ at $B_n$ must be at least $k + 1$ since $F(A^*, x) - F(B_n, x)$ has $k$ zeros. Thus if $\| F(B_n, x) - F(A^*, x) \| < \epsilon/3$ it follows that $F(B_n, x) - f_n(x)$ alternates in some interval $[x_j - 1/n, x_j + 1/n]$ so that $\| F(B_n, x) - F(A^*, x) \| > \epsilon/9$. Since $\| F(A, x) \|$ is a continuous function of $A$, we have

$$\lim_{n \to \infty} \| F(B_n, x) - F(A^*, x) \| = \| F(A_1, x) - F(A^*, x) \| \geq \epsilon/9.$$

This concludes the proof.

For the next lemma we need to introduce the concept of a function being between two other functions. The definition is a natural one and is as follows: $F(A, x)$ *is said to be between $F(A_1, x)$ and $F(A_2, x)$ if*

$$|F(A_1, x) - F(A, x)| + |F(A, x) - F(A_2, x)| = |F(A_1, x) - F(A_2, x)|$$

*for all $x \in [0, 1]$.*

We further note that Property $A$ and Property $Z$ (and hence Property $NS$) are sufficient for the proof of Theorem 7–1 with the modified conclusion that given $A^*$ there is a neighborhood $N(A^*)$ such that $A \in N(A^*)$ implies $m(A) \geq m(A^*)$. This fact is used in the following lemma.

**Lemma 7–11.** *Let $F$ have Property $NS$ of degree $m(A^*)$ for every $A^* \in P$. Given $A^* \in P$ of degree $m$ let $A \in N(A^*)$ be such that $F(A^*, x) - F(A, x)$ changes sign at $m - 1$ points. Then given $x_0$ and any $y_0$ between $F(A^*, x_0)$ and $F(A, x_0)$, there is an $A_0 \in N(A^*)$ such that*

$$F(A_0, x_0) = y_0 \tag{7–8.4}$$

*and $F(A_0, x)$ is between $F(A, x)$ and $F(A^*, x)$.*

*Proof.* Since $F$ has Property $NS$ of degree $m$ at $A^*$, it follows that $F$ has Property $Z$ of degree $m$ at $A^*$; and hence $F(A^*, x) - F(A, x)$ has exactly $m - 1$ zeros.

For concreteness assume $F(A, x_0) > F(A^*, x_0)$ and set

$$I = [F(A^*, x_0), F(A, x_0)].$$

If $I$ consists of one point, then $A_0 = A$ satisfies (7–8.4). Further let $E$ be the subset of $I$ for which the lemma is true, i.e. $y_0 \in E$ implies the existence of $A_0 \in P$ for which (7–8.4) is valid. Clearly $E$ is not empty for $F(A^*, x_0) \in E$.

It is now shown that $E$ is a closed set. Let

$$\{y_j \mid y_j \in E, j = 1, 2, \ldots\}$$

be given with

$$\lim_{j \to \infty} y_j = y_0.$$

Corresponding to $\{y_j\}$ there is a sequence

$$\{F(A_j, x) \mid F(A_j, x_0) = y_j\}$$

of functions between $F(A^*, x)$ and $F(A, x)$. Theorem 7–2 is applicable to this sequence, and hence $\{F(A_j, x)\}$ contains a pointwise convergent subsequence. Since $F$ is closed under pointwise convergence, this subsequence has a limit $F(A_0, x)$. We have

$$F(A_0, x_0) = y_0$$

and hence $y_0 \in E$.

It is now shown that $I - E$ does not contain an open interval. This implies that $I - E$ is empty for the only open set on the real line which does not contain an open interval is the empty set. Assume that $I - E$ contains the open interval $(y_1, y_2)$ with $y_1, y_2 \in E$. One can always take an interval of maximum length and hence ensure that $y_1, y_2 \in E$. Since $y_1 \in E$ there is an $A_1 \in P$ such that $F(A_1, x)$ is between $F(A^*, x)$ and $F(A, x)$ and

$$F(A_1, x_0) = y_1.$$

However, Lemma 7–10 may be applied to show the existence of an $A_2 \in P$ such that $F(A_2, x)$ is between $F(A^*, x)$ and $F(A, x)$ and

$$y_1 < F(A_2, x_0) < y_2.$$

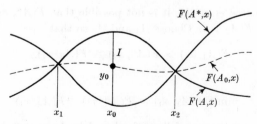

FIG. 7–8.   The construction of Lemma 7–11.

This contradicts the assumption that $(y_1, y_2)$ is in $I - E$ and completes the proof.

**Lemma 7–12.** *Let $F$ have Property NS of degree $m(A^*) = m$ for every $A^* \in P$. Then $F$ is solvent of degree $m(A^*) = m$ at $A^*$.*

*Proof.* The proof is done by an induction argument. The statement to be verified by induction is: *Let $A^* \in P$, $\epsilon > 0$ and a set*

$$\{x_j \mid 0 \leq x_1 < x_2 < \cdots < x_m \leq 1\}$$

*be given. Then there is a $\delta(A^*, \epsilon, k, x_j) > 0$ such that*

$$|F(A^*, x_j) - y_j| \leq \delta, \qquad j = 1, 2, \ldots, k \tag{7-8.5}$$

*implies that there is an $A \in P$ such that*

$$F(A, x_j) = y_j, \qquad j = 1, 2, \ldots, k \tag{7-8.6}$$

$$F(A, x_j) = F(A^*, x_j), \qquad j = k+1, \ldots, k \tag{7-8.7}$$

$$\|F(A^*, x) - F(A, x)\| < \epsilon. \tag{7-8.8}$$

The induction is on $k$, and for $k = m(A^*)$ the statement implies that $F$ is solvent of degree $m(A^*)$. See Definition 7–2.

The comments preceding Lemma 7–11 imply the existence of a neighborhood $N(A^*)$ of $A^*$ such that $A \in N(A^*)$ implies $m(A) \geq m(A^*)$. This neighborhood is defined by

$$N(A^*) = \{A \mid \|F(A, x) - F(A^*, x)\| \leq \epsilon^*\}. \tag{7-8.9}$$

It is assumed throughout the remainder of this proof that all functions $F$ are chosen from $N(A^*)$.

For $k = 1$ the induction statement follows from Lemma 7–10 and 7–11. One may determine $F(A_1, x)$, $F(A_2, x) \in N(A^*)$ by Lemma 7–10 so that

$$F(A_1, x_j) = F(A_2, x_j) = F(A^*, x_j), \qquad j = 2, 3, \ldots, m$$

$$\|F(A_1, x) - F(A^*, x)\| < \epsilon,$$

$$\|F(A_2, x) - F(A^*, x)\| < \epsilon.$$

Since $F$ is of degree $m$ at $A^*$, it is not possible that $F(A^*, x_1) = F(A_1, x_1)$ or $F(A^*, x_1) = F(A_2, x_1)$. Choose $A_1$ and $A_2$ so that

$$F(A_1, x_1) > F(A^*, x_1) > F(A_2, x_1).$$

Take

$$\delta(A^*, \epsilon, 1, x_j) = \min\left(|F(A_1, x_1) - F(A^*, x_1)|, |F(A_2, x_1) - F(A^*, x_1)|\right)$$

and the induction statement follows for $k = 1$ by Lemma 7–11.

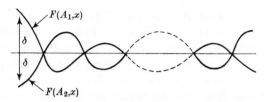

FIG. 7–9.  The construction for $k = 1$.

Before proceeding with the induction the following construction is required: Let $\mathbf{y} = (y_1, y_2, \ldots, y_k)$ be a point in $E_k$ and set

$$Y_k = \{\mathbf{y} \mid |y_i - F(A^*, x_i)| \leq \tfrac{1}{2}\delta(A^*, \epsilon, k, x_j), i = 1, 2, \ldots, k\}.$$

Define two subsets $P_1(\mathbf{y})$ and $P_2(\mathbf{y})$ of $P$ as follows: for $A \in P_1$ or $A \in P_2$

$$|F(A, x) - F(A^*, x)| < \epsilon,$$

$$F(A, x_j) = y_j, \qquad\qquad j = 1, 2, \ldots, k, \qquad\qquad (7\text{–}8.10)$$

$$F(A, x_j) = F(A^*, x_j), \qquad j = k + 2, \ldots, m,$$

and for $A_1 \in P_1$, $A_2 \in P_2$

$$F(A_2, x_{k+1}) < F(A^*, x_{k+1}) < F(A_1, x_{k+1}). \qquad (7\text{–}8.11)$$

$P_1$ and $P_2$ are the sets of all $A \in P$ that satisfy (7–8.10) and (7–8.11).  Let

$$\delta_1(\mathbf{y}) = \sup_{A \,\in\, P_1(\mathbf{y})} |F(A^*, x_{k+1}) - F(A, x_{k+1})|$$

$$\delta_2(\mathbf{y}) = \sup_{A \,\in\, P_2(\mathbf{y})} |F(A^*, x_{k+1}) - F(A, x_{k+1})|.$$

The numbers $\delta_1$ and $\delta_2$ are the furthest one can get from $F(A^*, x_{k+1})$ and still satisfy (7–8.10). If $P_1(\mathbf{y})$ and $P_2(\mathbf{y})$ are nonempty, then $\delta_1(\mathbf{y}) > 0$ and $\delta_2(\mathbf{y}) > 0$.

It is now shown that $P_1(\mathbf{y})$ and $P_2(\mathbf{y})$ are nonempty for each $\mathbf{y} \in Y_k$. The construction is illustrated in Fig. 7–10. By the induction hypothesis, there exists a function $F(A, x)$ satisfying (7–8.6), (7–8.7) and (7–8.8). Lemma 7–11 may now be applied to $F(A, x)$ to obtain the functions $F(A_1, x)$, $F(A_2, x)$ shown in Fig. 7–10. These functions are in $P_1(\mathbf{y})$ and $P_2(\mathbf{y})$, respectively.

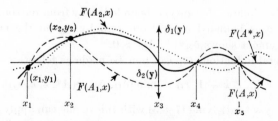

FIG. 7–10.  The construction of an element of $P_1(\mathbf{y})$, $P_2(\mathbf{y})$ for $k = 2$, $m = 5$.

The procedure illustrated in Fig. 7–10 gives a construction which allows one to carry out the construction of $F(A_m, x)$ satisfying (7–8.7) with $k = m$ in the following sense: given $x_1$ and $\delta(A^*, \epsilon, 1, x_1)$ we can find $F(A_1, x)$ satisfying (7–8.7) with $k = 1$. With this $F(A_1, x)$ we can, for $y_2$ in some interval about $F(A^*, x_2)$, find $F(A_2, x)$ satisfying (7–8.7) with $k = 2$ and so forth. The difficulty is that one does not have a lower bound on the lengths of the intervals about $F(A^*, x_k)$ obtained in this manner. It is for this purpose that the sets $P_1(\mathbf{y})$, $P_2(\mathbf{y})$ have been introduced, for they have no other use.

It is now shown that $\delta_1(\mathbf{y})$ and $\delta_2(\mathbf{y})$ are bounded away from zero as a function of $\mathbf{y} \in Y_k$ for each $k$.

The first step is to show that for any $\mathbf{y}' \in Y_k$ there is a neighborhood $N(\mathbf{y}')$ of $\mathbf{y}'$ (in the ordinary $E_k$ topology) such that $\mathbf{y} \in N(\mathbf{y}')$ implies

$$\delta_1(\mathbf{y}) \geq \tfrac{1}{2}\delta_1(\mathbf{y}'). \qquad (7\text{–}8.12)$$

There is an $A_1 \in P_1(\mathbf{y}')$ such that

$$F(A_1, x_{k+1}) \geq F(A^*, x_{k+1}) + \tfrac{1}{2}\delta_1(\mathbf{y}').$$

By the induction hypothesis applied to $F(A_1, x)$ there is a $\delta'(A_1, \eta, k, x_j) > 0$ such that for every $\mathbf{y}$ with $|y_j - y_j'| < \delta$ there is a $A \in P$ so that (7–8.6) is satisfied and

$$F(A, x_{k+1}) = F(A_1, x_{k+1}) \geq F(A^*, x_{k+1}) + \tfrac{1}{2}\delta_1(\mathbf{y}').$$

Further

$$\| F(A_1, x) - F(A, x) \| < \eta$$

and for $\eta$ sufficiently small (7–8.8) is satisfied. Hence (7–8.10) is satisfied and $\delta'$ defines the required neighborhood $N(\mathbf{y}')$.

The set $Y_k$ is a compact set. This follows from the less than or *equal* sign in the definition of $Y_k$, the assumption that $F$ is closed under pointwise convergence, and Theorem 7–2. Each set $Y_k$ has an open covering by neighborhoods which may be reduced to a finite covering

$$N(\mathbf{y}_1), N(\mathbf{y}_2), \ldots, N(\mathbf{y}_p).$$

From (7–8.12) it follows that $\delta_1(\mathbf{y})$ is bounded away from zero on each of these sets. Hence it is bounded away from zero by $\delta_{1k}$ on the entire set $Y_k$. A similar argument shows $\delta_2(\mathbf{y}) \geq \delta_{2k} > 0$.

The general induction step can now be made as follows: set

$$\delta(A^*, \epsilon, k + 1, x_j) = \min [\delta_{1k}, \delta_{2k}, \delta(A^*, \epsilon, k, x_j)].$$

Thus given any set satisfying (7–8.5) with this $\delta$, one can apply Lemma 7–11 to obtain an $F(A, x)$ satisfying (7–8.6), (7–8.7) and (7–8.8). This concludes the induction step and the proof of the lemma.

These four lemmas have established Theorem 7–8. This theorem is comparable with (but not exactly equivalent to) Theorem 3–12. There it is shown for linear approximating functions that Theorems 3–10(a), 3–10(b) (see Chapter 3) are valid if and only if $P = E_n$ and the set $\{\phi_i(x)\}$ is a Tchebycheff set. In order for Theorem 7–8 to be equivalent to this result it would be necessary for Property $NS$ and the assumption of existence of best approximations for all $f(x)$ to imply Assumption $\mathscr{A}2$. Assumption $\mathscr{A}2$ on $F$ does imply that every continuous function possesses a best approximation. On the other hand it is not clear that the existence of a best approximation for every continuous function implies that $\{F(A, x)\}$ is closed under pointwise convergence. There is the possibility that a sequence from $\{F(A, x)\}$ can converge pointwise to a discontinuous function which cannot possibly be a best approximation to any continuous function. Thus best approximations may exist for every continuous function, and yet $\{F(A, x)\}$ might not be closed under pointwise convergence. An example of this is seen in the case of exponential approximation.

However, when the degree $m(A)$ is assumed to be constant, the situation is changed. This problem is examined in the next section.

## 7–9   THE LIMITS OF A TCHEBYCHEFF TYPE THEORY— CHARACTERIZATION AND EXISTENCE

We begin with

**Definition 7–7.** $F(x)$ *is said to be locally unisolvent if $F$ is locally solvent and has Property Z with fixed degree n.*

Thus $F(x)$ is varisolvent of fixed degree. That this is weaker than unisolvence is seen from the example at the end of this section.

This section is concerned with determining what conditions on $F(A, x)$ are equivalent to the existence of best approximations (for all continuous functions) and Property $NS$ *with constant degree n*. The assumption that the degree $m(A)$ is constant is essential to the techniques (and probably to the validity) of this section. The main result is

**Theorem 7–9.** *F has Property NS and there exists a best approximation for every continuous function if and only if F is closed and locally unisolvent.*

A portion of the proof of this theorem is already complete. There are two points which remain to be established. The first and simplest is that the closure of $F$ (along with Property Z) implies the existence of best approximations for every continuous function. The second is that the hypothesis implies that $F$ is closed.

**Lemma 7–13.** *If F is closed and has Property Z then every continuous function possesses a best approximation.*

*Proof.* Let $f(x)$ be a given function continuous on $[0, 1]$ and $F(A', x)$ an approximating function. Denote by $P'$ the parameters

$$P' = \{A \mid \|F(A, x) - f(x)\| \leq \|F(A', x) - f(x)\|\}.$$

This set is not empty since it contains $A'$. Furthermore it is a bounded set, i.e. there exists an $M < \infty$ such that $|F(A, x)| \leq M$ for $A \in P'$.

There is a sequence $\{A_k\}$ in $P'$ such that

$$\lim_{k \to \infty} \|F(A_k, x) - f(x)\| = \inf_{A \in P} \|F(A, x) - f(x)\|.$$

It follows from Theorem 7–2 that there exists a pointwise convergent subsequence of every infinite sequence in $P'$. If $P'$ contains only a finite number of parameter sets then the lemma is clearly valid for $f(x)$. Otherwise, the sequence $\{F(A_k, x)\}$ contains a pointwise convergent subsequence and, by the hypothesis of closure, this subsequence possesses a limit $F(A_0, x)$ which is a best approximation to $f(x)$. This concludes the proof.

In order to establish the second point, one would like to construct for a limiting function $G(x)$ a continuous function $f(x)$ such that $f(x) - G(x)$ alternates $n$ times at $n + 1$ specified points in $[0, 1]$. This would imply (after some arguments) that $G(x)$ is a best approximation to $f(x)$ and hence that $G(x) \equiv F(A_0, x)$. However, it is not possible at this point to construct such an $f(x)$ since $G(x)$ is an unknown and possibly highly discontinuous function. This difficulty is circumvented in Lemma 7–14 where two functions associated with $G(x)$ are introduced for which one may construct the required continuous function $f(x)$. These two functions are

$$G^+(x) = \max [G(x), \limsup_{|x - y| \to 0} G(y)],$$

$$G^-(x) = \min [G(x), \liminf_{|x - y| \to 0} G(y)].$$

Since $G(x)$ is a bounded function, both of these functions are well defined.

**Lemma 7–14.** *Given $G(x)$ bounded on $[0, 1]$, $M > 0$, $\delta_0 > 0$ and $x_0 \in [0, 1]$ there exists a continuous function $f(x)$ such that*

$$f(x) - G^+(x)$$

*has a minimum $-M$ at $x_0$ in the interval $|x - x_0| \leq \delta_0$. Further*

$$f(x_0 \pm \delta_0) - G^+(x_0 \pm \delta_0) = 0.$$

*Proof.* Set

$$\omega^+(\delta) = \sup [G^+(y) - G^+(x_0)], \qquad 0 < |x_0 - y| < \delta.$$

This is an *upper modulus of continuity* of $G^+(x)$ at $x_0$. It is also the upper-semicontinuous function $u(x)$ (upper boundary function) described in

Goffman, 1953. If

$$G(x_0) = G^+(x_0) > \limsup_{|x_0 - y| \to 0} G(y) \qquad (7\text{–}9.1)$$

then clearly

$$\lim_{\delta \to 0} \omega^+(\delta) < 0.$$

When (7–9.1) does not hold then we have the following assertion:

$$\lim_{\delta \to 0} \omega^+(\delta) = 0. \qquad (7\text{–}9.2)$$

The basic reason that this assertion is true is that $G^+(x)$ itself is upper-semicontinuous. Assume (7–9.2) to be false, then there is an $\epsilon > 0$ and a sequence $\{x_i \mid i = 1, 2, \ldots\}$ tending to $x_0$ such that

$$G^+(x_0) < G^+(x_i) - \epsilon, \qquad i = 1, 2, \ldots.$$

This contradicts the fact that

$$G^+(x_0) > \limsup_{|x_0 - y| \to 0} G^+(y)$$

which may be established by a straightforward argument.

A construction is now given to establish the following

*Assertion.* There exists a continuous function $\omega(\delta)$ such that for $0 \le \delta \le \delta_0$

$$\omega^+(\delta) \le \omega(\delta)$$

and if (7–9.2) holds then $\omega(0) = 0$.

Note that $\omega^+(\delta)$ is a monotonic nondecreasing function. Define

$$\omega(\delta) = \frac{1}{\delta} \int_{\delta}^{2\delta} \omega^+(x)\, dx, \qquad \delta > 0,$$

$$\omega(0) = \limsup_{|x_0 - y| \to 0} [G(y) - G^+(x_0)].$$

It follows immediately from the mean value theorem that

$$\omega^+(\delta) \le \omega(\delta) \le \omega^+(2\delta), \qquad \delta > 0.$$

It is clear that $w(\delta)$ is a continuous function and further if (7–9.2) holds then $\omega(0) = 0$.

The function $f(x)$ required in this proof is now constructed. If $\omega(\delta_0) \le 0$ set

$$f(x) = G^+(x_0) - M + 2|x - x_0|. \qquad (7\text{–}9.3)$$

Then if $|x - x_0| \le \delta_0$ one has

$$f(x) - G^+(x) = G^+(x_0) - G^+(x) - M + 2|x - x_0| \ge -M + 2|x - x_0|.$$

If $\omega(\delta_0) > 0$ set $\omega'(\delta) = \max[\omega(\delta), 0]$ and

$$f(x) = G^+(x_0) - M + 2\omega'(|x - x_0|). \qquad (7\text{-}9.4)$$

Then

$$\begin{aligned} f(x) - G^+(x) &= G^+(x_0) - G^+(x) - M + 2\omega'(|x - x_0|) \\ &\geq -M + 2\omega'(|x - x_0|) - \omega^+(|x - x_0|) \\ &\geq -M + \omega'(|x - x_0|) \geq -M. \end{aligned}$$

This construction gives an $f(x)$ satisfying the minimum requirement of the lemma. The construction may be easily modified so that

$$f(x_0 \pm \delta_0) = G^+(x_0 \pm \delta_0).$$

It is clear that the same type of construction is applicable to the

**Corollary.** *Given $G(x)$ bounded on $[0, 1]$, $M > 0$, $\delta_0 > 0$ and $x_0 \in [0, 1]$ then there exists a continuous function $f(x)$ such that*

$$f(x) - G^-(x)$$

*has a local maximum of $M$ at $x_0$ in the interval $|x - x_0| \leq \delta_0$. Further*

$$f(x_0 \pm \delta_0) - G^-(x_0 \pm \delta_0) = 0.$$

The next lemma is required to establish the second point of the proof of the theorem. The proof is to be given as Problem 9–7.

**Lemma 7–15.** *Assume $F$ has Property NS. If*

$$\max_{x_i}|F(A, x_i) - f(x_i)| \leq 2M, \qquad i = 1, 2, \ldots, n + 1$$

*then either (a) $F(A, x) - f(x)$ alternates $n$ times on $\{x_i\}$ with deviation $2M$ or (b) there is an $A_0 \in P$ such that*

$$|F(A_0, x_i) - f(x_i)| < 2M, \qquad i = 1, 2, \ldots, n + 1.$$

The next lemma establishes the second point required for the proof of Theorem 7–9.

**Lemma 7–16.** *If $F$ has Property NS and there exists a best approximation for every continuous function then $F$ is closed.*

*Proof.* Assume that

$$\lim_{k \to \infty} F(A_k, x) = G(x), \, x \in [0, 1]$$

with

$$|F(A_k, x)| \leq M.$$

Let $n + 1$ points be given

$$0 \leq x_1 < x_2 < \cdots < x_{n+1} \leq 1$$

and set $\delta_0 = \frac{1}{4} \min |x_j - x_{j+1}|$.

By Lemma 7-14 a continuous function $f_1(x)$ may be defined by (7–9.3) and (7–9.4) so that

$$f_1(x_j) - G^-(x_j) = +2M, \qquad j = 1, 3, 5, \ldots,$$
$$f_1(x_j) - G^+(x_j) = -2M, \qquad j = 2, 4, \ldots$$

and these points are local extrema of $f_1(x) - G^+(x)$ and $f_1(x) - G^-(x)$ in $[x_j - \delta_0, x_j + \delta_0]$. Further, the definition of $f_1(x)$ may be extended to the remainder of $[0, 1]$ so that

$$|f_1(x) - G(x)| \leq M, \quad |x - x_j| > \delta_0.$$

Since $f_1(x)$ is continuous, the assumption of existence implies that $f_1(x)$ possesses a best approximation $F(A^1, x)$. The assumption of Property $NS$ implies that $F$ has Property $Z$. This fact is used essentially in the remainder of the proof.

The following assertion is now established:

*Assertion 1.*

$$\|f_1(x) - F(A^1, x)\| \leq 2M. \tag{7–9.5}$$

There are $n + 1$ points $\{y_j \mid y_j < y_{j+1}\}$ such that

$$F(A^1, y_j) - f_1(y_j) = (-1)^j K,$$

where $K = \pm \|f_1(x) - F(A^1, x)\|$. If $|K| > 2M$ then since

$$|G(y_j) - f_1(y_j)| \leq 2M < |K|$$

one has

$$[F(A^1, y_j) - G(y_j)](-1)^j \operatorname{sgn}[K] \geq |K| - 2M > 0.$$

For $k$ sufficiently large one has

$$|F(A_k, y_j) - G(y_j)| < \tfrac{1}{2}(|K| - 2M)$$

and hence

$$\operatorname{sgn}[F(A^1, y_j) - F(A_k, y_j)] = (-1)^j \operatorname{sgn}[K].$$

This implies that $F$ does not have Property $Z$ which contradicts the assumption of Property $NS$. This establishes the assertion (7–9.5).

We now establish

*Assertion 2.*

$$|F(A^1, x_j) - f_1(x_j)| = 2M, \qquad j = 1, 2, \ldots, n + 1. \qquad (7\text{-}9.6)$$

It follows from the first assertion that

$$|F(A^1, x_j) - f_1(x_j)| \leq 2M, \qquad j = 1, 2, \ldots, n + 1. \qquad (7\text{-}9.7)$$

Lemma 7–15 implies that either (7–9.6) follows from (7–9.7) or there is an $A_0 \in P$ such that

$$|F(A_0, x_j) - f_1(x_j)| < 2M, \qquad j = 1, 2, \ldots, n + 1. \qquad (7\text{-}9.8)$$

It is now shown that the alternative (7–9.8) leads to a contradiction.
Set

$$\epsilon = \min_j \left[ 2M - |F(A_0, x_j) - f_1(x_j)| \right] > 0.$$

There is an $\eta > 0$ such that $|x - x_j| < \eta$ implies

$$|F(A_0, x_j) - F(A_0, x)| < \frac{\epsilon}{3}, \qquad j = 1, 2, \ldots, n + 1.$$

Further, there exists a $y_j$ with $|y_j - x_j| < \eta$ so that

$$|G(y_j) - G^{\pm}(x_j)| < \frac{\epsilon}{3}, \qquad j = 1, 2, \ldots, n + 1.$$

One may choose $k$ so large that

$$|G(y_j) - F(A_k, y_j)| < \frac{\epsilon}{3}, \qquad j = 1, 2, \ldots, n + 1.$$

With alternative (7–9.8) it follows from these estimates that

$$F(A_0, y_j) > F(A_k, y_j), \qquad j \text{ odd},$$
$$F(A_0, y_j) < F(A_k, y_j), \qquad j \text{ even}.$$

This implies that $F(A_0, x) - F(A_k, x)$ has $n$ zeros, which is impossible. This establishes the assertion.

These two assertions imply that

$$\begin{aligned} F(A^1, x_j) &= G^-(x_j), \qquad j \text{ odd}, \\ F(A^1, x_j) &= G^+(x_j), \qquad j \text{ even}. \end{aligned} \qquad (7\text{-}9.9)$$

A similar construction of a continuous function $f_2(x)$ and an analysis of a best approximation $F(A^2, x)$ to it leads to

$$\begin{aligned} F(A^2, x_j) &= G^+(x_j), \qquad j \text{ odd}, \\ F(A^2, x_j) &= G^-(x_j), \qquad j \text{ even}. \end{aligned} \qquad (7\text{-}9.10)$$

It follows from (7–9.9) and (7–9.10) that

$$[F(A^2, x_j) - F(A^1, x_j)](-1)^{j+1} \geq 0, \qquad j = 1, 2, \ldots, n + 1.$$

Since $F$ must have Property $Z$, this implies that

$$F(A^2, x_j) \equiv F(A^1, x_j).$$

Since

$$G^+(x) \geq G(x) \geq G^-(x)$$

it follows that

$$G(x_j) = F(A^1, x_j), \qquad j = 1, 2, \ldots, n + 1. \tag{7–9.11}$$

One may fix $n$ distinct points and let the $(n + 1)$st point be variable. Then (7–9.11) is valid with $A^1$ replaced by a new parameter set $A_0$. However, on the $n$ fixed points one has $F(A^1, x_j) = F(A_0, x_j), j = 1, 2, \ldots, n$, which implies that $F(A^1, x) = F(A_0, x)$. Thus one has for any $x$,

$$G(x) = F(A^1, x).$$

This is the approximating function required in this lemma and concludes the proof.

*Proof of Theorem* 7–9. There are two implications to be established:

(a)   local unisolvence and closure imply existence and Property $NS$ and

(b)   vice-versa.

For the first implication we have shown (Lemma 7–13) that local unisolvence (which includes Property $Z$) and closure imply existence. It is already known (Theorem 7–8) that local unisolvence and closure imply Property $NS$.

For the second implication it is known (Lemma 3–10) that Property $NS$ implies Property $Z$. We have shown (Lemma 7–16) that existence and Property $NS$ imply closure. It is known (Theorem 7–8 and remarks after proof) that Property $NS$ and closure (and hence Property $NS$) imply unisolvence. This concludes the proof.

EXAMPLE.   For linear approximating functions, it is known (Theorem 3–14) that the classical approximating functions (i.e. linear approximating functions from Tchebycheff sets) are the only ones for which the classical results are all valid for all continuous functions. The simplest and most classical nonlinear approximating functions are the unisolvent functions. It is known that the classical results are valid for these approximating functions. One might conjecture then that these are the only approximating functions for which these results are all valid. That this is not true is seen by the simple example

$$F(A, x) = \frac{a}{1 + ax}, \qquad -1 < a < +1, \qquad -1 \leq x \leq +1.$$

One may easily verify that the three classical results of existence, characterization and uniqueness are valid for all continuous functions. The range of this approximating function is shown in Fig. 7–11.

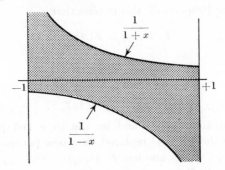

$$\frac{1}{1+x}$$

$$\frac{1}{1-x}$$

$-1$      $+1$

FIG. 7–11.   The range of $F(A, x) = a/(1 + ax)$.

## 7–10   AREAS OF DIFFICULTY AND UNSOLVED PROBLEMS

In the actual application of the theory of varisolvent functions, there are three principal areas of difficulty. They are

(a)   discovery of the exact form of the approximating function to be used in order to obtain an existence theorem;

(b)   proof of solvency;

(c)   the possible nonexistence of best approximations on finite point sets.

The difficulties are present, in varying degrees, for all the known and suspected examples of varisolvent functions.

It is very desirable for every continuous function to possess a best approximation. This means that one must essentially choose an approximating function so that the set

$$\{F(A, x) \,\big|\, \|F(A, x)\| \le M < \infty\} \tag{7–10.1}$$

is compact. This can be done in two ways. One may add elements to the set (7–10.1) or one may identify limit points of (7–10.1) with elements of the set (7–10.1). Both of these methods are used for exponential approximation. For some varisolvent functions (polynomial rational functions) this problem is trivial, but for others it requires a detailed analysis of the approximating function.

The second area of difficulty is well illustrated by the example of exponential approximation. The proof of solvency given in the next chapter is long and tedious. This is due to the fact that we are considering a nonlinear function, and, furthermore, this function has a variety of explicit representations. Generally speaking it is considerably easier to establish Property $Z$ than solvence. Thus in exploring the possibility that a given approximating function is varisolvent, one should consider Property $Z$ first. This has the dual advantage of avoiding the harder question of solvency if Property $Z$ is missing and of determining the degree of varisolvency if Property $Z$ is present. It is to be expected that the proof of solvency will present a problem of considerable importance for most non-linear approximating functions.

The third problem is one that generally arises in the computation of best approximations. Many computation schemes require that best approximations be computed on certain subsets, and hence the existence of best approximations on the subsets is normally required. In some situations it may be possible to devise special methods to circumvent the lack of existence of best approximations. The reason that this problem arises is that the beneficial properties of continuity are lost for approximation on a finite point set. An example of the nonexistence of best approximations on a finite point set by a varisolvent function is the following (see also Chapter 3):

EXAMPLE.

$$F(A, x) = \frac{1}{a + bx + cx^2}$$

$$X = \{-1, 0, 1\}$$

$$f(-1) = 0, f(0) = 1, f(1) = 0.$$

The function $1/(1 + nx^2)$ has a maximum deviation of $1/(n + 1)$ from $f(x)$. Hence the deviation of the best approximation should be zero. However, there is no function of the form $F(A, x)$ which attains this deviation.

The table overleaf gives a list of some known and conjectured varisolvent functions along with an indication of the degree of difficulty of the three problem areas: definition, Property $Z$ and solvence.

## PROBLEMS

7–1. With the notation of Section 7–8 establish the following result:
If $P$ is arcwise connected and $F$ is varisolvent, then $R = R_0$. (Rice, 1960).

7–2. Prove that

$$R(A, x) = s(x) \frac{\sum_{i=0}^{n} a_i x^{i-u}}{\sum_{i=0}^{m} b_i x^{i-v}}, \qquad s(x) > 0,$$

is a varisolvent function of degree $n + m + 1 - d$ where $d = \min(u, v)$.

TABLE 7.1. SOME KNOWN AND CONJECTURED VARISOLVENT FUNCTIONS

| Function | Known to be Varisolvent | Difficulty of | | | Remarks |
| --- | --- | --- | --- | --- | --- |
| | | Area 1 | Area 2 | Area 3 | |
| $F(A, x) = s(x) \dfrac{P_n(x)}{Q_m(x)}$, $s(x) > 0$, $P_n(x) = \sum_{i=0}^{n} a_i x^i$, $Q_m(x) = \sum_{i=0}^{m} b_i x^i$ | Yes | Minor | Medium | Major | Some linear techniques are applicable to this function. |
| $E(A, x) = \sum_{i=1}^{n} a_i e^{b_i x}$ | Yes | Medium | Major | Major | See Chapter 8. |
| $F(A, x) = ab^x \cos(\theta + \phi x) + c$ $0 \le |\theta| \le \pi \quad 0 \le \phi \le \pi$ | No | ? | Major | ? | See Problem 9–3. |
| $F(A, x) = \sum_{i=1}^{n} a_i \log(1 + b_i x)$ $x \in [-1, 1],\ |a_i| < \infty,\ |b_i| < 1$ | No | ? | Medium | ? | Property Z may be established. |
| $F(A, x) = \sum_{i=1}^{n} \alpha_i x^{\beta_i}$ | Yes | Medium | Major | Major | See Chapter 8. |
| $F(A, x) = s(x) \dfrac{P_n(x)}{Q_m(x)}$, $s(x) > 0$ $P_n(x) = \sum_{i=0}^{n} a_i \cos ix,\ Q_m(x) = \sum_{i=0}^{n} b_i \cos ix$ | Yes | Minor | Major | Major | See Cheney and Loeb (1965). Loeb (1965). |
| Weibul Distribution | No | ? | ? | ? | |

7–3. Show that the solution for $c$ to the system of equations

$$ab^n \cos (\theta + n\phi) + c = f_n + (-1)^n d, \qquad n = 0, 1, 2, 3, 4$$

is given by

$$c = \frac{2s_1 s_2 s_3 + s_4(s_0 s_2 - s_1^2) - s_0 s_3^2 - s_2^3}{2s_2(s_0 + 2s_1 - 3s_2 + 2s_3 + s_4) - 2(s_1 - s_3)^2 - 4(s_1 s_4 + s_0 s_3) + 2s_0 s_4}$$

where $s_n = \frac{1}{2}(f_n + f_{n+1})$.

7–4. Set

$$F(A, x) = F(a, b, c, \theta, \phi, x) = ab^x \cos (\theta + \phi x) + c$$

with $|a| < \infty, 0 < b < \infty, |c| < \infty, 0 \leq \theta \leq \pi, 0 < \phi < \pi$. Show

(a) If $F(A_1, n) = F(A_2, n)$, $n = 0, 1, 2, 3$ with $c_1 = c_2 = 0$,
   then $a_1 = a_2, b_1 = b_2, \theta_1 = \theta_2$ and $\phi_1 = \phi_2$.

(b) Set
$$\begin{aligned}
D(t, A) = {} & t^4 \cos (\theta + 2\phi) \cos (\theta + 4\phi) + t^3(2 \cos \phi - 2 \cos 3\phi) \\
& + t^2[\cos \theta \cos (\theta + 4\phi) - 5 \cos {}^2(\theta + 2\phi)] \\
& \qquad\qquad\qquad\qquad + t[4 \cos (\theta + 2\phi) \cos (\theta + \phi) \\
& - 2 \cos \theta \cos (\theta + 3\phi)] - \sin {}^2 \theta.
\end{aligned}$$

Show that if $F(A_1, n) = F(A_2, n)$, $n = 0, 1, 2, 3, 4$, and if either $D(b_1, A_2) \neq 0$ or $D(b_2, A_1) \neq 0$, then $A_1 = A_2$.

7–5. Discuss Tchebycheff approximation by

$$E_2(A, x) = \frac{1}{a_1 e^{t_1 x} + a_2 e^{t_2 x}}$$

$$E_3(A, x) = \frac{a_1 e^{t_1 x} + a_2 e^{t_2 x}}{1 + b_1 e^{s_1 x}}.$$

7–6. Let $F(A, x)$ be a varisolvent function. Consider the family of curves from $\{F(A, x)\}$ which assume a fixed value $a$ at a point $x_0$. Let $G(A, x)$ denote this approximating function. Prove that $G(A, x)$ is a varisolvent function in the remaining open intervals of definition of $F(A, x)$.

7–7. Establish Lemma 7–15.

7–8. Modify Assumption $\mathscr{A}2$ to read: *Assumption $\mathscr{A}1$ is included, P is arcwise connected, and F is closed in the following sense:*

$$\lim_{m \to \infty} F(A_m, x_k) = G(x_k), \qquad k = 1, 2, \ldots, n \text{ with } (x_k, G(x_k)) \in R$$

*implies there exists $A_0 \in P$ such that $G(x) = F(A_0, x)$.*

Show that the only approximating functions satisfying this assumption and Theorem 3–10 are the unisolvent functions. (Rice, 1960.)

# 8

# The Exponential Function
# and Related Functions

## 8-1  INTRODUCTION

The purpose of this chapter is to study an important example of a vari-solvent function in some detail. The exponential function exhibits some characteristic properties of varisolvent functions. These properties have complications in two areas where we might not expect them, namely the definition of the approximating function and approximation on finite point sets.

The definition of the approximating function is made in the next section and, though essential, this problem is not overly difficult. The third section discusses approximation from a curve of functions. This includes the exponential as a special case. Some existence theorems and a fact about the strict monotonicity of the error are established. The next section establishes sufficient conditions for such approximating functions to be varisolvent. The exponential function is included. Other special cases are presented in the sixth section.

The second possibly unsuspected area of difficulty is considered in the seventh section. We show examples of the problems encountered and, for the simple case of $ae^{tx} + b$, the so-called *pseudo-functions* are introduced to allow a complete theoretical description of the situation.

The final section presents several aspects of the computation problem, including the use of pseudo-functions for computations on finite point sets.

The Tchebycheff norm of approximation is assumed through this chapter.

## 8-2  THE EXPONENTIAL APPROXIMATING FUNCTION

The first area of difficulty for the exponential function is that the definition of the approximating function must be extended. One would normally define the approximating function as

$$\{F(A, x)\} = \left\{ \sum_{i=1}^{n} a_i e^{t_i x} \ \middle|\ |a_i| < \infty, |t_i| < \infty \right\}. \qquad (8\text{--}2.1)$$

The functions in (8–2.1) have a serious deficiency. This set is not closed under pointwise convergence and, for example, the function $f(x) = 1 + x$ does not possess a best approximation in this set. This is seen as follows: let $n = 2$, and set $t_2 = 0$. Then we have

$$F(A, x) = a_1 e^{t_1 x} + a_2. \qquad (8–2.2)$$

If we now expand $e^{t_1 x}$ in a Taylor's series, we obtain

$$F(A, x) = a_1 + a_2 + a_1 t_1 x + a_1 (t_1 x)^2 \sum_{i=0}^{\infty} \frac{(x t_1)^i}{(i + 2)!}. \qquad (8–2.3)$$

One can now choose the sequence

$$\{a_1 = k, t_1 = 1/k, a_2 = 1 - k\}$$

and (8–2.3) becomes

$$F(A_k, x) = 1 + x + (1/k)x^2 \sum_{i=0}^{\infty} \frac{(x/k)^i}{(i + 2)!}.$$

One can make the coefficient of $x^2$ arbitrarily small by choosing $k$ sufficiently large. Thus there exist functions from (8–2.1) arbitrarily close to $1 + x$, but $1 + x$ does not belong to the set (8–2.1).

It may be shown by a similar analysis that any polynomial of degree $n$ or less is the limit of a uniformly convergent sequence from (8–2.1). In fact all the functions

$$\sum_{i=1}^{k} \left( \sum_{j=0}^{m_i} p_{ij} x^j \right) e^{t_i x} \qquad (8–2.4)$$

with

$$\sum_{i=1}^{k} (m_i + 1) \leq n$$

are limits of pointwise convergent sequences from (8–2.1). This phenomenon is well known in the theory of linear ordinary differential equations with constant coefficients. See Problem 8–8.

The natural remedy to this problem is to include all of the functions of (8–2.4) in the definition of the approximating function. Thus one defines the exponential approximating function as

$$\{E(A, x)\} = \left\{ \sum_{i=1}^{k} \left( \sum_{j=0}^{m_i} p_{ij} x^j \right) e^{t_i x} \,\middle|\, \sum_{i=1}^{k} (m_i + 1) \leq n, \, |p_{ij}| < \infty, \, |t_i| < \infty \right\}. \qquad (8–2.5)$$

This definition illustrates the difficulty, mentioned earlier, of defining a reasonable topology in the space $P$. While there are nominally $2n$ parameters of $E(A, x)$ one has great difficulty in embedding $P$ in $E_{2n}$. However if one considers the family of curves in the $(x, E)$-plane defined by (8–2.5), then there are no difficulties in using the neighborhood definition (7–2.2) to define the topology of $P$.

The set (8–2.5) of approximating functions is still closed under pointwise convergence. It is possible to choose a sequence of $(p_{ij}, t_i)$ such that the corresponding sequence from (8–2.5) converges to the discontinuous function

$$D(A_0, x) = \begin{cases} d_0 & x = 0 \\ d_1 & x = 1 \\ E(A_0, x) & x \in (0, 1) \end{cases} \qquad (8\text{–}2.6)$$

The following lemma shows that these functions may be disregarded in the theory of approximation on $[0, 1]$.

**Lemma 8–1.** *Let $f(x)$ be continuous on $[0, 1]$. If $D(A_0, x)$ is a best approximation to $f(x)$ on $[0, 1]$, then so is $E(A_0, x)$.*

*Proof.* We have

$$\sup_{x \in [0, 1]} |D(A_0, x) - f(x)|$$
$$= \max \left[ |f(0) - d_0|, |f(1) - d_1|, \sup_{x \in (0, 1)} |E(A_0, x) - f(x)| \right]$$
$$\geq \sup_{x \in (0, 1)} |E(A_0, x) - f(x)| = \max_{x \in [0, 1]} |E(A_0, x) - f(x)|.$$

Thus the deviation of $D(A_0, x)$ from $f(x)$ is greater than or equal to the deviation of $E(A_0, x)$ from $f(x)$. This establishes the lemma.

The above lemma is an example of the general fact that one cannot improve upon the approximation to a continuous function by modifying a continuous approximating function on a countable subset of the interval $[0, 1]$. This is due to the fact that the continuity of $f(x)$ and $F(A^*, x)$ automatically determines $\sup |f(x) - F(A^*, x)|$ on any interval containing such a subset.

In order to remove the ambiguity presented by the function (8–2.6), the following assumption is made.

ASSUMPTION. *The function $D(A_0, x)$ is identified with $E(A_0, x)$.*

With the above identification it follows that the set (8–2.5) is compact in the sense that every pointwise convergent subsequence from (8–2.5) converges to a member of (8–2.5). In order to establish this fact, we first show that $E(A, x)$ has Property Z.

We note again that when one is investigating the possibility that a function $F$ is varisolvent, one usually should begin with the consideration of Property Z. The two reasons for this are that Property Z is usually much more tractable, and hence one should verify or disprove it first and, secondly, once the degree of Property Z is known then the degree of solvence of $F$ must be the same. This makes the analysis of solvence more straightforward.

**Lemma 8–2.** *The function*

$$E(A, x) = \sum_{i=1}^{k} \left( \sum_{i=1}^{m_i} p_{ij}x^j \right) e^{t_i x}$$

*has at most*

$$\sum_{i=1}^{k} (m_i + 1) - 1 \tag{8-2.7}$$

*zeros.*

**Proof.** Set

$$F_1(x) = e^{-t_1 x}E(A, x) = \sum_{j=0}^{m_1} \rho_{ij}x^j + e^{-t_1 x}E(A_1, x) \tag{8-2.8}$$

where the $\rho_{ij}$ are generic constants and $E(A_1, x)$ is the appropriate function from (8–2.5). Since $e^{-t_1 x} \neq 0$, the function $F_1(x)$ has the same number of zeros as $E(A, x)$.

One may differentiate (8–2.8) $m_1 + 1$ times to obtain

$$F_1{}^{(m_1+1)}(x) = \frac{d^{m_1+1}}{dx^{m_1+1}}[e^{-t_1 x}E(A_1, x)] = \sum_{i=2}^{k} \left[ \sum_{j=0}^{m_i} \rho_{ij}x^j \right] e^{-t_1 x}.$$

Then set

$$F_2(x) = e^{-t_2 x}F_1{}^{(m_1+1)}(x)$$

and $F_2(x)$ has the same number of zeros as $F_1{}^{(m_1+1)}(x)$. Furthermore the number of zeros of $F_1{}^{(m_1+1)}(x)$ is an upper bound on the number of zeros of $E^{(m_1+1)}(x)$. Hence the number of zeros of $F_2{}^{(m_2+1)}(x)$ is an upper bound on the number of zeros of $E^{(m_1+m_2+2)}(x)$. This process may be continued until one obtains

$$F_k{}^{(m_k)}(x) = \text{constant.} \tag{8-2.9}$$

One may now apply the mean value theorem for derivatives to conclude that $F_k(x)$ has at most $m_k$ zeros. Hence $F_{k-1}(x)$ has at most $m_{k-1} + 1 + m_k$ zeros. This argument is applied to the $F_i(x)$ recursively to obtain the upper bound (8–2.7) on the number of zeros of $E(A, x)$.

**Corollary.** *Let $E(A, x)$ be explicitly given by (8–2.5). Then $E(A, x)$ has property Z of degree*

$$m(A) = n + \sum_{i=1}^{k} (m_i + 1). \tag{8-2.10}$$

**Proof.** The difference $E(A^*, x) - E(A, x)$ has at most

$$\sum_{i=1}^{k^*} (m_i{}^* + 1) + \sum_{i=1}^{k} (m_i + 1) - 1 \leq n + \sum_{i=1}^{k} (m_i + 1) - 1$$

zeros.

We may now state

**Theorem 8–1.** *The set*

$$\{E(A, x)\,|\ \max_{x\,\in[0,\,1]}\ |E(A, x)| \leq M < \infty\} \tag{8–2.11}$$

*is closed under pointwise convergence.*

*Proof.* We must show that every infinite sequence of (8–2.11) contains a pointwise convergent subsequence and further that the limit of this subsequence is contained in (8–2.11). From the corollary of Lemma 8–2 it is seen that $E$ has Property $Z$ of degree at most $2n$. Theorem 7–2 may now be applied to show that every infinite sequence from (8–2.11) contains a pointwise convergent subsequence.

The set (8–2.5) was found by taking the closure of the set (8–2.1) under pointwise convergence. However, no formal proof has been given that (8–2.5) and (8–2.6) actually comprise the closure of (8–2.1). Such a proof is a complicated exercise in expanding (8–2.1) in a Taylor series (as is done for the simple example in (8–2.3)) and examining the various possibilities. This fact is a consequence of some more general results presented in the next sections.

## 8–3  APPROXIMATION FROM A CURVE OF FUNCTIONS

In this section we consider a more general approximation problem which is analysed by the same methods as the exponential approximation problem (Hobby and Rice, 1967). In Section 8–4 we establish some existence theorems. The next section establishes that some approximating functions of this type (including exponential sums) are varisolvent. Concrete interpretations and special cases are presented in Section 8–6.

We consider a curve $\Gamma$ in $L_p[0, 1]$ which is the continuous image of the interval $I$. The mapping is denoted by $\gamma(t, x)$ and

$$\Gamma = \{\gamma(t, x) \mid t \in I\}.$$

From $\Gamma$ we form the *$\gamma$-polynomial* of order $n$

$$P_n(A, T, x) = \sum_{i=1}^{n} a_i \gamma(t_i, x)$$

where $A = (a_1, a_2, \ldots, a_n)$ and $T = (t_1, t_2, \ldots, t_n)$. Interesting examples of $\Gamma$ occur when $\gamma(t, x)$ is $e^{tx}$, $x^t$, $(x - t)_+^k$, and $(1 + tx)^{-1}$. Let $\mathscr{P}_n$ denote the set

$$\{P_n(A, T, x) \mid -\infty < a_i < \infty;\ t_i\ \text{distinct}\}.$$

We assume throughout that any set $\{\gamma(t_i, x)\}$ with distinct $t_i$ is a linearly independent set of functions of $x$.

We have the

Γ-APPROXIMATION PROBLEM. *Given* $f \in L_p[0, 1]$, *determine a* $\gamma$-*polynomial* $P_n(A^*, T^*)$ *of order* $n$ *so that*

$$\|f - P_n(A^*, T^*)\|_p \le \|f - P_n(A, T)\|_p$$

*for all* $\gamma$-*polynomials* $P_n(A, T)$ *of order* $n$.
Here $\| \ \|_p$ denotes the norm in $L_p[0, 1]$.

Not unexpectedly, this problem does not always have a solution. The concept of $\gamma$-polynomial is extended in Section 8–4 and three existence theorems are established. The first, Theorem 8–5, is for $1 \le p \le \infty$, $I$ compact and $\gamma(t, x)$ sufficiently differentiable. The important case when $I$ is not compact is considered in Theorem 8–6 for $1 \le p < \infty$ and Theorem 8–7 for $p = \infty$.

In this section we note the interesting fact that if $\Gamma$ spans $L_p[0, 1]$ (as in the above examples), then the error of the best $L_p$-approximation, for $1 < p < \infty$, *strictly* decreases as a function of $n$ until it reaches zero.

We denote the error of the best $L_p$-approximation $P_n(A^*, T^*)$ to $f(x) \in L_p[0, 1]$ by

$$E_p^n(f) = \|f - P_n(A^*, T^*)\|_p.$$

We show that $E_n^p(f)$ is a strictly decreasing function of $n$ for $1 < p < \infty$ as long as $E_n^p(f)$ is not zero. Let $[\Gamma]$ denote the smallest linear subspace of $L_p[0, 1]$ which contains the curve $\Gamma$.

**Lemma 8–3.** *Assume that* $[\Gamma] = L_p[0, 1]$ *and* $1 < p < \infty$. *Then either* $\|f\|_p = 0$ *or*

$$E_1^p(f) < \|f\|_p.$$

*Proof.* For each value of $t$ there is a coefficient $a_t$ so that

$$\int_0^1 |f(x) - a_t\gamma(t, x)|^p \, dx$$

is minimized for all $a$. This implies (by differentiation) that

$$\int_0^1 |f(x) - a_t\gamma(t, x)|^{p-1} \operatorname{sgn} [f(x) - a_t\gamma(t, x)]\gamma(t, x) \, dx = 0.$$

Suppose that $\|f\|_p = E_1^p(f)$. Then $a_t = 0$ for every $t$ and

$$\int_0^1 |f(x)|^{p-1} \operatorname{sgn} [f(x)]\gamma(t, x) \, dx = 0$$

for every $t$. Thus

$$\int_0^1 |f(x)|^{p-1} \operatorname{sgn} [f(x)] \sum_{i=1}^n a_i\gamma(t_i, x) \, dx = 0$$

for arbitrary $a_i$, $t_i$ and $n$.

The assumption that $|f(x)|^{p-1} \geq \epsilon > 0$ on a set $I\epsilon$ of positive measure leads to a contradiction as follows. Consider

$$h(x) = \begin{cases} 0 & x \notin I_\epsilon \\ \text{sgn}\,[f(x)] & x \in I_\epsilon \end{cases}$$

which is clearly in $L_p[0, 1]$. Since $[\Gamma] = L_p[0, 1]$, given any $\eta > 0$ there is a $\gamma$-polynomial $P_m(A, T)$ so that $\|h(x) - P_m(A, T)\|_p \leq \eta$. Hence we have, with $r = (p-1)/p$,

$$0 = \int_0^1 |f(x)|^{p-1}\,\text{sgn}\,[f(x)][h(x) - h(x) + P_m(A, T)]\,dx$$
$$\geq \epsilon\mu(I_\epsilon) - \|f\|_p^r\|P_m(A, T) - h(x)\|_p$$
$$\geq \epsilon\mu(I_\epsilon) - \eta\|f\|_p^r$$

where $\mu(I_\epsilon)$ is the measure of $I_\epsilon$. Thus $\eta\|f\|_p^r \geq \epsilon\mu(I_\epsilon)$, and since $\eta$ is arbitrary we have $\epsilon\mu(I_\epsilon) = 0$, which is a contradiction. Thus if $\|f\|_p = E_1^p(f)$ we have $\|f\|_p = 0$ and the result is established.

**Theorem 8–2.** *Suppose a best $L_p$-approximation exists for each $n$ and that $[\Gamma] = L_p[0, 1]$ and $1 < p < \infty$. Then either $E_n^p(f) = 0$ or*

$$E_{n+1}^p(f) < E_n^p(f).$$

*Proof.* Set $g(x) = f(x) - P_n(A^*, T^*, x)$. Then

$$E_n^p(f) = \|g\|_p \geq E_1^p(g) \geq E_{n+1}^p(f).$$

By Lemma 8–3 we have either $0 = \|g\|_p = E_n^p(f)$ or $\|g\|_p > E_1^p(g)$. This completes the proof.

This result is not true for $p = \infty$. The case $p = 1$ is open.

## 8–4 THE EXISTENCE THEOREMS FOR $L_p$-APPROXIMATION

As in many approximation problems, the problem as initially stated does not always have a solution. The usual remedy is to enlarge the set of admissible approximation functions appropriately. Thus we set

$$\overline{\mathscr{P}}_n = \{P_n(A, T) = \sum_{i=1}^k \sum_{j=0}^{m_i} a_{ij}\gamma^{(j)}(t_i, x) \mid \sum_{i=1}^k (m_i + 1) \leq n\}$$

where $\gamma^{(j)}(t, x)$ denotes the $j$th derivative of $\gamma(t, x)$ with respect to $t$. The symbols $A$ and $T$ denote generically the parameters $\{a_{ij}\}$ and $\{t_i\}$ of this expression.

In this section we establish three existence theorems for $L_p$-approximations from $\overline{\mathscr{P}}_n$. We require some preliminary results. The first is a variation of Gauss elimination applied to a Vandermonde matrix.

**Lemma 8–4.** *Let $D^j = (d_1^j, d_2^j, \ldots, d_n^j)$.*

*Suppose that $D^j \to 0$ as $j \to \infty$ and that*

$$\sum_{i=1}^{n} a_i^j (d_i^j)^l$$

*is bounded for each $l = 0, 1, \ldots, n - 1$.*

*Let $a_i^j(1) = a_i^j$ and $a_i^j(r) = a_i^j \prod_{q=1}^{r-1} (d_i^j - d_q^j)$ for $1 < r \le i$.*

*Then, for each $l = 0, 1, \ldots, n - r$,*

$$\sum_{i=r}^{n} a_i^j(r)(d_i^j)^l \tag{8–4.1}$$

*is bounded.*

*Proof.* There is nothing to prove if $r = 1$. For simplicity of notation the superscripts $j$ are omitted. If (8–4.1) is bounded for $l = 0, 1, \ldots, n - r$, then

$$\sum_{i=r}^{n} a_i(r)(d_i - d_{r-1})^{q-l}$$

is bounded for $0 \le l \le q \le n - r$. It follows that if we set

$$F = \sum_{l=0}^{q} \left[ \binom{q}{l}(d_{r-1} - d_r)^l \sum_{i=r}^{n} (d_i - d_{r-1})^{q-l} a_i(r) \right]$$

then $F$ is bounded. But, for $1 \le q \le n - r$,

$$F = \sum_{i=r}^{n} a_i(r) \sum_{l=0}^{q} \binom{q}{l}(d_i - d_{r-1})^{q-l}(d_{r-1} - d_r)^l$$

$$= \sum_{i=r}^{n} a_i(r)(d_i - d_r)^q = \sum_{i=r+1}^{n} a_i(r + 1)(d_i - d_r)^{q-1}$$

$$= \sum_{l=0}^{q-1} \left[ \sum_{i=r+1}^{n} a_i(r + 1)(d_i)^{q-1} \right] (-d_r)^{q-1-l}.$$

The proof follows immediately by induction on $q$, then on $r$.

The following *conditions $G$* on $\gamma(t, x)$ are required:

(G1)  *the $\gamma^{(j)}(t, x)$ exist and are linearly independent functions of $x$ for $j = 0, 1, 2, \ldots, n$,*

(G2)  *$\gamma^{(n-1)}(t, x)$ is absolutely continuous,*

(G3)  *$\gamma^{(n)}(t, x)$ is bounded in the domain $I \otimes [0, 1]$.*

**Theorem 8–3.** *Condition G3 on $\gamma(t, x)$ is assumed. If $D^j \to 0$ and if for each $l = 0, 1, 2, \ldots, n - 1$,*

$$\sum_{i=1}^{n} a_i^j (d_i^j)^l$$

*is bounded, then with*

$$R^j(t, x) = \sum_{i=1}^{n} a_i^j \int_0^{d_i^j} (d_i^j - \tau)^{n-1} \gamma^{(n)}(t + \tau, x) \, d\tau$$

*for $t \in I$ we have $\| R^j(t, x) \|_\infty \to 0$ for $t \in I$.*

*Proof.* The proof is by induction on $n$. For simplicity of notation, the superscripts $j$ are omitted during this proof. All limits are taken as $j \to \infty$ unless otherwise stated. When $n = 2$

$$\| R \|_\infty \leq \| \int_0^{d_1} [(a_1 d_1 + a_2 d_2) - (a_1 + a_2)\tau] \gamma^{(2)}(t + \tau, x) \, d\tau \|_\infty$$

$$+ \| a_2 \int_{d_2}^{d_1} (d_2 - \tau) \gamma^{(2)}(t + \tau, x) \, d\tau \|_\infty.$$

Since $a_1 d_1 + a_2 d_2$ and $a_1 + a_2$ are bounded and $d_1 \to 0$, the norm of the first integral tends to zero. Likewise, since $a_2(d_2 - d_1) = (a_1 d_1 + a_2 d_2) - d_1(a_1 + a_2)$ is bounded, the norm of the second integral tends to zero.

Suppose now that the theorem is true for integers less than $n$. By Lemma 8–4,

$$\sum_{i=r}^{n} (d_i - d_{r-1})^l a_i(r)$$

is bounded as $D \to 0$ for $l = 0, 1, \ldots, n - r$. When $r > 1$ the induction hypothesis ensures that

$$\| \sum_{i=r}^{n} a_i(r) \int_0^{d_i - d_{r-1}} (d_i - d_{r-1} - \tau)^{n-r} \gamma_1(\tau, x) \, d\tau \|_\infty$$

tends to zero as $D \to 0$ whenever $\gamma_1(t, x)$ is integrable.

Let

$$S_r = \sum_{i=r}^{n} a_i(r) \frac{1}{d_i - d_1} \int_0^{d_i - d_1} (d_i - d_1 - \tau)^{n-r+1} \frac{\tau^{r-2}}{E(r - 1)} \gamma^{(n)}(d_1 + \tau, x) \, d\tau$$

where

$$E(l) = \prod_{i=2}^{l} (d_i - d_1).$$

Then

$$R = \sum_{i=1}^{n} a_i \int_0^{d_1} (d_i - \tau)^{n-1} \gamma^{(n)}(t + \tau, x)\, d\tau$$

$$+ \sum_{i=2}^{n} a_i \int_{d_1}^{d_i} (d_i - \tau)^{n-1} \gamma^{(n)}(t + \tau, x)\, d\tau$$

$$= \sum_{i=1}^{n} a_i \int_0^{d_1} (d_i - \tau)^{n-1} \gamma^{(n)}(t + \tau, x)\, d\tau + S_2.$$

Note that $\| R \|_\infty \to \| S_2 \|_\infty$ as $D \to 0$, since

$$\sum_{=1}^{n} a_i \int_0^{d_1} (d_i - \tau)^{n-1} \gamma^{(n)}(t + \tau, x)\, d\tau =$$

$$\sum_{l=0}^{n-1} \binom{n-1}{l} \left[ \sum_{i=1}^{n} a_i d_i^{n-1-l} \right] \int_0^{d_1} (-\tau)^l \gamma^{(n)}(t + \tau, x)\, d\tau$$

and each coefficient $\sum_{i=1}^{n} a_i d_i^{n-1-l}$ is bounded.

We show that $S_r \to S_{r+1}$ as $D \to 0$ for $r = 2, \ldots, n-1$. Let $\epsilon_i = d_i - d_1$. Then

$$S_r = \sum_{i=r}^{n} a_i(r) \int_0^{\epsilon_i} (\epsilon_i - \tau)^{n-r} \frac{\epsilon_i - \tau}{\epsilon_i} \frac{\tau^{r-2}}{E(r-1)} \gamma^{(n)}(d_1 + t + \tau, x)\, d\tau.$$

We assume that the terms are ordered so that $|\epsilon_i| \geq |\epsilon_{i+1}|$. Since

$$\frac{\epsilon_i - \tau}{\epsilon_i} = \frac{\epsilon_r - \tau}{\epsilon_r} + \frac{\epsilon_i - \epsilon_r}{\epsilon_i \epsilon_r} \tau,$$

we have

$$S_r = R_r + \sum_{i=r}^{n} a_i(r) \left( \frac{\epsilon_i - \epsilon_r}{\epsilon_i} \right) \int_0^{\epsilon_i} (\epsilon_i - \tau)^{n-r} \frac{\tau^{r-1}}{E(r)} \gamma^{(n)}(d_1 + t + \tau, x)\, d\tau,$$

where

$$R_r = \sum_{i=r}^{n} a_i(r) \int_0^{\epsilon_i} (\epsilon_i - \tau)^{n-r} \frac{\epsilon_r - \tau}{\epsilon_r} \frac{\tau^{r-2}}{E(r-1)} \gamma^{(n)}(d_1 + t + \tau, x)\, d\tau.$$

That is $S_r = R_r + S_{r+1}$.

We now show that $\| R_r \|_\infty \to 0$ as $D \to 0$. Let

$$\gamma_1(\tau, x) = \frac{\epsilon_r - \tau}{\epsilon_r} \frac{\tau^{r-2}}{E(r-1)} \gamma^{(n)}(d_1 + t + \tau, x).$$

Since $|\epsilon_r| \geq |\epsilon_i|$ for $i \geq r$, $\gamma_1(\tau, x)$ is integrable. Thus it follows from Lemma 8–4 and the induction hypothesis that

$$\| Q \|_\infty = \| \sum_{i=r}^{n} a_i(r) \int_0^{d_i - d_{r-1}} (d_i - d_{r-1} - \tau)^{n-r} \gamma_1(\tau, x)\, d\tau \|_\infty \to 0$$

3

as $D \to 0$. Observe that

$$R_r = \sum_{i=r}^{n} a_i(r) \int_0^{\epsilon_{r-1}} (\epsilon_i - \tau)^{n-r} \gamma_1(\tau, x) \, d\tau + Q$$

where we have used the fact that $\epsilon_i - \epsilon_{r-1} = d_i - d_{r-1}$. Since

$$(\epsilon_i - \tau)^{n-r} = \sum_{l=0}^{n-r} \binom{n-r}{l} (\epsilon_i - \epsilon_{r-1})^{n-r-l} (\epsilon_{r-1} - \tau)^l$$

we have

$$R_r - Q = \sum_{l=0}^{n-r} \binom{n-r}{l} \left[ \sum_{i=r}^{n} a_i(r)(\epsilon_i - \epsilon_{r-1})^{n-r-l} \right] \int_0^{\epsilon_{r-1}} (\epsilon_{r-1} - \tau)^l \gamma_1(\tau, x) \, d\tau.$$

By Lemma 8–4, each coefficient $\sum_{i=r}^{n} a_i(r)(\epsilon_i - \epsilon_{r-1})^{n-r-l}$ is bounded and thus each term in the sum tends to zero in norm as $D \to 0$. Hence $\|R_r\|_\infty \to 0$, $\|S_r - S_{r+1}\|_\infty \to 0$ and $\|R - S_n\|_\infty \to 0$.

We examine

$$S_n = a_n(n) \frac{1}{d_n - d_1} \int_0^{d_n - d_1} (d_n - d_1 - \tau) \frac{\tau^{n-2}}{E(n-1)} \gamma^{(n)}(d_1 + t + \tau, x) \, d\tau.$$

By Lemma 8–4, $a_n(n)$ is bounded and clearly

$$\left\| \frac{1}{d_n - d_1} \int_0^{d_n - d_1} (d_n - d_1 - \tau) \frac{\tau^{n-2}}{E(n-1)} \gamma^{(n)}(d_1 + t + \tau, x) \, d\tau \right\|_\infty$$
$$\leq \left| \frac{(d_n - d_1)^{n-1}}{E(n)} \right| \int_0^{d_n - d_1} \int_0^1 |\gamma^{(n)}(d_1 + t + \tau, x)| \, dx \, d\tau.$$

Since $E(n) = \prod_{i=2}^{n} \epsilon_i$ and $|\epsilon_i| \geq |\epsilon_{i+1}|$, we have

$$\|S_n\|_\infty \leq \int_0^{d_n - d_1} \int_0^1 |\gamma^{(n)}(d_1 + t + \tau, x)| \, dx \, d\tau$$

and $\|S_n\|_\infty \to 0$ as $D \to 0$. This implies that $\|R\|_\infty \to 0$ and completes the induction step and the proof.

**Theorem 8–4.** *Conditions $G$ on $\gamma(t, x)$ are assumed. Further assume $\{P_k(A^j, T^j)\} \subset \mathscr{P}_k, \|P_k(A^j, T^j)\|_p \leq 1, k \leq n$ and each for $i$*

$$\lim_{j \to \infty} t_i^j = t_0.$$

*Then there is a convergent subsequence, also denoted by $\{P_k(A^j, T^j)\}$, and numbers $b_i$ so that as $j \to \infty$*

$$\left\| P_k(A^j, T^j) - \sum_{i=0}^{k-1} b_i \gamma^{(i)}(t_0, x) \right\|_p \tag{8–4.2}$$

*converges to zero.*

*Proof.* For simplicity of notation, the superscripts $j$ are omitted during this proof. All limits are taken as $j \to \infty$ unless otherwise stated. Since $\gamma(t, x)$ satisfies conditions $G$, we have the Taylor series

$$\gamma(t_i, x) = \sum_{l=0}^{k-1} \frac{(t_i - t_0)^l}{l!} \gamma^{(l)}(t_0, x) + \frac{1}{(k-1)!} \int_{t_0}^{t_i} (t_i - \tau)^{k-1} \gamma^{(k)}(\tau, x)\, d\tau.$$

Set $d_i = (t_i - t_0)$ and obtain

$$P_k(A, T) = \sum_{l=0}^{k-1} \left[ \sum_{i=1}^{k} a_i(d_i)^l \right] \frac{\gamma^{(l)}(t_0, x)}{l!} + R(t_0, x),$$

where

$$R(t_0, x) = \frac{1}{(k-1)!} \sum_{i=1}^{k} a_i \int_0^{d_i} (d_i - \tau)^{k-1} \gamma^{(k)}(t_0 + \tau, x)\, d\tau.$$

Since the $\gamma^{(l)}(t_0, x)$ are linearly independent functions of $x$, the co-efficients

$$\frac{1}{l!} \sum_{i=1}^{k} a_i(d_i)^l$$

are bounded as $j \to \infty$. Hence we choose a subsequence $\{P_k(A^j, T^j)\}$ so that each coefficient converges and we denote the limits by $b_l$ for $l = 0, 1, 2, \ldots, k - 1$. Then (8–4.2) is $\| R(t_0, x) \|_p$. The hypothesis of Theorem 8–3 is satisfied and $\| R(t_0, x) \|_p \leq \| R(t_0, x) \|_\infty \to 0$ to complete the proof.

We establish our first existence theorem

**Theorem 8–5.** *Let $I$ be compact and $\gamma(t, x)$ satisfy conditions $G$. Then given $f(x) \in L_p[0, 1]$ there is a best $L_p$-approximation $P_n(A^*, T^*) \in \overline{\mathscr{P}}_n$ to $f(x)$.*

*Proof.* We show that $\overline{\mathscr{P}}_n$ is boundedly compact which immediately establishes the theorem by standard arguments. We show that $\overline{\mathscr{P}}_n$ is bound-edly compact by showing that $\overline{\mathscr{P}}_n$ is the closure of $\mathscr{P}_n$ and that $\mathscr{P}_n$ is bound-edly compact in $\overline{\mathscr{P}}_n$.

Given distinct $d_i^j$, $i = 1, 2, \ldots, k$ there are $a_i^j$ so that

$$\frac{1}{l!} \sum_{i=1}^{k} a_i^j(d_i^j)^l = b_l$$

for $l = 0, 1, 2, \ldots, k - 1$. Hence given a term

$$\sum_{l=0}^{k-1} b_l \gamma^{(l)}(t_0, x)$$

we choose $P_k(A^j, T^j) \in \mathscr{P}_n$ with $T^j = (t_0 + d_1^j, \ldots, t_0 + d_k^j)$ and Theorem 8–4 implies that

$$\left\| P_k(A^j, T^j) - \sum_{l=0}^{k-1} b_l \gamma^{(l)}(t_0, x) \right\|_p$$

tends to zero as $d_i^j \to 0$. It follows immediately that $\overline{\mathscr{P}}_n$ is contained in the closure of $\mathscr{P}_n$.

Consider now $\{P_n(A^j, T^j)\} \subset \mathscr{P}_n$ with $\| P_n(A^j, T^j)\|_p \leq M$. Since $I$ is compact we may choose a subsequence so that $t_i^j$ converges for each $i$. Denote by $T^* = \{t_l^*|l = 1, 2, \ldots, k\}$ the set of distinct limiting values. Partition the sequences $\{t_i^j\}$ into $k$ classes according to limiting values and relabel $t_i^j$ as $t_{lq}^j$ if $t_i^j$ is the $q$th member of the $l$th class. Similarly relabel the $a_i$ and write $P_n(A^j, T^j)$ as

$$\sum_{i=1}^{k} \sum_{q=1}^{m_i} a_{iq}^j \gamma(t_{iq}^j, x).$$

Since the $\gamma(t_i^*, x)$ are linearly independent, each of the inner sums is individually bounded. Theorem 8–4 implies that there is a further subsequence and numbers $b_{iq}^*$ so that

$$\left\| P_n(A^j, T^j) - \sum_{i=1}^{k} \sum_{q=1}^{m_i} b_{iq}^* \gamma^{(q)}(t_i^*, x) \right\|_p$$

tends to zero. This limiting function is in $\overline{\mathscr{P}}_n$ and $\mathscr{P}_n$ is boundedly compact in $\overline{\mathscr{P}}_n$. This implies that the closure of $\mathscr{P}_n$ is in $\overline{\mathscr{P}}_n$ and hence $\overline{\mathscr{P}}_n$ is the closure of $\mathscr{P}_n$ and $\overline{\mathscr{P}}_n$ is boundedly compact.

For reference we state

**Corollary.** *Let $I$ be compact and $\gamma(t, x)$ satisfy conditions $G$. Then $\overline{\mathscr{P}}_n$ is boundedly compact in $L_p [0, 1]$.*

In many interesting situations the interval $I$ is not compact. The next theorem applies to some of these situations, in particular for $\gamma(t, x) = e^{tx}$ and $I = (-\infty, +\infty)$.

**Theorem 8–6.** *Let $I$ be the half open interval $[\alpha, \beta)$ and let $\gamma(t, x)$ satisfy conditions $G$ in $I$. Assume that for $k \leq n$ and any bounded sequence $\{P_k(A^j, T^j)\} \subset \overline{\mathscr{P}}_k$ with $t_i^j \to \beta$, there is a subsequence, an element $P_k(A_0, T_0) \in \overline{\mathscr{P}}_k$ and a set $I_0$ of zero measure so that*

$$\lim_{\to \infty} P_k(A^j, T^j, x) = P_k(A_0, T_0, x), \ x \notin I_0.$$

*Further assume that the convergence is in a norm on closed subsets of $[0, 1]$ not containing points of $I_0$. Then given $f(x) \in L_p[0, 1]$, $1 \leq p < \infty$, there is a best $L_p$-approximation $P_n(A^*, T^*) \in \overline{\mathscr{P}}_n$ to $f(x)$.*

*Proof.* There is a minimizing sequence so that

$$\lim_{\to \infty} \| P_n(A^j, T^j) - f\|_p = \inf_{\overline{\mathscr{P}}_n} \| P_n(A, T) - f\|_p. \tag{8–4.3}$$

Choose a subsequence so that the $t_i^j$ converge or tend to $\beta$. Those terms of

$P_n(A^j, T^j)$ with $t_i^j \le \beta - \delta < \beta$ for some $\delta > 0$ are known to have a limit $P_{n-q}(A_1, T_1) \in \overline{\mathscr{P}}_{n-q}$ by Theorem 8–5.

With $q \le \sum_{i=1}^{k} (m_i + 1)$ set

$$g_j(x) = \sum_{i=1}^{k} \sum_{l=0}^{m_i} a_{il}^j \gamma^{(l)}(t_{il}^j, x)$$

where $t_{il}^j \to \beta$. The hypothesis implies that there is a $P_q(A_0, T_0) \in \overline{\mathscr{P}}_q$ so that for $x \notin I_0$

$$\lim_{j \to \infty} g_j(x) = P_q(A_0, T_0, x).$$

We show that $P_n(A^*, T^*) = P_q(A_0, T_0) + P_{n-q}(A_1, T_1)$ is a best $L_p$-approximation to $f(x)$.

Let $I_\epsilon$ be a set of open intervals of total length less than $\epsilon$ which covers $I_0$. Given $\eta > 0$ consider

$$\|f - P_{n-q}(A_1, T_1) - g_j\|_p^p - \|f - P_n(A^*, T^*)\|_p^p$$

$$= \int_{[0,1]-I_\epsilon} [|f - P_{n-q}(A_1, T_1) - g_j|^p - |f - P_n(A^*, T^*)|^p] \, dx$$

$$+ \int_{I_\epsilon} |f - P_{n-q}(A_1, T_1) - g_j|^p \, dx - \int_{I_\epsilon} |f - P_n(A^*, T^*)|^p \, dx.$$

Since the convergence of $g_j$ to $P_q$ on $[0, 1] - I_\epsilon$ is in norm, there is a $j(\epsilon)$ so that for $j \ge j(\epsilon)$ the first integral is less than $\eta/2$ in absolute value. Further, there is an $\epsilon_1 > 0$ so that for $\epsilon \le \epsilon_1$ the last integral is less than $\eta/2$. Thus for $j \ge j(\epsilon)$, $\epsilon \le \epsilon_1$

$$\|f - P_{n-q}(A_1, T_1) - g_j\|_p^p$$

$$\ge \|f - P_n(A^*, T^*)\|_p^p - \eta + \int_{I_\epsilon} |f - P_{n-q}(A_1, T_1) - g_j|^p \, dx.$$

Since $\eta$ is arbitrary and the integral over $I_\epsilon$ is nonnegative we have

$$\lim_{j \to \infty} \|f - P_{n-q}(A_1, T_1) - g_j\|_p \ge \|f - P_n(A^*, T^*)\|_p.$$

This concludes the proof.

It follows immediately that

$$\int_{I_\epsilon} |g_j - P_q(A_0, T_0)|^p \, dx$$

tends to zero and hence we have

**Corollary 1.** *With the hypothesis of Theorem 8–6, every minimizing sequence (i.e. one for which (8–4.3) holds) is compact in $\overline{\mathscr{P}}_n$.*

Equivalently, this is expressed by the statement that $\overline{\mathscr{P}}_n$ is *approximatively compact*. We have then (Efimof and Steckin, 1961).

**Corollary 2.** *Every $f(x) \in L_p[0, 1]$, $1 < p < \infty$, has a unique best $L_p$-approximation in $\overline{\mathscr{P}}_n$ if and only if $\overline{\mathscr{P}}_n$ is convex.*

A similar argument establishes the following theorem, but the corresponding corollaries are not valid.

**Theorem 8–7.** *With $p = \infty$ and the hypothesis of Theorem 8–6, assume further that $I_0$ is nowhere dense in $[0, 1]$. Then given $f(x) \in L_\infty [0, 1]$ there is a best $L_\infty$-approximation $P_n(A^*, T^*) \in \overline{\mathscr{P}}_n$ to $f(x)$.*

## 8–5  TCHEBYCHEFF APPROXIMATION AND VARISOLVENCE

In this section we consider approximation in the $L_\infty$-norm. All functions are continuous for $x \in [0, 1]$ unless otherwise indicated.

We must further extend the concept of $\gamma$-polynomial. Henceforth, the domain $I$ of the $t$ variable is an open region in the complex plane and $\gamma(t, x)$ is analytic in $t$ for $t \in I$ and $\gamma(t, x)$ is continuous in $I \otimes [0, 1]$. These assumptions are included in the statement that $\gamma(t, x)$ is *analytic*. Let $P_n(A, T) \in \overline{\mathscr{P}}_n$. We may suppose that $P_n(A, T)$ has the explicit form

$$\sum_{i=1}^{k} \sum_{j=0}^{m_i} a_{ij} \gamma^{(j)}(t_i, x). \qquad (8\text{–}5.1)$$

Then the *degree* $m(A, T)$ of $P_n(A, T)$ is defined by

$$m(A, T) = n + \sum_{i=1}^{k} (m_i + 1) \qquad (8\text{–}5.2)$$

and thus $m(A, T) \leq 2n$.

This extension implies that $P_n(A, T, x)$ is a complex-valued function of the real variable $x$ and hence we might consider approximation of complex-valued functions $f(x)$. We do not do this here, but in the first part of this section we allow $t$, $\gamma(t, x)$, etc., to be complex valued. Thus Theorem 8–9 below is valid for complex functions, but it is not known what the consequences of Theorem 8–9 are for the Tchebycheff approximation of complex-valued functions. Theorem 8–10 states that the subset of $\overline{\mathscr{P}}_n$ of real $P_n(A, T, x)$ is varisolvent. Thus the known uniqueness and characterization theorems for real varisolvent functions can be applied. The results for the approximation of real functions are given in the Corollary of Theorem 8–10.

The following definitions are normally given for real functions, but are meaningful for complex functions and we use them for complex functions. We restate some previous definitions in this context.

**Definition 8–1.** *The set $\{\phi_i(x) \mid i = 1, 2, \ldots, n\}$ is a Tchebycheff set if the matrix $(\phi_i(x_j))$, $i, j = 1, 2, \ldots, n$ is nonsingular for every set of $n$ distinct $x_j \in [0, 1]$.*

**Definition 8–2.**   *The function $\gamma(t, x)$ is extended totally positive if $\{\gamma^{(j)}(t_i, x)\}$ $\{(\gamma_1^{(q)}(t_r, x), \gamma_2^{(q)}(t_r, x)\}$ is a Tchebycheff set where $j = 0, 1, 2, \ldots, m_i$, $i = 1, 2, \ldots, k'$ and $q = 0, 1, 2, \ldots, m_r, r = k' + 1, \ldots, k$ and $\gamma_1^{(q)}(t, x)$, $\gamma_2^{(q)}(t, x)$ are the real and complex parts of $\gamma(t, x)$.*

These and related functions are studied in depth by Karlin, 1967. The example $e^{tx}$ is extended totally positive, and further cases are presented in Section 8–6.

**Definition 8–3.**   *$P_n(A, T)$ is varisolvent of degree $m = m(A', T')$ at $(A', T')$ if given $\{x_l | 0 \le x_1 < x_2 < \cdots < x_m \le 1\}$ and $\epsilon > 0$, there is a $\delta(A', T', x_l, \epsilon) > 0$ so that $|w_l - P_n(A', T', x_l)| < \delta$ implies there is a unique solution to*

$$P_n(A, T, x_l) = w_l, \qquad l = 1, 2, \ldots, m, \qquad (8\text{–}5.3)$$

*and $\| P_n(A, T) - P_n(A', T') \|_\infty \le \epsilon$.*

The following lemma is readily established.

**Lemma 8–5.**   *Let $\gamma(t, x)$ be analytic and extended totally positive. Then the solution of (8–5.3) is unique if it exists.*

In preparation for the proof of Theorem 8–8, we establish

**Lemma 8–6.**   *Suppose that $y_1, y_2, \ldots, y_{2n}$ are numbers such that, with $R_j = (y_j, y_{j+1}, \ldots, y_{j+n-1})$, the matrix*

$$Y = \begin{pmatrix} R_1 \\ R_2 \\ \cdot \\ \cdot \\ \cdot \\ R_n \end{pmatrix} \qquad (8\text{–}5.4)$$

*is nonsingular. Let $e = (e_1, e_2, \ldots, e_n)$ be the solution of*

$$eY = R_{n+1} \qquad (8\text{–}5.5)$$

*and set $p(z) = z^n - \sum_{j=1}^n e_j z^{j-1}$. Let $d_1, d_2, \ldots, d_s$ be the distinct roots of $p(z)$, where $d_j$ has multiplicity $m_j$. Let $V_j$ be the column vector whose entries are $1, d_j, \ldots, d_j^{n-1}$. Then $V_j$ is a characteristic vector of the companion matrix $E$ of $p(z)$ and $E V_j = d_j V_j$. Let $V_j^{(q)}$ denote the qth formal derivative of $V_j$ with respect to $d_j$ and let $V$ denote the $n \times n$ matrix whose columns are*

$$V_1^{(0)}, V_1^{(1)}, \ldots, V_1^{(m_1-1)}, V_2^{(0)}, \ldots, V_s^{(0)}, \ldots, V_s^{(m_s-1)}.$$

*Then $V$ is nonsingular and if $b' = (b_1, \ldots, b_n)$ satisfies*

$$Vb = R_1',$$

*then* $E^n Vb = R'_{n+1}$. *Furthermore, if the rth column of $V$ is $V_j^{(q)}$, then the rth column of $E^n V$ is the qth formal derivative of $d_j^n V_j^{(0)}$ with respect to $d_j$. Let $\Lambda_q(Y)$ be the first component of $E^{q-1} Vb$. Then, if $\| E \| < 1$ and $j \geq 1$, we have*

$$| \Lambda_{2n+j}(Y) | \leq n \| Y^{-1} \| \| R_{n+1} \|^2.$$

*Proof.* We first show that $V$ is nonsingular. Suppose that $U = (u_1, \ldots, u_n)$ is a vector such that $UV = 0$. Let $u(z) = \sum_{j=1}^{n} u_j z^{j-1}$. It is immediate that $d_j$ is a root of $u(z)$ of multiplicity $m_j$. Hence $u(z)$ has $n$ roots and is identically zero. Thus $V$ is nonsingular.

Next note that $E R'_j = R'_{j+1}$ for $1 \leq j \leq n$. This is clear for the first $n - 1$ components of $R'_{j+1}$ since the first $n - 1$ rows of $E$ are zero except for a superdiagonal of ones. The last entry is correct since the last row of $E$ is $e$, given by (8–5.5). Therefore $E^n Vb = R'_{n+1}$.

If the $r$th column of $V$ is $V_j = V_j^{(0)}$, then $E^n V_j = d_j^n V_j$ since $V_j$ is a characteristic vector associated with the characteristic value $d_j$ of $E$. It follows immediately that, for any $q$,

$$E^n V^{(q)} = \frac{d^q(E^n V_j^{(0)})}{dd_j^q} = \frac{d^q(d_j^n V_j^{(0)})}{dd_j^q}.$$

For the final point note that, for $q \geq 1$,

$$\Lambda_{2n+q}(Y) = E^{2n+q-1} Vb = E^{q-1} \sum_{j=1}^{n} e_j E^{j-1} R'_{n+1}$$

where the last equality follows from the fact that $p(E) = 0$. Therefore

$$| \Lambda_{2n+q}(Y) | \leq \| R_{n+1} \| n \max_j | e_j | \max [1, \| E^{n+q-2} \|].$$

Since $e = R_{n+1} Y^{-1}$, $\max | e_j | \leq \| R_{n+1} \| \| Y^{-1} \|$ and since $\| E \| < 1$, the result is established.

For the next theorem let $Q$ be a nonsingular $n \times n$ matrix and let $X$ and $Y$ be $n$-vectors. Define the norm of $X$ by

$$\| X \|^2 = \sum_{i=1}^{n} (x_i)^2$$

where $X = (x_1, x_2, \ldots, x_n)$ and let $o(X)$ denote a continuous vector-valued function of $X$ such that

$$\lim_{\| X \| \to 0} \| o(X) \| = 0. \tag{8–5.6}$$

**Theorem 8–8.** *There exists a $\delta(Q) > 0$ such that $\| Y \| < \delta$ implies the existence of a solution $X$ of the equation*

$$QX = Y + Xo(X). \tag{8–5.7}$$

*Proof.* Set

$$M = \min_{\|X\|=1} \|QX\|.$$

Since $Q$ is nonsingular, $M$ is positive. Choose $K$, $1 \geq K > 0$ so that $0 < \|X\| \leq K$ implies

$$\|o(X)\| < \frac{M}{2}$$

or

$$\|Xo(X)\| < \frac{\|QX\|}{2}. \tag{8-5.8}$$

Define $\delta(Q)$ as

$$\delta(Q) = \min_{\|X\|=K} \|QX - Xo(X)\|.$$

It follows that $\delta(Q)$ is positive since, for $\|X\| = K \leq 1$

$$\|QX - Xo(X)\| \geq \|QX\| - \|Xo(X)\| \geq \frac{K\|QX\|}{2}.$$

It is now asserted that if $\|Y\| < \delta(Q)$, then a solution exists to (8–5.7). The equation (8–5.7) defines a continuous mapping of the sphere $\|X\| \leq K$ in $E_n$ into a distorted hyperellipsoid $H$ in $E_n$. The set $H$ is connected. From (8–5.8) it follows that the sphere $\|Y\| < \delta$ is contained in the interior of the set $H$. This concludes the proof.

The theorem is closely related to the implicit function theorem of analysis. In the application to be made here, the matrix $Q$ is the Jacobian of the system (8–5.3).

The main theorem of this section is

**Theorem 8–9.** *Let $\delta(t, x)$ be analytic and extended totally positive. Then $P_n(A, T)$ is varisolvent and if $P_n(A, T)$ is given by (8–5.1) with $a_{im_i} \neq 0$, $i = 1, 2, \ldots, k$, then the degree of varisolvence of $P_n(A, T)$ is given by (8–5.2).*

*Proof.* We know from Lemma 8–5 that the solution of (8–5.3) is unique if it exists. Suppose then that $P_n(A', T')$ is given explicitly by (8–5.1) with $a'_{im'_i} \neq 0$ where we distinguish symbols from $P_n(A', T')$ with primes. Further let $\epsilon > 0$ and distinct $x_l$, $l = 1, 2, \ldots, m(A', T')$ be given. Set

$$\eta_l = w_l - P_n(A', T', x_l).$$

We first show that (8–5.3) possesses a solution if the $|\eta_l|$ are sufficiently small.

In order to determine the exact form of $P_n(A, T)$ we set

$$y_{i,q+1} = c_{iq} - a'_{iq}, \qquad q = 0, 1, \ldots, m'_i - 1$$
$$y_{i,q+1} = c_{iq}, \qquad q = m'_i, \ldots, 2m'_i - 1,$$

and for each $i$ form the row vectors $R_{ij}$ and $2m_i' \times 2m_i'$ of matrix $Y_i$ as in (8–5.4). Set

$$M = \max |c_{iq}|$$

and note that since $a_{im_i'}' \neq 0$, there is a $\delta_1 > 0$ so that $M < \delta_1$ implies that $Y_i$ is nonsingular. Thus, the construction of Lemma 8–6 associates with each $\{c_{iq} | q = 0, \ldots, 2m_i' - 1\}$ through $Y_i$ a set of roots $d_{ij}$, $j = 1, 2, \ldots, k_i$ of multiplicity $m_{ij}$ and corresponding coefficients $a_{ijr}$ (corresponding to the $b$ vector) for $r = 0, 1, \ldots, m_{ij}$, $j = 1, 2, \ldots, k_i$.

The structure of the $V$ matrix associated with each $Y_i$ is such that we have, after manipulations and collection of terms,

$$\sum_{j=1}^{k_i} \sum_{r=0}^{m_{ij}} a_{ijr} \gamma^{(r)}(t_i' + d_{ij}, x) = \sum_{q=0}^{\infty} \frac{\Lambda_q(Y_i)}{q!} \gamma^{(q)}(t_i', x)$$

$$= \sum_{q=0}^{2m_i'-1} \frac{\Lambda_q(Y_i)}{q!} \gamma^{(q)}(t_i', x) + S(Y_i, x), \qquad (8–5.9)$$

where $S(Y_i, x)$ is defined by the last equality. Note that $\| R_{i,n+1} \| \leq M$ for each $i$ and hence if $M$ is small then from (8–5.5) the coefficients $e$ are small, and the roots $d_{ij}$ are small. Thus for $M < \delta_2$ we have $\| E \| < 1$ for each $i$ and hence by Lemma 8–6, we obtain for $q > 2m_i' + 1$

$$\Lambda_q(Y_i) \leq 2m_i' \| Y_i^{-1} \| M^2.$$

For $M < \min(\delta_1, \delta_2)$ the quantity $\| Y_i^{-1} \|$ is bounded independently of $\{c_{iq}\}$ and we have a constant $K$ so that

$$\| S(Y_i, x) \|_{\infty} \leq KM^2. \qquad (8–5.10)$$

Set $h = 2n - m(A', T')$ and if $h > 0$ choose $h$ distinct real values $t_j$ different from the $t_i'$, $i = 1, 2, \ldots, k$. Consider now the system

$$\sum_{i=1}^{k'} \left[ \sum_{q=0}^{2m_i'-1} c_{iq} - \sum_{q=0}^{m_i'} a_{iq}' \right] \frac{\gamma^{(q)}(t_i', x_l)}{q!} + \sum_{i=1}^{h} a_{i+k'} \gamma(t_i, x_l) \qquad (8–5.11)$$

$$+ \sum_{i=1}^{k'} S(Y_i, x_l) = \eta_l.$$

The linearized form of (8–5.11) is obtained by deleting the $S(Y_i, x_l)$ terms. Since $\gamma(t, x)$ is extended totally positive, the coefficient matrix of $\{c_{iq}, a_{i+k'}\}$ is nonsingular and the linearized system may be solved for any set

$$\{\eta_l \mid l = 1, 2, \ldots, m(A', T')\}.$$

From the relation (8–5.10) it follows from Theorem 8–8 that there is a $\delta_3 > 0$ so that $|\eta_l| < \delta_3$ implies that the nonlinear system (8–5.11) has a solution. Thus for $M < \min(\delta_1, \delta_2, \delta_3)$, (8–5.11) has a solution $\{c_{iq}, a_{i+k'}\}$. From this solution we obtain $\{a_{ijr}, d_{ij}, k_i, m_{ij}\}$ and choose $P_n(A, T)$ to be

$$\sum_{i=1}^{k'} \sum_{j=1}^{k_i} \sum_{r=1}^{m_{ij}} a_{ijr} \gamma^{(r)}(t_i' + d_{ij}, x) + \sum_{i=1}^{h} a_{i+k'} \gamma(t_i, x).$$

It is immediately verified from (8–5.9) that $P_n(A, T)$ solves (8–5.3).

To establish the final point recall that for any Tchebycheff set $\{\phi_i(x)\}$ and distinct points $\{x_l\}$ where $i, l = 1, 2, \ldots, n$, there is a constant $K_1$ so that

$$\left\| \sum_{i=1}^{n} b_i\,\phi_i(x) \right\|_\infty \le K_1 \max_j \left| \sum_{i=1}^{n} b_i\phi_i(x_j) \right|.$$

Let $K_1$ be the constant for the Tchebycheff set $\{\gamma^{(q)}(t_i', x), \gamma(t_i)\}$ in (8–5.11) and given $\epsilon > 0$ choose $\delta_4 > 0$ so that $|\eta_l| < \delta_4$ implies that

$$\sum_{i=1}^{k'} \| S(Y_i, x) \|_\infty \le k'KM^2 \le \frac{\epsilon}{2}.$$

Then

$$\left\| P_n(A, T) - P_n(A', T') - \sum_{i=1}^{k'} S(Y_i, x) \right\|_\infty \le K_1 \max_l |\eta_l|$$

and if $|\eta_l| \le \dfrac{\epsilon}{2K_1}$ we obtain

$$\| P_n(A, T) - P_n(A', T') \|_\infty \le \epsilon.$$

Thus with the $P_n(A, T)$ specified above and $\delta(A', T', x_l, \epsilon) = \min(\delta_1, \delta_2, \delta_3, \delta_4, \epsilon/2K_1)$ the theorem is established.

We are still interested in real-valued approximation. If $P_n(A, T)$ includes a term $a\gamma(t, x)$ where $a$ and $t$ are not real, and if $P_n(A, T)$ also contains the term $\overline{a\gamma(t, x)}$ we have that $P_n(A, T)$ is still a real-valued function. Thus a typical real element $P_n(A, T)$ of $\overline{\mathscr{P}}_n$ appears as

$$\sum_{i=1}^{k_r} \sum_{j=0}^{m_i} a_{ij}\gamma^{(j)}(t_i, x) + \sum_{i=k_r+1}^{k} \sum_{j=0}^{m_i} [a_{ij}\gamma^{(j)}(t_i, x) + \bar{a}_{ij}\gamma^{(j)}(\bar{t}_i, x)], \qquad (8\text{–}5.12)$$

where the $a_{ij}, t_i$ are real for $i \le k_r$ and complex for $i > k_r$. The *degree* of (8–5.12) is seen to be

$$m(A, T) = n + \sum_{i=1}^{k_r} (m_i + 1) + 2 \sum_{i=k_r+1}^{k} (m_i + 1). \qquad (8\text{–}5.13)$$

Note that there is another representation of $P_n(A, T)$ in terms of the real and complex parts, $\gamma_1(t, x)$ and $\gamma_2(t, x)$, of $\gamma(t, x)$. We have

$$a\gamma(t, x) + \bar{a}\gamma(\bar{t}, x) = 2[\alpha\gamma_1(t, x) - \beta\gamma_2(t, x)],$$

where $a = \alpha + i\beta$. This is well illustrated by the example of $e^{tx}$ where

$$ae^{tx} + \bar{a}e^{\bar{t}x} = 2e^{\tau x}[\alpha \cos \theta x - \beta \sin \theta x]$$

where $t = \tau + i\theta$, $a = \alpha + i\beta$ and $\alpha, \beta, \tau, \theta$ are real parameters.

We now present the result pertinent to the approximation of real-valued functions by real elements of $\overline{\mathscr{P}}_n$.

**Theorem 8–10.** *Let $\gamma(t, x)$ be analytic and extended totally positive. Then the subset of $\overline{\mathscr{P}}_n$ consisting of real elements is varisolvent and the degree of the function (8–5.12) is given by (8–5.13).*

*Proof.* We need only establish that if the $w_l$ are real and if $P_n(A', T')$ is given by (8–5.12), then the solution of (8–5.3) may also be represented in the form (8–5.12). It follows from the proof of Theorem 8–9 that the uniqueness condition and the condition involving $\epsilon$ are satisfied.

We note that if $a_{ijr}, d_{ij}$ are derived from the matrix $Y_i$ by the construction of Lemma 8–6 and Theorem 8–9, then a manipulation shows that the analog of (8–5.9) is

$$\sum_{j=1}^{k_i} \sum_{r=0}^{m_{ij}} [a_{ijr}\gamma^{(r)}(t_i' + d_{ij}, x) + \bar{a}_{ijr}\gamma^{(r)}(\bar{t}_i + \bar{d}_{ij}, x)]$$

$$= \sum_{q=0}^{\infty} \left[ \frac{2 \operatorname{Re}[\Lambda_q(Y_i)]}{q!} \gamma_1^{(q)}(t_i', x) - \frac{2 \operatorname{Im}[\Lambda_q(Y_i)]}{q!} \gamma_2^{(q)}(t_i', x) \right]$$

$$= \sum_{q=0}^{2m_i'-1} \left[ \frac{2 \operatorname{Re}[\Lambda_q(Y_i)]}{q!} \gamma_1^{(q)}(t_i', x) \right.$$
$$\left. - \frac{2 \operatorname{Im}[\Lambda_q(Y_i)]}{q!} \gamma_2^{(q)}(t_i', x) \right] + S(Y_i, x)$$

and the relation (8–5.10) applies to $S(Y_i, x)$ for $M$ sufficiently small.

We modify (8–5.11) by replacing the linear terms for $k_r' + 1 \leq i \leq k'$ by

$$2\left[ \sum_{q=0}^{2m_i'-1} \operatorname{Re}(c_{iq}) - \sum_{q=0}^{m_i'-1} \alpha_{iq}' \right] \gamma_1^{(q)}(t_i', x) - 2\left[ \sum_{q=0}^{2m_i'-1} \operatorname{Im}(c_{iq}) - \sum_{q=0}^{m_i'} \beta_{iq}' \right] \gamma_2^{(q)}(t_i', x),$$

where $\alpha_{ij}' = \operatorname{Re}[a_{ij}']$, $\beta_{ij}' = \operatorname{Im}[a_{ij}']$. Since $\gamma(t, x)$ is extended totally positive and since a complex matrix is nonsingular only if its real and imaginary parts are nonsingular, it follows that the coefficient matrix of the linear terms in the modified (8–5.11) is still nonsingular. Thus the remainder of the argument of Theorem 8–9 may be carried through. Note that some of the $d_{ij}$ may be complex for $i \leq k_r$, but since $Y_i$ is real and the $d_{ij}$ are roots of the polynomial with coefficients determined by (8–5.5), it follows that these $d_{ij}$ occur in complex pairs. So $P_n(A, T)$ can still be represented in the form (8–5.12), even though $k_r$ may differ from $k_r'$. This concludes the proof.

Using the results of Chapter 7 we obtain the

**Corollary.** *Let* $\gamma(t, x)$ *be analytic and extended totally positive. Let* $f(x)$ *be a real continuous function of* $x$. *Then the best Tchebycheff approximation* $P_n(A^*, T^*)$ *by real elements of* $\overline{\mathscr{P}}_n$ *is unique and is characterized by the fact that* $f(x) - P_n(A^*, T^*)$ *alternates at least* $m(A^*, T^*)$ *times on* $[0, 1]$.

Note that this corollary does not imply that $P_n(A^*, T^*)$ exists.

## 8–6  CONCRETE INTERPRETATIONS

The primary concrete example to which Theorem 8–10 and its Corollary can be applied is the function $\gamma(t, x) = e^{tx}$. Note, however, that we do not obtain a positive statement on existence, uniqueness and characterization simultaneously. In order to obtain the characterization and uniqueness results in Theorem 8–10 we must allow the domain of $t$ to be an *open* set. This, of course, implies that we cannot in general establish an existence theorem. If we take the domain of $t$ to be a closed set, then we immediately obtain an existence theorem, but we lose varisolvence (and hence the characterization theorem) on the boundary of this set.

It is surprising how little is known about Tchebycheff approximation in the complex plane. Some results on polynomial approximation were developed by workers in the early 1900's, but very little has been done since then except for questions on the degree of convergence. For example, very few examples of Tchebycheff sets are known for complex functions of a complex variable. The results of the preceding section only require knowledge about the simpler case of complex functions of a real variable. Even here very little is known. The basic properties of Tchebycheff sets have not been developed and it is not even sure what is the appropriate definition of a Tchebycheff set in these situations. We are able to avoid the questions here because we eventually restrict our attention to real functions of a real variable.

There is a great deal known about extended total positivity and related concepts. This theory is rich and it is not appropriate to attempt to present it here. The interested reader is referred to the presentation in Karlin, 1967. It is developed only for real functions of a real variable. Thus there is a gap to be filled before this theory can be carried over to the present situation. One would like to have a statement such as the following:

(a) *Suppose* $\gamma(t, x)$ *is extended totally positive as a function of the real variables* $x \in [0, 1]$ *and* $t \in [a, b]$

(b) *Suppose that* $\gamma(t, x)$ *is analytic in* $t$ *in some region* $I$ *which contains the interval* $[a, b]$.

*Then* $\gamma(t, x)$ *is extended totally positive in some region* $I_0$ *which contains the interval* $[a, b]$.

It is not known if this is a true statement. Note that one cannot blindly apply continuity arguments to the matrices involved in the definition of Tchebycheff sets (and thence to extended total positivity).

In spite of these negative facts, there is hope that the gap between the real and complex cases will be filled in a pleasant manner. In anticipation of this, we indicate some of the criteria for *real* extended total positivity and some methods for constructing new examples from known examples. This material and much more is presented in depth in Karlin, 1967. A function $\gamma(t, x)$ is said to be *strictly totally positive* if $\{\gamma(t_i, x) \mid \text{distinct } t_i\}$ is a Tchebycheff set.

### A. *Conditions for extended total positivity*

(a)  Suppose that $\gamma(t, x) = f(t + x)$ and $f(u)$ is infinitely differentiable in $(a, b)$. Then if $\gamma(t, x)$ is strictly totally positive, it is extended totally positive for $t + x \in (a, b)$.

(b)  Suppose that

$$\gamma(t, x) = g(x/t)$$

and $g(u)$ is infinitely differentiable in $(0, \infty)$. Then if $\gamma(t, x)$ is strictly totally positive, it is extended totally positive for $0 < x, t < \infty$.

(c)  Suppose that $\gamma(t, x) = f(tx)$ where

$$f(z) = \sum_{i=0}^{\infty} a_i z^i.$$

Assume we have convergence for $|z| < \rho$ and $a_i \geq 0$ with inequality for infinitely many $i$. Then $\gamma(t, x)$ is extended totally positive for $0 < x, t$ and $tx < \rho$.

### B. *Changes of variable*

(a)  Suppose $\gamma(t, x) = f(t + x)$ is extended totally positive for $t + x \in (a, b)$. Let $\phi(t)$ and $\psi(x)$ be infinitely differentiable with strictly positive first derivatives. Then $\gamma_1(t, x) = f(\phi(t) + \psi(x))$ is extended totally positive for $\phi(t) + \psi(x) \in (a, b)$.

(b)  Let $\phi(t)$ and $\psi(x)$ be infinitely differentiable with strictly positive first derivatives. Then

$$\gamma(t, x) = e^{\phi(t)\psi(x)}$$

is extended totally positive.

### C. *Specific cases of extended totally positive real functions.* The following

cases are from Karlin, 1967. Other examples are given there and the techniques of B (and others) may be used to generate more examples.

$$x^t; \qquad x, t > 0$$

$$\frac{1}{x + t}; \qquad x, t > 0$$

$$\cosh{(xt)}; \qquad \text{all } x, t$$

$$e^{-(x-t)^2}; \qquad \text{all } x, t$$

$$e^{-(x+t)}(x/t)^{\alpha/2}I_\alpha(2\sqrt{xt}); \qquad x, t > 0$$

$$p(t, x) = \int_0^\infty \exp\left[-\tfrac{1}{2}(t\sqrt{\tau/2\alpha} - x)^2\right]\tau^{\alpha-1}e^{-\tau/2}d\tau; \qquad \text{all } x, t.$$

(This is the noncentral $t$-density in statistics)

$$\frac{1}{\cosh{(x + t)}}; \qquad \text{all } x, t.$$

## 8–7  FINITE POINT SETS AND PSEUDO-APPROXIMATIONS

In most problems of analysis there is usually considerable simplification when one considers functions defined on a finite point set rather than on an interval. This, however, is an area of difficulty for most varisolvent approximating functions. Since $E(A, x)$ is a varisolvent function, best Tchebycheff approximations on a finite point set are unique and are characterized in the usual manner, *if they exist*. There is no counterpart of Lemma 8–1 or Theorem 8–1 for approximation on finite point sets and indeed best approximations by exponentials need not exist on finite point sets.

The following example illustrates the nonexistence of best approximations.

EXAMPLE.

$$E(A, x) = ae^{tx} + b$$

$$X = \{1, 2, 3, 4\}$$

$$f(1) = 2, f(2) = 1, f(3) = 0, f(4) = 1.$$

If $d$ is the deviation of the best approximation to $f$ on $X$, then the alternation of $f(x) - E(A, x)$ on $X$ leads to

$$ae^t + b - d = 2$$
$$ae^{2t} + b + d = 1$$
$$ae^{3t} + b + d = 0 \qquad\qquad (8\text{--}7.1)$$
$$ae^{4t} + b + d = 1.$$

Consider (8–7.1) with $d = \frac{1}{2}$, $b = \frac{1}{2}$, $e^t = \epsilon$, $a = \epsilon^{-1}$. The residues in (8–7.1) for these parameter values are $0$, $\epsilon$, $\epsilon^2$, $\epsilon^3$, respectively. As $\epsilon$ tends to zero, the values of $E(A, x)$ on $X$ tend to $\frac{3}{2}, \frac{1}{2}, \frac{1}{2}, \frac{1}{2}$. Clearly no better approximation exists, but there is no function of the form $ae^{tx} + b$ which assumes these values.

In Section 8–2, we closed the set of approximation functions when we discovered that best approximations did not always exist. This led to the inclusion of combinations of polynomials and exponentials as approximating functions, a step which is natural from any point of view. If we attempt to close the set of approximating functions for finite point sets, we are led to approximating elements which are not even functions in the usual sense of the word. Nevertheless these *pseudo-functions* are useful in computations, as seen in the next section.

The actual theory has been developed so far only for the very special case of approximation by $ae^{tx} + b$. These results are presented in the remainder of this section. This special case indicates what one should expect for more general exponential sums.

A *pseudo-function* $P_0$ is defined on the interval $[0, 1]$ as follows:

$$P_0(a, b, x_0, x) = -\infty \cdot \text{sgn}\,(b), \qquad x < x_0,$$
$$P_0(a, b, x_0, x_0) = a, \tag{8–7.2}$$
$$P_0(a, b, x_0, x) = a + b, \qquad x > x_0.$$

A similar pseudo-function $P_1$ is defined by

$$P_1(a, b, x_0, x) = a + b, \qquad x < x_0,$$
$$P_1(a, b, x_0, x_0) = a, \tag{8–7.3}$$
$$P_1(a, b, x_0, x) = -\infty \cdot \text{sgn}\,(b), \qquad x > x_0.$$

The parameters $a$, $b$ and $x_0$ satisfy

$$|a| < \infty,\ 0 \le x_0 \le 1,\ 0 < |b| < \infty.$$

The parameters $a$, $b$ and $x_0$ are often denoted by $B$ and the subscripts 0 and 1 are omitted if no ambiguity results. The approximating function is now defined to be

$$E(A, x) = \{ae^{tx} + b, a + cx, P_0(B, x), P_1(B, x)\}. \tag{8–7.4}$$

The parameters $A$ in $E(A, x)$ refer to the parameters in any of the four possible forms which $E$ may take.

The definition of the *deviation* $d$ on a set $Y$ has the natural extension

$$d = \inf_{A} \max_{x \in Y} |f(x) - E(A, x)|.$$

If a best approximation in the usual sense exists, then the usual deviation is obtained.

**Lemma 8–7.** *Given f defined on X then there exists a best Tchebycheff approximation to f by the extended exponential (8–7.4).*

*Proof.* We need only consider the case where

$$\lim_{j \to \infty} \max_{x \in A} |f(x) - E(A_j, x)| = \inf_A \max_{x \in X} |f(x) - E(A, x)| = d$$

and $\{E(A_j, x) \mid j = 1, 2, \ldots\}$ does not converge in the usual sense. This exceptional case can occur only when $t$ tends to $\pm \infty$ or zero. If $t$ tends to zero then the usual convergence takes place for $\{E(A_j, x)\}$ is uniformly bounded on $X$. When $t$ tends to $\pm \infty$ it is clear that the only bounded limiting functions of such sequences are the pseudo-functions (8–7.2) and (8–7.3).

A best approximation by the extended exponential is said to be a *pseudo-best approximation* whether it is a pseudo-function or of the usual form. Pseudo-best approximations are further constrained by two conditions. The first is that a discontinuity is permitted only where there exists no continuous best approximation. The second is that the "jump" of a pseudo occurs at a point of $X$ and is as small as possible consistent with obtaining a best approximation. These constraints are introduced to make the best approximation by pseudo-functions unambiguously defined.

There are two properties of the pseudo-functions which are similar to properties of varisolvent functions. These are given in the following simple lemmas.

**Lemma 8–8.** *Let $P(B_1, x)$ and $P(B_2, x)$ have the same interval of finiteness. Then there is a pseudo-function $P(B_3, x)$ such that*

$$P(B_1, x) - P(B_3, x) = P(B_2, x).$$

*Proof.* Since $P(B_1, x)$ and $P(B_2, x)$ have the same interval of finiteness, it follows that they are discontinuous at the same point in that interval. One can then choose $P(B_3, x) = P(B_1, x) - P(B_2, x)$.

**Lemma 8–9.** *Let $P(B_1, x)$ and $P(B_2, x)$ be two distinct pseudo-functions. Then $P(B_1, x) - P(B_2, x)$ has at most two sign changes in the interval (if any) where both $P(B_1, x)$ and $P(B_2, x)$ are finite. Further, if $P(B_1, x)$ and $P(B_2, x)$ are both infinite at a common point then $P(B_1, x) - P(B_2, x)$ has at most one sign change.*

*Proof.* $P(B_1, x) - P(B_2, x)$ is constant in the interior of the interval in question and thus any sign changes take place at the end points of the interval. Clearly there are at most two sign changes (the constant zero is not considered to change sign in this context).

If $P(B_1, x)$ and $P(B_2, x)$ are infinite at a common point then there is only one (at most) end point where the sign can change. This concludes the proof.

We may now establish a general theorem for Tchebycheff approximation by the extended exponential (8–7.4).

**Theorem 8–11.** *Let $f(x)$ be defined on a finite point set $X$. Then:*

(a) $f(x)$ *possesses a pseudo-best approximation.*

(b) *The pseudo-best approximation is unique.*

(c) $E(A^*, x)$ *is the pseudo-best approximation to $f(x)$ if and only if $f(x) - E(A^*, x)$ alternates $k$ times where $k = 2$ if $E(A^*, x)$ is a pseudo-function or a constant and $k = 3$ otherwise.*

*Proof.* Part (a) follows from Lemma 8–7. If $E(A^*, x)$ is not a pseudo-function then part (c) follows from the usual analysis. Further it is clear that $f(x) - E(A^*, x)$ must alternate at least once in any case as an arbitrary constant may be added to $E(A^*, x)$.

Assume that the pseudo-function $P(B^*, x)$ is a pseudo-best approximation to $f(x)$ on $X$ and that $f(x) - P(B^*, x)$ does not alternate twice. The deviation $\alpha$ must be assumed at the point $x_0$ of discontinuity of $P(B^*, x)$. There is a pseudo-function $P(B_1, x)$ such that

$$P(B_1, x) = P(B^*, x) + \epsilon$$

in the interval of finiteness of $P(B^*, x)$ and such that

$$|P(B_1, x_0) - f(x_0)| < |P(B^*, x_0) - f(x_0)|.$$

One may choose $\epsilon$ so that $P(B_1, x)$ is a better approximation than $P(B^*, x)$ which is a contradiction. This establishes the "only if" portion of point (c).

To establish the "if" portion assume that $f(x) - P(B^*, x)$ alternates twice on $x_0, x_1, x_2$ in $X$, and

$$\max_{x \in X} |P(B_1, x) - f(x)| < \max_{x \in X} |P(B^*, x) - f(x)|. \qquad (8\text{–}7.5)$$

Then $P(B_1, x) - P(B^*, x)$ has at least two sign changes and $P(B_1, x)$ and $P(B^*, x)$ are not infinite at a common point. If $P(B^*, x)$ is discontinuous on the left then the deviation $d_1$ of $P(B_1, x)$ satisfies

$$d_1 \geq \tfrac{1}{2}(f(x_0) + f(x_1)) \geq d^*.$$

This contradicts (8–7.5) and shows that $f(x)$ has no better approximations by pseudo-functions. Clearly a continuous approximation is not better than $P(B^*, x)$.

In order to prove part (b) assume that $f(x)$ has two distinct pseudo-best approximations $P(B_1, x)$ and $P(B_2, x)$ (it is clear that they must both be pseudo-functions) with deviations $d^*$. Since the error curve alternates twice, it follows that $P(B_1, x) - P(B_2, x)$ has at least two sign changes. Thus, by Lemma 8–9, one, say $P(B_1, x)$, is discontinuous on the left and the other, $P(B_2, x)$, is discontinuous on the right. There is a maximum interval $[x_1, x_2]$, where both of these functions are finite. Consider then

$|P(B_2, x_1) - f(x_1)|$ and $|P(B_1, x_2) - f(x_2)|$. It is clear that if these values are less than or equal to $d^*$, as they must be, then no jump discontinuity occurs at these points. This contradicts the definition of the interval $[x_1, x_2]$ and concludes the proof.

This theorem is very similar to the usual result for varisolvent functions and leads to the definition of the *degree of the extended exponential:* The degree $m(A)$ of (8–7.4) is defined by

$$m(A) = \begin{cases} 2, & E(A, x) \text{ constant or pseudo-function} \\ 3, & E(A, x) \text{ otherwise.} \end{cases}$$

The following analog of Theorem 7–5 for varisolvent functions may be established for the extended exponential by the same line of proof as for Theorem 7–5.

**Theorem 8–12.** *Let $E(A^*, x)$ be the pseudo-best approximation to $f(x)$ on $X$. Then there is a subset of $m(A^*) + 1$ points of $X$ such that $E(A^*, x)$ is the pseudo-best approximation to $f(x)$ on this subset. Further this subset is a subset which maximizes the deviation of the pseudo-best approximation to $f(x)$ among all subsets of $X$ of $m(A^*) + 1$ points.*

## 8–8  COMPUTATION

There are no direct methods for computing best Tchebycheff approximations by exponentials and the iterative methods are divided between the methods of descent and methods of ascent (see Chapter 6).

Furthermore, no one has proposed any methods of descent especially designed for exponential approximation, though of course the general approach may be used.

The methods of ascent, such as the one-for-one exchange and the Remes algorithms, may be stated for this approximation problem. However, there is an essential difficulty in the use of these methods in that they operate by successively finding best approximations on finite point sets. Since best approximations need not exist on finite point sets, these algorithms become undefined. There are further complications introduced due to the fact that $E(A, x)$ is varisolvent and hence the number of alternations of the error curve is not known *a priori.* Even if these difficulties have been circumvented, there remains a serious numerical problem of solving certain simultaneous nonlinear equations for the parameter values.

If one assumes that a best approximation exists on a certain set $\{x_j \mid x_j < x_{j+1}, j = 1, 2, \ldots, 2n + 1\}$, then, in general, one must solve for the $a_i, t_i$ from the system.

$$\sum_{i=1}^{2m} a^i e^{t_i x_i} + (-1)^j d = f(x_j), \qquad j = 1, 2, \ldots, 2n + 1. \qquad (8–8.1)$$

Obvious modifications are required if the form of $E(A, x)$ has some poly-nomial terms. The system (8–8.1) rapidly becomes very delicate as $n$ increases or as the $t_i$ coalesce. For the special case considered below an effective method of solution is given in Problem 8–2.

For the special case of $E(A, x) = ae^{tx} + b$, the difficulties of vari-solvence and nonexistence have been overcome (Rice, 1961b). The remainder of this section presents a procedure for this special case. This procedure is actually a modification which one may make to any of the method-of-ascent algorithms. The essential character of these algorithms remains unchanged. It is clear that similar but more complicated modifications must be made for more general situations.

It is conceivable that an algorithm exists which would never encounter a situation where best approximations do not exist in the usual sense. Such an algorithm would obviously be more desirable than one (such as is to be pre-sented) which encounters such situations. In Problem 8–4 an example is given which shows that all algorithms of the one-for-one exchange type encounter such situations. Further in Problem 8–5 an example is given where the Remes algorithm encounters a situation where best approximations do not exist.

Since the methods of ascent consider only four points at a time, it is sufficient to consider only this case in detail.

The purpose of the pseudo-functions and pseudo-best approximations is to allow the computation of a "deviation" and an "error curve" when a best approximation does not exist in the usual sense. The test of the usefulness of pseudo-approximations comes when we attempt to apply Theorem 8–12. Suppose $Y = \{x_1 < x_2 < x_3 < x_4\}$ and consider approximation on $X = Y \cup \{x\}$. There are sixteen distinct regions where $(x, f(x))$ may lie in rela-tion to the points of $Y$. See Fig. 8–1.

If $(x, f(x))$ lies in the shaded region, then the deviation on $X$ is the same as on $Y$. If $(x, f(x))$ lies in the other region, then the deviation of the best approximation is larger than $d$. Thus the pseudo-function does indeed define an "error curve", which may be used in the method-of-ascent algorithms.

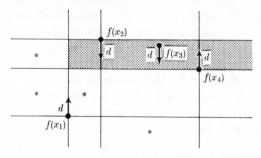

FIG. 8–1.   A typical pseudo-best approximation.

There are twelve basic combinations of four points in the $(x, f(x))$-plane for which best approximations do not exist. One may verify by enumeration that a situation similar to that shown in Fig. 8–1 is present in each case.

There is a simple test for the existence of a best approximation in the usual sense. From the set $Y$ one forms

$$s = \frac{f(x_1) - f(x_3)}{f(x_2) - f(x_4)}. \qquad (8\text{–}8.2)$$

Then, a best approximation exists if $s > 0$ and does not exist if $s < 0$. The case $s = 0$ is analysed in Fig. 8–2. In Fig. 8–1 an ordinary best approximation exists if $(x, f(x))$ lies in one of the regions with an asterisk. In the other regions a pseudo-function must be used.

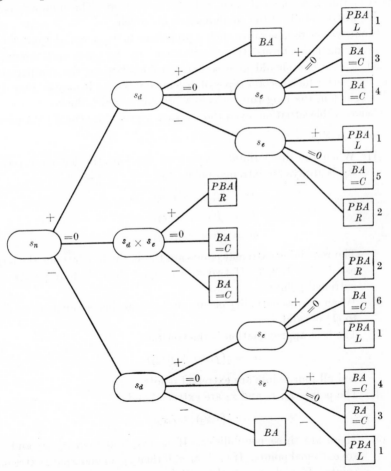

Fig. 8–2. Systematic classification of the possible situations which may arise for four points. The numbers refer to notes in the text.

A systematic classification of the possible situations which may arise for four points may be made in terms of the quantitative

$$s_n = f(x_1) - f(x_3)$$
$$s_d = f(x_2) - f(x_4)$$
$$s_e = f(x_1) - f(x_4).$$

The complete classification is given in Fig. 8–2.

In this figure BA denotes a situation where an ordinary best approximation exists and is not a constant. PBA denotes a situation where a pseudo-best approximation must be used. In this case $R$ and $L$ signify that the discontinuity occurs on the right and left, respectively. When the best approximation is a constant then $BA = C$ is written. The numbers refer to notes where details of the computations are given.

If one wishes to generalize such a procedure to exponential approximation involving more terms, the classification tree becomes very complex. In such a case one should give serious consideration to the comparative frequency with which certain types of degeneracy occur. It may be that it is more efficient in the long run to have a procedure which does not work in every conceivable situation, even though such a procedure could be devised.

*Notes on Fig. 8–2.*

(1)   When the discontinuity occurs on the left, the left-most point, $x_4$, is always an extremal point. Set

$$d_1 = |f(x_1) - f(x_2)|$$
$$d_2 = |f(x_1) - f(x_3)|$$
$$d_3 = |f(x_2) - f(x_3)|.$$

The remaining extremal points are those which determine the largest $d_i$, $i = 1, 2, 3$. If two $d_i$ are equal then all four points are extremal points.

(2)   When the discontinuity occurs on the right then an analysis similar to (1) is valid.

(3)   The best approximation is the constant

$$c = \tfrac{1}{2}\big(f(x_2) + f(x_3)\big)$$

and all four points are extremal points.

(4)   The points $x_2$, $x_3$ and $x_4$ are extremal and

$$c = \tfrac{1}{2}\big(f(x_2) + f(x_3)\big)$$

(5)   There are three possibilities. If $s_n + s_d > 0$ then $x_1$, $x_2$ and $x_4$ are extremal points. If $s_n + s_d < 0$ then $x_1$, $x_3$ and $x_4$ are extremal points. If $s_n + s_d = 0$ then all four points are extremal points, but the error curve only alternates twice.

(6)  The situation is the converse of that of (5).

(7)  All four points are extremal points. If $s_e = 0$ then the error curve alternates twice, if $s_d = 0$ the error curve alternates three times. The best approximation is

$$c = \tfrac{1}{2}\big(f(x_2) + f(x_3)\big).$$

(8)  The extremal points are $x_1$, $x_2$ and $x_3$.

## PROBLEMS

8–1.  Consider the Tchebycheff approximation of the values $Y_1$, $Y_2$, $Y_3$, $Y_4$ on the points $x_1 < x_2 < x_3 < x_4$ by $ae^{tx} + b$. Show that the parameters and the deviation $d$ are given by

$$\frac{e^{tx_4} - e^{tx_2}}{e^{tx_3} - e^{tx_1}} = \frac{Y_4 - Y_2}{Y_3 - Y_1} = u$$

$$b = \frac{(Y_1 + Y_2)(Y_3 + Y_4) - (Y_2 + Y_3)^2}{2[Y_1 - Y_2 - Y_3 + Y_4]}$$

$$a = \frac{(Y_1 - Y_3)^3 e^{-tx_1}}{(Y_1 - Y_3)^2 - (Y_1 - Y_4)^2}$$

$$d = \frac{(Y_1 - Y_3)^2(Y_4 - Y_3) + (Y_2 - Y_4)^2(Y_1 - Y_2)}{2[(Y_1 - Y_3)^2 - (Y_2 - Y_4)^2]}.$$

8–2.  Set $\phi(t)$ equal to the left side of the first equation of Problem 8–1 and consider the equation

$$g(t) = \ln \phi(t) = \ln u = v.$$

Show that $\dfrac{dg}{dt}$ is positive and monotone for all $t$ and hence that the equation $g(t) = v$ may be solved by Newton's method with an arbitrary starting point (Maehly, 1962).

8–3.  Assume that

$$x_2 = x_1 + H\Delta x$$
$$x_3 = x_2 + K\Delta x$$
$$x_4 = x_3 + L\Delta x$$

and set $z = e^{t\Delta x}$. Let $s$ be given by (8–8.2) and show that $z$ of the best approximation satisfies the polynomial equation

$$P(z) = sz^{(H+K+L)} - z^{(H+K)} - sz^{H} + 1 = 0.$$

This equation has exactly two positive roots including the trivial root $z=1$. Show that if the best approximation is a straight line then $P(z)$ has a double root at $z = 1$.

8–4. Consider the approximation by $ae^{tx} + b$ to the tabular function

| $x_i$ | 0 | $\frac{1}{9}$ | $\frac{2}{9}$ | $\frac{1}{3}$ | $\frac{2}{3}$ | $\frac{7}{9}$ | $\frac{8}{9}$ | 1 |
|-------|------|------|------|------|------|-------|-------|------|
| $f(x_i)$ | 0.05 | 3.1 | 3.15 | 0.25 | 0.35 | −0.05 | −3.15 | 0.85 |

Show that the best approximation to $f$ on $\{x_1, x_4, x_5, x_8\}$ is

$$E(A_1, x) = \frac{8^x}{10}$$

and the deviation is 0.05. For every other $x$ we have

$$|E(A_1, x_i) - f(x_i)| > 0.05.$$

Show that no best approximation exists on any set $\{x_1, x_4, x_5, x_8, x_i\}$ for $i = 2, 3,$ 6, 7. The best approximation on the entire set is

$$E(A^*, x) = 5.06825(.325387)^x - 2.90870.$$

8–5. Set $X = \left\{ x_i = \dfrac{i-1}{9} \middle| i = 1, 2, \ldots, 10 \right\}$ and consider the tabular

function

| $i$ | 1 | 2 | 3 | 4 | 5 | 6 | 7 | 8 | 9 | 10 |
|-----|-----|-----|-----|-----|-----|-----|-----|-----|-----|-----|
| $f(x_i)$ | 0.8 | 0.6 | 0.5 | 2.3 | 5.5 | 6.3 | 6.6 | 7.5 | 8.0 | 8.6 |

The best approximation by $ae^{tx} + b$ on $\{x_1, x_4, x_7, x_{10}\}$ is

$$E(A_1, x) = 32.250(1.2816)^x - 32.090$$

and the deviation is 0.64008. Determine the set of extremal point estimates which are obtained by the Remes algorithm and show that no best approximation exists on these points. The best approximation on $X$ is

$$E(A^*, x) = 0.00530098 (1533.12)^x - 3.23048$$

and the deviation is 2.75754. The extremal points are $x_2, x_3, x_6$ and $x_{10}$.

8–6. Define the approximating function $E_1(A, x)$ by appropriately extending the approximating function

$$P_0(x) + \sum_{i=1}^{m} P_i(x)e^{t_i x}$$

where

$$P_i(x) = \sum_{j=0}^{m} p_{ij}x^i.$$

Show that $E_1(A, x)$ is a varisolvent function and determine the degree $m(A)$.

8–7. Consider the system of equations

$$\sum_{i=1}^{n} a_i e^{t_i x_j} = f(x_j) + (-1)^j d, \qquad i = 1, 2, \ldots, 2n + 1.$$

Show that the $e^{t_i}$ are the roots of the equation

$$
\det
\begin{pmatrix}
1 & Y & \cdots & Y^{n-1} & Y^n \\
f_1 & f_2 & \cdots & f_n & f_{n+1} \\
f_2 & f_3 & \cdots & f_{n+1} & f_{n+2} \\
\cdot & & & & \cdot \\
\cdot & & & & \cdot \\
\cdot & & & & \cdot \\
f_n & f_{n+1} & \cdots & f_{2n-1} & f_{2n}
\end{pmatrix}
= 0,
$$

where $f_j = f(x_j) - f(x_{j+2})$.

# 9

# Rational Functions

## 9–1  INTRODUCTION

In this chapter a second important nonlinear approximating function is considered in some detail. The polynomial rational function

$$\frac{a_0 + a_1x + \cdots + a_n x^n}{b_0 + b_1x + \cdots + b_m x^m},$$

$$b_0 + b_1x + \cdots + b_m x^m > 0 \text{ for } x \in [0, 1], \ \sum_{i=0}^{m} (b_i)^2 = 1, \quad (9\text{–}1.1)$$

was partially treated in Chapter 3 by the application of techniques of a linear nature. The result Theorem 3–9 given there shows that (9–1.1) is a varisolvent function. We initially consider in this chapter the more general rational function

$$R(C, x) = \frac{N(A, x)}{D(B, x)} = \frac{\sum_{i=1}^{n} a_i\phi_i(x)}{\sum_{i=1}^{m} b_i\psi_i(x)}, \qquad D(B, x) > 0 \text{ for } x \in [0, 1]$$

$$\sum_{i=0}^{m} (b_i)^2 = 1. \quad (9\text{–}1.2)$$

The parameter vector $C$ stands for the vector $(A, B)$ and this convention is used throughout this chapter. We assume that the functions $\phi_i(x)$ and $\psi_i(x)$ are continuous in the interval $[0, 1]$ and that the sets $\{\phi_i(x)\}$ and $\{\psi_i(x)\}$ are linearly independent. We also assume that the functions $\psi_i(x)$ are such that the set defined in (9–1.2) is not empty.

We consider first the existence question and the results are of two types. First we have an existence theorem for approximation on the interval $[0, 1]$. This analysis is similar to that of Chapter 3 and the main idea is to discover a set of hypotheses on (9–1.2) to allow one to establish such an existence theorem. Second we have the concept of *stability* (Goldstein, 1963) which is used to attack the existence problem in a general setting. This concept seems to be one of the keys to understanding the existence problem for rational functions.

After this we consider the uniqueness and characterization questions for generalized rational functions. The approach is a somewhat natural extension of the polynomial case, but there are certain additional difficulties present. It is more difficult to make this extension than it is to extend the ordinary polynomial results to results involving Tchebycheff sets. The results here are due primarily to Cheney and Loeb, 1964, Cheney, 1965, and Loeb, 1965, but the presentation here is somewhat reformulated. Similar results were obtained independently by Brosowski, 1965b, 1965c.

In Section 9–5 we give a résumé of the results already established for (9–1.1) and consider in some detail the continuity of the operator which associates with each $f(x)$ its best Tchebycheff approximation by polynomial rational functions.

The final three sections are concerned with computational methods for rational approximations. A large number of methods have been proposed and several are described in this chapter. A rather long analysis is given of the Remes algorithm as applied to rational functions as it has been successfully used by a variety of people. There are many variants of this algorithm indicated in the presentation given here and even more have been described in the literature. The Remes algorithm encounters real difficulties for functions whose best rational approximation is (or almost is) degenerate (e.g., the degree $m(C^*)$ of the best approximation is less than $n + m + 1$). Some of the other computational methods proposed for rational approximation do not, in theory, encounter these difficulties, but this has not yet been verified by actual experiment.

The reader is forewarned that conditions for the convergence of some of the methods for rational approximations are unknown. As Maehly's second method shows, a few preliminary experiments may fail to indicate the true nature of the computational behavior of a particular method.

As in the preceding chapter we consider best approximation only in the Tchebycheff norm and use the convention that

$$\max_{x \in [0, 1]} |f(x)| = \|f(x)\| = \|f\|$$

when no ambiguity is possible.

The study of $L_2$-approximation by rational functions has been initiated by Cheney and Goldstein, 1967. A few of their results are presented in Problem 9–19.

## 9–2  EXISTENCE THEOREMS FOR THE INTERVAL $[0, 1]$

In this section we are concerned with the existence of a general rational function $R(C^*, x)$ so that

$$\|f(x) - R(C^*, x)\| \le \|f(x) - R(C, x)\|$$

for all $C \in P$. Following the definition for polynomial rational functions, we take $P$ to be given as

$$P = \{C = (A, B) \mid \sum_{i=1}^{m} b_i^2 = 1; \qquad D(B, x) > 0, x \in [0, 1]\}. \quad (9\text{--}2.1)$$

The existence problem is intimately related to the closure of the set $\{R(C, x)\}$ under convergence in $P$, and for general rational functions one cannot conclude anything about closure without further assumptions. Let us consider five examples which show some of the phenomena which may arise in this connection.

EXAMPLE 1. $f(x) = |x - \frac{1}{2}|$, $R(C, x) = (a_1 + a_2 x)/(b_1 + b_2 x)$, $x \in [0, 1]$. It is known from the results of Chapter 3 that $R(C^*, x) = \frac{1}{4}$ is the best approximation. Note, however, that $R(C, x) = \frac{1}{4}(x - k)/(x - k)$ is an equally good approximation except that it is undefined for $x = k$. We have, of course, assumed that the factors $x - k$ have been canceled, but this may not always be possible for other rational functions. See Fig. 9–1.

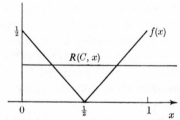

FIG. 9–1.   The best approximation $R(C, x) = \frac{1}{4}(x - k)/(x - k)$ to $f(x)$.

EXAMPLE 2. $f(x) = |x - \frac{1}{2}|$, $R(C, x) = (a_1 + a_2 x)/(b_1 + b_2 x)$, $x = 0, \frac{1}{4}, \frac{1}{2}, 1$. The best approximation in the usual sense is again $R(C^*, x) = \frac{1}{4}$, but note that $R(C, x) = \frac{3}{8}(x - \frac{1}{2})/(x - \frac{1}{2})$, i.e. $C = (-\frac{3}{16}, \frac{3}{8}, -\frac{3}{16}, \frac{3}{8})$, has a deviation of $\frac{1}{8}$ except where it is undefined.

EXAMPLE 3. $f(x) = |x - \frac{1}{2}|$, $R(C, x) = (a_1 + a_2 x)/(b_1 + b_2 x)$; $x_i = 0, \frac{1}{4}, \frac{1}{2}, \frac{3}{4}$. It is seen that

$$\inf_{C \in P} \max_{x_i} |f(x) - R(C, x)| = \frac{1}{8}$$

but no function of the form $R(C, x)$ achieves this value for the deviation. (See Fig. 9–2.) Note that the approximations which tend to minimize the error converge to the constant value $\frac{1}{8}$ except for $x = 0$. Thus $x = 0$ is a removable singularity and the "best" approximation here i s $R(C, x) = \frac{1}{8}x/x$, i.e. $C = (0, \frac{1}{8}, 0, 1)$. Note that this is the same type as in the preceding example.

EXAMPLE 4. $f(x) = \frac{1}{2} - \sin(3\pi x)$, $x \in [0, 1]$

$$R(C, x) = \frac{a_1}{b_1 + b_2 \phi(x)}$$

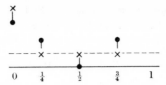

FIG. 9–2. A case of the nonexistence of best approximations. The dots are $f(x)$ values and the $x$'s are limiting values of rational approximations.

where

$$\phi(x) = \begin{cases} 3x, & 0 \le x \le \frac{1}{3} \\ 1, & \frac{1}{3} \le x \le \frac{2}{3} \\ 3(1 - x), & \frac{2}{3} \le x \le 1. \end{cases}$$

Consider the function (we have omitted here the normalization of the denominator for the sake of simplicity of notation)

$$R(C, x) = \frac{a}{1 + a - \phi(x)}, \qquad C = (a, 1 + a, -1). \qquad (9\text{–}2.2)$$

The limit of this function as $a$ tends to zero is shown in Fig. 9–3 along with $f(x)$. The limiting value of the deviation of these approximations is $\frac{1}{2}$ and it is seen that no smaller deviation may be achieved, nor is the value $\frac{1}{2}$ achieved by any continuous approximation of this form.

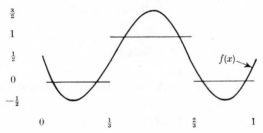

FIG. 9–3. The limiting values $R(0, 1, -1)$ of (9–2.2) as $a$ tends to zero along with $f(x)$.

EXAMPLE 5. $f(x) = x$, $R(C, x) = \dfrac{a_1 x^2}{b_1 + b_2 x}$,    $x \in [0, 1]$. It is clear that

$$\inf_{C \in P} \| f(x) - R(C, x) \| = 0$$

and this value is achieved for $C = (1, 0, 1)$. However, the parameter $C = (1, 0, 1)$ is not in $P$, for these values give $D(B, 0) = 0$. Thus a best approximation does not exist for this function.

Recall from Chapter 1 that the existence was approached by means of Condition E.

**Condition E.** *An approximating function $F(A, x)$ with $P \subset E_m$ is said to satisfy Condition E for the norm $\| \ \|$ if, given $M < \infty$, there is an $N < \infty$ such that*

$$\| F(A, x) \| \leq M$$

*implies that*

$$\max_i |a_i| \leq N.$$

In the case at hand we do have $P \subset E_m$ and the next lemma shows that Condition E is satisfied. Thus Theorem 1–4 says that the existence question reverts to the question of the compactness of bounded subsets of $P$. Since $P \subset E_m$, the compactness of bounded subsets is equivalent to the closure of $P$ in the usual Euclidean topology. In each of the above examples the lack of a best approximation resulted from the fact that $P$ was not a closed set.

**Lemma 9–1.** *The general rational function $R(C, x)$ defined by (9–1.2) satisfies Condition E for the Tchebycheff norm.*

The proof parallels that of Lemma 3–5 for polynomial rational functions.
*Proof.* Assume that

$$\| R(C, x) \| \leq M.$$

We have

$$|R(C, x)| \geq \frac{|N(A, x)|}{\| D(B, x) \|} \geq \frac{1}{mK} |N(A, x)|$$

where

$$K = \max_i \| \psi_i(x) \|.$$

Since the $\psi_i(x)$ are continuous we have that $K$ is well defined and finite. Hence

$$|N(A, x)| \leq mKM$$

which implies that the $|a_i|$ are bounded and the $b_i$ are bounded by the normalization of $P$. This concludes the proof.

We should note that we really do not have to show that $P$ is closed, but rather only that parts of $P$ are closed. This is due to the fact that for rational functions the converse of Condition E is not satisfied. That is to say that there are unbounded rational functions with bounded parameters. We need not be concerned whether $P$ is closed near these unbounded functions, for they cannot possibly be best approximations. Even for approximation on finite point sets we do not consider a rational function as an admissible candidate for best approximation if it is unbounded in the interval between two of the points.

All of this discussion implies that the topology of $E_n$ is actually not very appropriate for $P$. One has a conceptually neater theory if one considers the topology of $P$ to be defined as suggested in Chapter 1. That is to say if one defines convergence in $P$ by means of the statement:

*The sequence $\{C_r\}$ is said to converge to $C^*$ if*

$$\lim_{r \to \infty} \| R(C_r, x) - R(C^*, x) \| = 0$$

where $\| \ \|$ denotes some suitable norm.

With this definition of the topology of $P$, we would not have the situation of considering whether only particular parts of $P$ are closed or not. However, we will not pursue this approach here.

Now let us turn to the consideration of some extra conditions on $R(C, x)$ which will make $P$ closed at the appropriate places and hence ensure the existence of best approximations for all continuous functions. We first consider the trivial condition; *there exists a $\delta > 0$ such that $C \in P$ implies $D(B, x) \geq \delta$ for all $x \in [0, 1]$.* That is to say that the denominators of $R(C, x)$ are uniformly bounded away from zero. It is easily shown that $P$ is closed in this case.

We have seen in Chapter 3 that best approximations do exist on the interval $[0, 1]$ for polynomial rational functions. Let us consider several examples of a similar nature in order to extract an appropriate abstraction of the properties of this approximating function.

EXAMPLE 6.     $R(C, x) = (a_1 + a_2 \sin x)/(b_1 + b_2 x)$,     $x \in [0, 1]$.

The function $f(x) = (\sin x)/x$ does not have a best approximation, yet in the case of approximation by $(a_1 + a_2 x)/(b_1 + b_2 x)$ the function $f(x) = x/x = 1$ does have a best approximation. This situation is exactly analogous to that of the preceding chapter when it was noted that $a + dx$ does not possess a best approximation by the form $ae^{tx} + b$. It was pointed out there that this is a defect in the definition of the approximating function more than anything else and that the natural remedy is to extend the definition of the approximating function to include the limiting cases which do not happen to have the same explicit representation.

For this particular case we would define the new approximating function

$$R'(a_1, a_2, b_1, b_2, x) = \begin{cases} a_2 \left( \dfrac{\sin x}{x} \right), & |a_1| + |b_1| = 0, & \dfrac{\sin 0}{0} = \\[3mm] a_2 \left( \dfrac{\sin 1 - \sin x}{1 - x} \right), & & \\[3mm] & \left| \dfrac{a_2}{a_1} + \sin 1 \right| + \left| \dfrac{b_2}{b_1} + 1 \right| = 0, \\[3mm] \dfrac{a_1 + a_2 \sin x}{b_1 + b_2 x} & \text{otherwise.} \end{cases}$$

With this extended definition of the approximating function, there is no difficulty in establishing the existence of best approximations on [0, 1] for any continuous function.

This same approach may be used for the approximating function of Example 5.

We now show how the approach for polynomial rational functions may be used for an extended class of general rational functions. We start with the following definition.

**Definition 9–1.** *The approximating function* $R'(C, x)$ *is said to be the parameter closure of* $R(C, x)$ *on* [0, 1] *if* $\{R'(C, x)\}$ *contains all functions such that*

(a)   $C^* = \lim_{k \to \infty} C_k, \qquad C_k \in P,$

(b)   $D(B^*, x) \neq 0$ *for* $x \in X_0$, *where* $X_0$ *is dense in* [0, 1].

This defines $R'(C^*, x)$ uniquely for $x \in X_0$ as

$$R'(C^*, x) = \frac{N(A^*, x)}{D(B^*, x)}, \qquad x \in X_0.$$

It is seen that $R'(C^*, x)$ is continuous on $X_0$ and hence has a unique continuous extension

$$R'(C^*, x) = \lim_{|x - x_0| \to 0} R'(C^*, x_0), \qquad x_0 \in X_0,$$

to the interval [0, 1]. We denote by $P'$ the parameter space of $R'(C, x)$.

This procedure is exactly analogous to the extension made in Section 8–2 for the exponential function.

It is clear that we can identify the parameters of $R$ and $R'$ when they represent the same function of $x$. If we have an element $R'(C, x)$ which is not represented by a point in $P$, then we represent it in $P'$ by the point which is naturally visualized as the limit of the sequence $\{C_k\}$.

The next lemma shows that the identification made in Definition 9–1 leads to no complications as far as approximation to *continuous functions on an interval* is concerned. This lemma has the same proof as Lemma 3–7.

**Lemma 9–2.** *Let* $F(A, x)$ *be a continuous approximating function and let* $g(x)$ *be such that* $g(x) = F(A, x)$ *for* $x \in X_0$ *where* $X_0$ *is dense in* [0, 1]. *If* $f(x)$ *is continuous on* [0, 1] *then*

$$\|f(x) - F(A, x)\| \leq \sup_{x \in [0, 1]} |f(x) - g(x)|.$$

*Proof.* We have

$$\sup_{x \in [0, 1]} |f(x) - g(x)|$$

$$= \max \left[ \sup_{\substack{x \in [0, 1] \\ x \notin X_0}} |f(x) - g(x)| \; ; \; \sup_{x \in X_0} |f(x) - g(x)| \right]$$

$$\geq \sup_{x \in X_0} |f(x) - g(x)| = \max_{x \in [0, 1]} |f(x) - F(A, x)|.$$

The closure procedure given in Definition 9–1 is not powerful in the sense that it extends the definition of the approximating function to include additional large classes of functions. Indeed, one normally will add only a relatively few functions to the set of admissible approximations. In Example 6, the only functions added are $(\sin x)/x$ and $(\sin 1 - \sin x)/(1 - x)$. The continuous function

$$f(x) = \frac{\frac{1}{2} - \sin x}{\pi/6 - x}$$

is not included, for it is not the limit of a sequence from $\{R(C, x)\}$. The next example shows that in some cases such functions may be included in the parameter closure.

EXAMPLE 7.        $R(C, x) = \dfrac{a_1 + a_2 \sin x + a_3 \sin^2 x}{b_1 + b_2 x + b_3 x^2}$ .

One approximating function of this form is

$$R(C_\epsilon, x) = \frac{(\frac{1}{2} - \sin x)^2}{\epsilon + (\pi/6 - x)^2}, \qquad \epsilon > 0$$

and hence the parameter closure of $R$ contains the approximating function

$$R'(C_0, x) = \frac{(\frac{1}{2} - \sin x)^2}{(\pi/6 - x)^2} .$$

A one parameter family of such functions is contained in the parameter closure of $R$, one for each possible zero in $[0, 1]$ of $a - \sin x$. In addition there are other functions included, namely

$$a_3 \frac{\sin x}{x} \left( \frac{a_1 + a_2 \sin x}{b_1 + b_2 x} \right)$$

$$a_3 \left( \frac{\sin 1 - \sin x}{1 - x} \right) \left( \frac{a_1 + a_2 \sin x}{b_1 + b_2 x} \right)$$

$$a_3 \frac{\sin x (\sin 1 - \sin x)}{x(1 - x)} .$$

This example shows how parameter closure may introduce considerable complication in nomenclature and notation since the new approximating function may take on a variety of explicit representations. This difficulty was felt rather acutely for exponential functions in the preceding chapter.

The next lemma fills the final gap in an existence proof for a large class of general rational functions. It has already been shown that Condition E is satisfied for the Tchebycheff norm and we now show that appropriate subsets of $P'$ (the result of parameter closure) are compact in the required sense. That is to say, given a sequence from

$$\{R'(C, x)\,\big|\, \| R'(C, x)\| \leq M < \infty, C \in P'\} \tag{9–2.3}$$

then there is a convergent subsequence which converges to a function of the form $R'(C^*, x)$.

A function $L(A, x) = \sum_i a_i d_i(x)$ is said to have the *dense nonzero property* if $L(A, x) \neq 0$ on a set dense in $[0, 1]$ for all $A \neq 0$.

**Lemma 9–3.** *Let $D(B, x)$ have the dense nonzero property, then the set (9–2.4) is compact.*

*Proof.* Let $\{R'(C_k, x)\}$ be a sequence from (9–2.3). By Lemma 9–1 the parameters $C_k$ are uniformly bounded and we may assume that $\{C_k\}$ is a convergent sequence with limit $C^*$. Since each $C_k$ must be the limit of a sequence in $P$ (rather than $P'$) it follows that $C^*$ is the limit of a sequence in $P$ and hence $C^* \in P'$. This concludes the proof.

These three lemmas establish the following theorem:

**Theorem 9–1.** *Let $f(x)$ be continuous on $[0, 1]$ and let $R(C, x)$ be such that $D(B, x)$ has the dense nonzero property. Let $R'(C, x)$ be the parameter closure of $R(C, x)$ on $[0, 1]$. Then there exists $C^* \in P'$ such that*

$$\| f(x) - R'(C^*, x) \| = \inf_{C \in P} \| f(x) - R(C, x)\| \leq \| f(x) - R'(C', x) \|$$

*for all $C' \in P'$.*

This result is a variation of the results given by Boehm, 1964. Boehm did not require functions in the parameter closure to be limits of functions in the original family of approximating functions. Thus $(\frac{1}{2} - \sin x)/(\pi/6 - x)$ would be included in the parameter closure of Example 6 with his treatment.

## 9–3 STABILITY AND EXISTENCE FOR GENERAL RATIONAL FUNCTIONS

While Theorem 9–1 gives a certain amount of satisfaction for the existence question, it leaves much to be desired, namely approximation on finite point sets. Furthermore the remaining existence problems seem to be very messy when one attempts to push further the abstraction of the polynomial approach as in the preceding section. However, there is another approach due to Goldstein, 1963, which gives the key to these remaining problems. In addition, this approach leads to the interesting concepts of *stability* and *stabilized best approximations*. It is probable that these concepts will lead to important computational results as well as clarify some difficult theoretical questions. At this writing the computational aspects of stabilized best approximations have not been extensively studied.

The approach of Goldstein is to consider a linear inequalities problem which is intimately related to the rational approximation problem. Thus let $X$ be an arbitrary subset of $[0, 1]$ and set

$$\rho^* = \inf_{C \in P} \sup_{x \in X} |f(x) - R(C, x)|. \qquad (9\text{–}3.1)$$

We are now concerned with the existence of a set of parameters $C^*$ so that

$$\left| f(x) - \frac{N(A^*, x)}{D(B^*, x)} \right| \leq \rho^*, \qquad \text{all } x \in X. \qquad (9\text{–}3.2)$$

If $D(B^*, x) \neq 0$ then we multiply both sides of (9–3.2) to obtain

$$|f(x)D(B^*, x) - N(A^*, x)| \leq \rho^* D(B^*, x), \qquad \text{all } x \in X. \quad (9\text{–}3.3)$$

We assume for concreteness that $D(B^*, x) \geq 0$ in $[0, 1]$. The systems (9–3.2) and (9–3.3) are not exactly equivalent for (9–3.3) may be satisfied at some point $x$ when $N(A^*, x) = D(B^*, x) = 0$, while (9–3.2) is undefined at such a point. It is exactly at these points that we encounter the difficulties in the existence problem.

In order to study the relation between (9–3.2) and (9–3.3) let us define

$$P = \{C \,|\, D(B, x) > 0, \, x \in [0, 1], \, \sum_{i=1}^{m} b_i^2 = 1\}$$

$$P_0 = \{C \,|\, D(B, x) \geq 0, \, x \in [0, 1], \, \sum_{i=1}^{m} b_i^2 = 1 \qquad\qquad (9\text{–}3.4)$$

$$\text{and } D(B, x) = 0 \text{ implies } N(A, x) = 0\}.$$

The first set is the same parameter set as defined in the introduction while the second set includes all those parameters for which the numerator and denominator have common zeros. We also require the notation

$$z(C) = \{x \,|\, D(B, x) = 0, C \in P_0\}$$

for the set of zeros that $N(A, x)$ and $D(B, x)$ have in common.

It is usual in approximation theory to exclude from consideration those functions $f(x)$ which are actually one of the forms of the approximating functions. In the present situation it is possible that $f(x)$ is not formally one of these forms, but yet that

$$\inf_{C, \; x \in X} \sup |f(x)D(B, x) - N(A, x)| = 0.$$

In the preceding section we included such functions $f(x)$ in the set of approximating functions by the procedure of parameter closure. Here we take a slightly different approach. The continuous function $f(x)$ is said to be *linearly dependent on* $R(C, x)$ on $X$ if there exists $C = (A, B)$ (not necessarily contained in $P$) such that

$$N(A, x) - f(x)D(B, x) = 0, \qquad x \in X.$$

In what follows we exclude from consideration those functions which are linearly dependent on $R$.

The next lemma formally establishes the equivalence of a certain approximation problem and a certain system of linear inequalities. Consider

$$\left| \frac{N(A, x)}{D(B, x)} - f(x) \right| \le \rho, \qquad x \in \{X - z(C)\}, C \in P_0 \qquad (9\text{-}3.5)$$

and

$$|N(A, x) - f(x)D(B, x)| \le \rho D(B, x), \qquad x \in X. \qquad (9\text{-}3.6)$$

Let $P_1$ and $P_2$ denote the solution of (9–3.5) and (9–3.6), respectively.

**Lemma 9–4.** *If $f(x)$ is linearly independent of $R(C, x)$ on $X$ then $P_1 = P_2$.*

*Proof.* Consider $C_1 \in P_1$. If $C_1 \in P$, then clearly $C_1$ satisfies (9–3.6) and $C_1 \in P_2$. Assume that $C_1 \in P_0$, $C_1 \notin P$. For those points in $z(C_1)$, (9–3.6) is trivially satisfied. If $x \notin z(C_1)$, then $D(B, x) > 0$ and again (9–3.5) implies (9–3.6).

Consider $C_2 \in P_2$. If $\rho = 0$ then

$$|f(x)D(B_2, x) - N(B_2, x)| \equiv 0, \qquad x \in X$$

which implies that $f(x)$ is not linearly independent of $R(C, x)$ on $X$. Hence $\rho > 0$ and $D(B, x) \ge 0$. If $C_2 \in P$ then clearly (9–3.5) is satisfied. If $C_2 \notin P_0$ then (9–3.6) is not satisfied and hence $C_2 \notin P_2$. If $C_2 \in P_0$, $C_2 \notin P$, then for $x \notin z(C_2)$, (9–3.5) is satisfied. For $x \in z(C_2)$ there is no condition in (9–3.5) and hence $C_2 \in P_1$. This concludes the proof.

The next lemma establishes the existence of a solution of (9–3.6) with the smallest possible value of $\rho$.

Set

$$\rho_0 = \inf \{\rho \,|\, (9\text{-}3.6) \text{ is consistent}\}. \qquad (9\text{-}3.7)$$

It is not yet established that this is the same number as defined in (9–3.1).

**Lemma 9–5.** *If $f(x)$ is linearly independent of $R(C, x)$ on $X$ then there exists $(A_0, B_0)$ such that*

$$|N(A_0, x) - f(x)D(B_0, x)| \le \rho_0 D(B_0, x), \qquad x \in X.$$

*Proof.* Recall that $P$ (and hence $P_0$) is assumed to be nonempty. Thus the set in (9–3.7) is not empty and $\rho_0$ is defined. Let $\{\rho_r\}$ be a sequence of values which converges to $\rho_0$ from above. Let $S_r \subset E_{n+m}$ be the set of solutions of (9–3.6) for $\rho = \rho_r$. The sets $S_r$ are compact in $E_{n+m}$, $S_{r+1} \subset S_r$ and hence the intersection $S = \bigcap_{k=1}^{\infty} S_r$ is not empty. Clearly any element of $S$ satisfies (9–3.6) with $\rho = \rho_0$.

These results allow us to establish an existence theorem for the approximation problem given by (9–3.5). The fact that we ignore what happens at points of $z(C)$ (i.e. where $R(C, x)$ is undefined) makes this approximation problem slightly different from the usual Tchebycheff approximation problem. However, Examples 2 and 3 of Section 9–2 show that such an extension of the concept of a best approximation is essential to an understanding of rational approximation on finite point sets. Note that so far we have used the fact that $X \subset [0, 1]$ only in the constraint that $D(B, x) \geq 0$, $x \in [0, 1]$. This constraint may be modified in various ways without essentially affecting the proofs. Thus one can use this approach to discuss rational approximations to functions defined on arbitrary sets. This is pursued further in Problems 9–11, 9–12.

**Theorem 9–2.** *Let $f(x)$ be linearly independent of $R(C, x)$ on $X$. Then $\rho_0$ defined in (9–3.7) is the smallest value for which (9–3.5) is consistent and there exists $C_0 \in P_0$ for which this value is assumed.*

*Proof.* From Lemma 9–5 we know there exists a pair $(A_0, B_0)$ which satisfies (9–3.6) with $\rho = \rho_0$. It follows from Lemma 9–4 that $(A_0, B_0)$ is also a solution of (9–3.5). It also follows from Lemma 9–4 that (9–3.5) is not consistent with any smaller value than $\rho_0$ and hence we may set $C_0 = (A_0, B_0)$.

Let us consider Examples 2 and 3 given at the beginning of Section 9–2. With the approximation problem as defined by (9–3.5) we see that the best approximation in Example 2 is $R(C, x) = \frac{3}{8}(x - \frac{1}{2})/(x - \frac{1}{2})$ with deviation $\frac{1}{8}$. Now this function is undefined for $x = \frac{1}{2}$, but the constant $\frac{3}{8}$ has a deviation of $\frac{3}{8}$ from $f(x)$ at that point. Thus it is questionable that we really want to consider $\frac{3}{8}(x - \frac{1}{2})/(x - \frac{1}{2})$ as the best approximation in this example.

For Example 3 (see Fig. 9–2) the best approximation in the present sense is given by $R(C, x) = \frac{1}{8}(x)/(x)$ with deviation $\frac{1}{8}$. Again this approximation is undefined at one point. And at this point the constant $\frac{1}{8}$ has a deviation of $\frac{3}{8}$ from $f(x)$. Nevertheless, it is very natural to consider this approximation as the best approximation to this function.

Let us examine the reasoning that leads us to accept one of these approximations as natural and to reject the other. In Example 3 the approximation $\frac{1}{8}(x)/(x)$ is the limit of *continuous* approximations which tend to minimize the deviation. However, in Example 2 there are no approximations continuous in $[0, 1]$ which approach $f(x)$ with deviation near $\frac{1}{8}$. Since the approximation

$\frac{3}{8}(x - \frac{1}{2})/(x - \frac{1}{2})$ is not close to a continuous approximation, we are inclined to discard it in favor of the approximation $\frac{1}{4}$ which *cannot* be improved upon by approximations *continuous on* $[0, 1]$.

We now introduce another mechanism, in the form of another system of inequalities, which allows us to distinguish between these two possibilities. This, in turn, allows us to define the concept of a *stabilized best approximation* which is a natural way to define best Tchebycheff approximations by rational functions when they do not exist in the narrow sense.

We have defined an approximation problem which may be stated as: *Determine the smallest value $\rho_0$ (and a corresponding $C_0$) for which* (9–3.6) *is consistent*. Consider a dual problem of this which is: *Determine the largest value $\rho^*$ for which the system*

$$|N(A, x) - f(x)D(B, x)| < \rho D(B, x, \qquad x \in X, \qquad (9\text{–}3.8)$$

*is inconsistent for $C \in P$*. Note that the system (9–3.8) cannot be consistent for parameter $C$ such that $D(B, x) = 0$ for some $x \in X$.

**Lemma 9–6.** *There exists a largest value $\rho^*$ for which* (9–3.8) *is inconsistent and $\rho^* > \rho_0$.*

*Proof.* Since $P$ is not empty there is a $C$ such that $D(B, x) > 0\ x \in X$ and hence for $\rho$ sufficiently large the system (9–3.8) is consistent for this choice of $C$. If $\rho < \rho_0$ then (9–3.6) is inconsistent which in turn implies that (9–3.8) is inconsistent. Hence $\rho^* \geq \rho_0$.

For Example 2 discussed above we see that $\rho^* = \frac{1}{4}$ and $\rho_0 = \frac{1}{8}$.

**Definition 9–2.** *The approximation $R(C^*, x)$ is said to be a stabilized best approximation with deviation $\rho^*$ to $f(x)$ if $R(C^*, x)$ satisfies* (9–3.6) *with $\rho = \rho^*$ and if $\rho^*$ is the largest value for which* (9–3.8) *is inconsistent.*

The stabilized best approximations are exactly those approximations (with parameters in $P_0$, but perhaps not in $P$) which are limits of approximations continuous on $[0, 1]$. The following theorem has been established.

**Theorem 9–3.** *If $f(x)$ is linearly independent of $R(C, x)$ on $X$ then $f(x)$ possesses a stabilized best approximation.*

In his original paper Goldstein did not make exactly the same definitions as have been presented here. He did not require that $C$ belong to $P$ in (9–3.8). This change leads, for example, to the conclusion that $\frac{3}{8}(x - \frac{1}{2})/(x - \frac{1}{2})$ is a stabilized best approximation in Example 2. This does not seem desirable in the consideration of approximation to functions defined on an interval. However, when one proceeds to more abstract situations, such as considered by Goldstein, it is not so obvious just how one should constrain the zeros of the denominator for (9–3.8). Goldstein chose no constraint at all which, by the nature of the system (9–3.8), excludes the zeros of $D(B, x)$ only from the set $X$.

## 9–4  CHARACTERIZATION AND UNIQUENESS FOR GENERAL RATIONAL FUNCTIONS

The results on characterization and uniqueness which are presented in this section are rather general in nature. As a consequence, considerable further analysis may be required for explicit results for specific situations. The two theorems given do, however, make clear exactly where further analysis may be required for specific cases.

We begin with a convexity property of the set $P$. Since $P$ has been normalized by $\sum b_i^2 = 1$, it is not possible to form the usual convex combination since $P$ itself is not convex. However, we adopt a simple convention which avoids this difficulty. The parameter $C$ is said to be a *convex combination* of $C_1$ and $C_2$ if

$$A = \sigma[\lambda A_1 + (1 - \lambda)A_2], \quad \lambda \geq 0$$
$$B = \sigma[\lambda B_1 + (1 - \lambda)B_2],$$

where

$$\sigma^2 = \sum_{i=1}^{m} (\lambda b_{1i} + (1 - \lambda)b_{2i})^2.$$

We will simply write $C = \lambda C_1 + (1 - \lambda)C_2$, etc., and convexity of subsets of $P$ is assumed to be defined in terms of this special form of combination.

**Lemma 9–7.**  *The set*

$$P\rho = \{C \mid C \in P, \|f(x) - R(C, x)\| \leq \rho\} \tag{9–4.1}$$

*is convex in the preceding sense.*

*Proof.* By direct calculation we have

$$|f(x) - R(\lambda C_1 + (1 - \lambda)C_2, x)|$$
$$= \frac{|\sigma f(x)[\lambda D(B_1, x) + (1 - \lambda)D(B_2, x)] - \sigma[\lambda N(A_1, x) + (1 - \lambda)N(A_2, x)]|}{\sigma|D(\lambda B_1 + (1 - \lambda)B_2, x)|}$$
$$\leq \frac{\lambda D(B_1, x)}{|D(\lambda B_1 + (1 - \lambda)B_2, x)|} \left| f(x) - \frac{N(A_1, x)}{D(B_1, x)} \right|$$
$$+ \frac{(1 - \lambda)D(B_2, x)}{|D(\lambda B_1 + (1 - \lambda)B_2, x)|} \left| f(x) - \frac{N(A_2, x)}{D(B_2, x)} \right|.$$

This concludes the proof.

We now turn to the question of characterizing a best approximation. Let us assume that $X$ is compact and

$$\rho = \max_{x \in X} |f(x) - R(C, x)|.$$

Then in the usual terminology we say $x_0 \in X$ is an *extremal point* if

$$|f(x_0) - R(C, x_0)| = \rho.$$

Assume that the approximation $R(C, x)$ has extremal points $x_i$, $i = 1$, $2, \ldots, q$ and set

$$\sigma_i = \text{sgn} [f(x_i) - R(C, x_i)].$$

Consider the possibility that a small change $\delta C$ in $C$ leads to a better approximation that $R(C, x)$. We would have then at the extremal points

$$\sigma_i \left[ f(x_i) - \frac{N(A + \delta A, x_i)}{D(B + \delta B, x_i)} \right] < \sigma_i \left[ f(x_i) - \frac{N(A, x_i)}{D(B, x_i)} \right] \qquad (9\text{-}4.2)$$

or, after manipulation,

$$\sigma_i[N(\delta A, x_i) - R(C, x_i)D(\delta B, x_i)] > 0, \qquad i = 1, 2, \ldots, q. \quad (9\text{-}4.3)$$

Thus we have heuristically concluded that the change $\delta C$ must satisfy (9–4.3) in order to achieve an improvement in the approximation. The next theorem places the conditions (9–4.3) on a firm basis and uses the system to characterize best approximations. This, in itself, says little, but there are conditions for the consistency of (9–4.3) which may be used to obtain more concrete forms of this characterizing property. See Fan, 1956, Cheney and Goldstein, 1962 and Problem 9–13.

In particular, the alternation of the error curve is one such condition in the case of polynomial rational functions.

**Theorem 9–4.** *Let $X$ be compact. A necessary and sufficient condition that $R(C, x)$ be a best Tchebycheff approximation to $f(x)$ is that (9–4.3) be inconsistent for all $\delta C \in P$ where the $x_i$ are the extremal points of the approximation $R(C, x)$.*

*Proof.* Assume that (9–4.3) is inconsistent for all $\delta C \in P$. If $R(C_1, x)$ were a better approximation than $R(C, x)$ then by Lemma 9–7 all convex combinations $R(\lambda C + (1 - \lambda)C_1, x)$ are as good as or better than $R(C, x)$. Let $R(C_2, x)$ be the one on this line with the same deviation on the extremal points and with the smallest value $\lambda_2$ of $\lambda$. We may then consider (9–4.2) with $C$ replaced by $C_2$ and $\delta C$ replaced by $\epsilon(C_1 - C)$ where $\epsilon$ is chosen small enough for the sign of $f(x_i) - R(C_2 + \delta C, x_i)$ to be the same as the sign of $f(x_i) - R(C_2, x_i)$. Then the inequality (9–4.2) and the manipulation leading to (9–4.3) are valid and (9–4.3) is consistent. This contradicts the original assumption and establishes the sufficiency portion of the proof.

Assume now that (9–4.3) is satisfied for some $(\delta A, \delta B)$. Since the functions involved are continuous, it follows that (9–4.3) is satisfied on a larger set than just the extremal points. Specifically there is an open set $X_e$ such that $x_i \in X_e$, $i = 1, 2, \ldots, \rho$ and

$$\sigma_i[N(\delta A, x) - R(C, x)D(\delta B, x)] \geq \delta > 0, \qquad x \in X_e.$$

We now consider $R(C + \lambda\delta C, x)$. Clearly there is a $\lambda_1$ so small that $0 < \lambda < \lambda_1$ implies

$$|f(x) - R(C + \lambda\delta C, x)| < \|f(x) - R(C, x)\|$$

for $x$ not contained in $X_e$. Furthermore there is a $\lambda_2 > 0$ such that for $\lambda < \lambda_2$

$$\mathrm{sgn}\,[f(x) - R(C, x)] = \mathrm{sgn}\,[f(x) - R(C + \lambda\delta C, x)] = \sigma(x)$$

for all $x \in X_e$. This equation defines the sign function $\sigma(x)$. In addition $D(B, x)$ is bounded from zero for $x \in [0, 1]$ and hence there is a $\lambda_3 > 0$ so that for $0 < \lambda < \lambda_3$, $D(B + \lambda\delta B, x)$ is bounded from zero for $x \in [0, 1]$. Set $\lambda_0 = \min\,[\lambda_1, \lambda_2, \lambda_3]$; then for $\lambda < \lambda_0$ we have

$$\|f(x) - R(C + \lambda\delta C, x)\| = \sup_{x \in X_e} \sigma(x)[f(x) - R(C + \lambda\delta C, x)].$$

Consider then for $x \in X_e$

$$\sigma(x)[f(x) - R(C + \lambda\delta C, x)] - \sigma(x)[f(x) - R(C, x)]$$

$$= -\frac{\sigma(x)}{D(B + \lambda\delta B, x)}\,[\lambda N(\delta A) - \lambda R(C, x)D(\delta B, x)] < \frac{\sigma\lambda}{D(B + \lambda\delta B, x)}\,.$$

$$(9\text{–}4.4)$$

Thus for $\lambda < \lambda_0$, the quantity (9–4.4) is negative. However, this quantity is exactly the deviation of $R(C + \lambda\delta C, x)$ less that of $R(C, x)$. This implies that $R(C + \lambda\delta C, x)$ is a better approximation to $f(x)$ than $R(C, x)$ and hence $R(C, x)$ cannot be a best approximation if (9–4.3) is consistent.

We note that at no point was the set of extremal points assumed to be finite and that the proof is valid in case $p$ is not finite. This concludes the proof.

If $X$ is not compact, then this characterization theorem is no longer valid. Indeed it is very possible that there are no extremal points at all for a best approximation. On the other hand the proof suggests one possibility of modification. If $X$ is not compact, let $\bar{X}$ be the closure of $X$, which is then compact. Since all functions involved are continuous we may extend their definition to $\bar{X}$ by continuity. It is clear that $R(C, x)$ is a best approximation to $f(x)$ on $X$ if and only if it is a best approximation to $f(x)$ on $\bar{X}$. This then gives a characterization theorem in case $X$ is not compact.

In order to discuss the uniqueness problem in general we are going to distinguish between two kinds of extremal point sets. The point is that there may well be extremal points which play no essential role in determining the best approximation. A similar situation occurs when there is a number of "extra" extremal points, each of which might be essential in determining the best approximation, but which, when taken as a group, actually overdetermine the best approximation. These possibilities are illustrated in Fig. 9–4. In Fig. 9–4(a), there are several combinations of three points which (in normal circumstances) would determine the parameters of a best approximation. The fact that there are actually five such points does not in any way further restrict the best approximation. In Fig. 9–4(b) there are whole intervals of extremal points and a best approximation is determined by choosing one representative point from each of these intervals. In each case there are more extremal points than actually required to determine the best approximation.

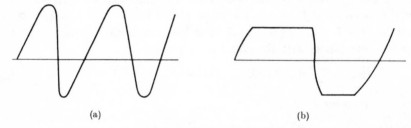

(a)                                             (b)

FIG. 9–4.  Extra extremal points in the error curve for approximation with two parameters.

The next definition makes it possible for us to distinguish between those sets of extremal points which essentially determine a best approximation and those sets which contain extraneous extremal points.

**Definition 9–3.** *A subset* $S = \{x_i \mid i = 1, 2, \ldots, p\}$ *of the extremal points of a best approximation* $R(C^*, x)$ *to* $f(x)$ *is said to be a critical point set if* $R(C^*, x)$ *is a best approximation to* $f(x)$ *on* $S$, *but is not a best approximation to* $f(x)$ *on any proper subset of* $S$.

That is to say if we remove one point from $S$ then there is an approximation to $f(x)$ which has a smaller deviation than $R(C^*, x)$.

Let us examine the characterization theorem in view of this definition. By Theorem 9–3 it follows that (9–4.3) is inconsistent if the $x_i$ are the extremal points. Likewise, it follows that the subsystem of (9–4.3) corresponding to any critical point set must be inconsistent. Otherwise, $R(C^*, x)$ would not be a best approximation to $f(x)$ on this subset of the extremal points. Now there is a concept in the theory of systems of linear inequalities which corresponds exactly to this situation. This is the concept of an *irreducibly* *inconsistent system of linear inequalities* (Carver, 1922): the system is said to be irreducibly inconsistent if

$$\sum_{i=1}^{p} a_i g_{ij} > \alpha_j, \qquad j = 1, 2, \ldots, q. \tag{9–4.5}$$

(9–4.5) is inconsistent, but every proper subsystem of (9–4.5) is consistent. We have the following result which is established, for example, by Fan, 1956, Theorem 5.

**Lemma 9–8.** *The system (9–4.5) is irreducibly inconsistent if and only if* (a) *any* $q - 1$ *of the* $q$ *vectors*

$$\mathbf{g}_j = (g_{1j}, g_{2j}, \ldots, g_{pj})$$

*are linearly independent and* (b) *there exist* $\lambda_j$, $j = 1, 2, \ldots, q$ *such that* $\lambda_j > 0$, $\sum_{i=1}^{q} \lambda_j = 1$, $\sum_{i=1}^{q} \lambda_j \alpha_j \geq 0$ *and*

$$\sum_{j=1}^{q} \lambda_j \mathbf{g}_j = 0. \tag{9–4.6}$$

For the particular application at hand we have that the $\alpha_j$ are all zero and the second condition of Lemma 9–8 is reduced to $\lambda_j > 0$ and (9–4.6). With

$$\begin{aligned} \mathbf{g}(C, x) = \sigma(x)\big(\phi_1(x), \phi_2(x), \ldots, \phi_n(x), \\ -R(C, x)\psi_1(x), -R(C, x)\psi_2(x), \ldots, -R(C, x)\psi_m(x)\big) \end{aligned} \tag{9–4.7}$$

and the dot product notation, the system (9–4.3) for a best approximation $R(C^*, x)$ appears as

$$\delta C \cdot \mathbf{g}(C^*, x_i) > 0, \qquad i = 1, 2, \ldots, q. \tag{9–4.8}$$

**Corollary 1.** *Let* $X$ *be compact. A necessary and sufficient condition that* $R(C^*, x)$ *be a best approximation to* $f(x)$ *is that the zero vector be in the convex hull of the set* $\{\mathbf{g}(C^*, x_i) \mid x_i \text{ an extremal point}\}$.

*Proof.* It is known (Fan, 1956, Corollary 5) that the system (9–4.5) with $\alpha_j = 0$, $j = 1, 2, \ldots, q$ is inconsistent if and only if (9–4.6) holds.

**Corollary 2.** *A critical point set contains at most* $n + m$ *points.*

*Proof.* The system (9–4.8) must be inconsistent and every subset of $q - 1$ vectors $\mathbf{g}(C, x_i)$ must be linearly independent. Since the vectors are of length $n + m$ we must have $q \leq n + m + 1$ for any set of $n + m + 1$ vectors in $E_{n+m}$ is linearly dependent. The normalization used, however, means that one parameter in $C$ may be assigned arbitrarily, thereby reducing the effective length of $\mathbf{g}(C, x)$ to $n + m - 1$.

This result may be obtained alternatively from Corollary 1 by the classical result of Caratheodory: *Let S be a set in $E_n$ and $H(S)$ the convex hull of S. Then any point of $H(S)$ is in the convex hull of a subset of S consisting of at most $n + 1$ points.*

With these results we may establish the following uniqueness theorem.

**Theorem 9–5.** *Let $X$ be compact and let $R(C^*, x)$ be a best approximation to $f(x)$ on $X$. If every set $\{g(C^*, x_i) \mid i = 1, 2, \ldots, n + m - 1; \; x_i \neq x_j\}$ of vectors is linearly independent then $R(C^*, x)$ is uniquely determined.*

*Proof.* Let $\{x_i \mid i = 1, 2, \ldots, p\}$ be a critical point set of the best approximation $R(C^*, x)$. Since all sets $\{g(C^*, x_i) \mid i = 1, 2, \ldots, n + m - 1\}$ are linearly independent, it follows from Lemma 9–8 that $p = n + m$. Further it is seen from (9–4.8) that there exist $\lambda_i > 0$ so that

$$\sum_{i=1}^{n+m} \lambda_i g(C^*, x_i) = 0.$$

We note that $C^* \cdot g(C^*, x_i) = 0$ and hence $C^*$ is orthogonal to the $n + m - 1$ dimensional subspace of $E_{n+m}$ spanned by the vectors $\{g(C^*, x_i)\}$. If $C_1 = (A, B^\perp)$ where $B^\perp \cdot B^* = 0$ (here we are taking the inner product of vectors of length $m$), then $C_1 \cdot g(C^*, x_i) \neq 0$ for some $i$ and

$$\sum_{i=1}^{n+m} \lambda_i (C_1 \cdot g(C^*, x_i)) = 0.$$

Thus, for some $i$, $C_1 \cdot g(C^*, x_i) > 0$ and, for $C$ of this form,

$$\alpha = \min_{B^\perp \cdot B^* = 0} \; \max_i \; C \cdot g(C^*, x_i) > 0. \tag{9–4.9}$$

Further, if $C_2 = (A^* + A, B^*)$, then by the same reasoning and noting that $C_2 \cdot g(C^*, x_i) = N(A, x_i)$ we have

$$\max_i \sigma_i N(A, x_i) \geq \beta \, \|N(A, x)\| \tag{9–4.10}$$

where $\beta > 0$.

Now consider any other approximation $R(C, x)$. We have

$$\sigma_i[f(x_i) - R(C, x_i)] = \sigma_i[f(x_i) - R(C^*, x_i)] + \sigma_i[R(C^*, x_i) - R(C, x_i)]$$

and hence, with $d^* = \|f(x) - R(C^*, x)\|$

$$\|f(x) - R(C, x)\| \geq d^* + \max_i \sigma_i[R(C^*, x_i) - R(C, x_i)]$$

$$\geq d^* + \frac{\max_i \sigma_i[D(B, x_i)R(C^*, x_i) - N(A, x_i)]}{\|D(B, x)\|}. \tag{9–4.11}$$

We introduce the notation $M = \max_B \|D(B, x)\|$ and $\cos \theta = B \cdot B^*$.

We consider first the case $\theta \neq 0$. We write $B = \sin \theta B^{\perp} + \cos \theta B^*$ and note for $\sin \theta > 0$ we have

$$(-A,\, B) \cdot \mathbf{g}(C^*, x_i) = \sin \theta \left[ -N\left( \frac{A - \cos \theta A^*}{\sin \theta},\, x_i \right) + R(C^*, x_i)D(B^{\perp}, x_i) \right].$$

Then we have from (9–4.9) and (9–4.11)

$$\|f(x) - R(C, x)\| \geq d^* + \frac{\sin \theta}{M} \max_i \sigma_i[(-A,\, B) \cdot \mathbf{g}(C^*, x_i)] \geq d^* + \frac{\alpha \sin \theta}{M}.$$

Thus if $\sin \theta > 0$, $R(C^*, x)$ is a better approximation than $R(C, x)$. For $\sin \theta < 0$ a similar analysis gives $-\alpha \sin \theta / M$.

When $\theta = 0$ we have from (9–4.11) that

$$\|f(x) - R(C, x)\| \geq d^* + \frac{1}{M} \max_i \sigma_i[N(A^*, x_i) - N(A, x_i)].$$

It follows from (9–4.10) that

$$\|f(x) - R(C, x)\| \geq d^* + \frac{\beta}{M}\|N(A, x) - N(A^*, x)\|$$

and thus $R(C^*, x)$ is a better approximation than $R(C, x)$ if $A \neq A^*$. This concludes the proof.

We have, in fact, established a somewhat stronger result than mere uniqueness. This is stated in the following *strong uniqueness theorem*.

**Corollary.** *Let $X$ be compact and $R(C^*, x)$ be a best approximation to $f(x)$ on $X$. If every set $\{\mathbf{g}(C^*, x_i) | i = 1, 2, \ldots, n + m - 1,\ x_i \neq x_j\}$ of vectors is linearly independent then, for any approximation $R(C, x)$*

$$\|f(x) - R(C, x)\| \geq \|f(x) - R(C^*, x)\| + \begin{cases} a \sin \theta, & \theta \neq 0 \\ b\|N(A, x) - N(A^*, x)\|, & \theta = 0 \end{cases}$$

$$(9\text{–}4.12)$$

*where $\cos \theta = B \cdot B^*$, $b > 0$ and $a \sin \theta > 0$.*

It is likely that even stronger estimates are possible, perhaps with the right hand term in (9–4.11) replaced by

$$a' \sin \theta + b'\|N(A, x) - \cos \theta N(A^*, x)\|.$$

It is to be shown in Problem 9–14 that the right hand term may be replaced with

$$a''\|R(C^*, x) - R(C, x)\|$$

where $a'' > 0$.

Some of these results may be reformulated and sharpened in terms of a number of indices associated with the approximating function. An $n$-dimensional subspace $\mathscr{L}$ of the continuous functions on $[0, 1]$ is called a *Haar subspace* if, for every set $\{x_i\}$ of $n$ distinct points in $[0, 1]$ the $n \times n$ determinant

$$\det \{\phi_i(x_j)\}$$

is nonzero where $\{\phi_i(x)\}$ is a basis for $\mathscr{L}$. It follows from Problem 3–7 that $\mathscr{L}$ is a Haar subspace if and only if $\{\phi_i(x)\}$ is a Tchebycheff set. For any subspace $\mathscr{M}$ we define the following indices

$\eta(\mathscr{M}) = $ maximum dimension of a Haar subspace of $\mathscr{M}$,

$\delta(\mathscr{M}) = $ dimension of $\mathscr{M}$,

$\nu(\mathscr{M}) = 1 + $ maximum number of variations of sign possessed by elements of $\mathscr{M}$,

$\zeta(\mathscr{M}) = 1 + $ maximum number of zeros possessed by nonzero elements of $\mathscr{M}$,

$\zeta^*(\mathscr{M}) = 1 + $ maximum number of zeros possessed by nonzero elements of $\mathscr{M}$, counting all double zeros as two.

The subspace spanned by

$$f(x) = (3x - 1)(3x - 2)^2$$

has indices 0, 1, 2, 3, 4, respectively. We note that, for any subspace

$$\zeta^* \geq \zeta \geq \nu \geq \delta \geq \eta \qquad (9\text{–}4.13)$$

and it follows from the results of Chapter 3 that if either $\eta = \delta$ or $\zeta = \delta$ then all of the indices are equal.

For stating the results in terms of these indices we define the subspaces

$$\mathscr{N} = \{N(A, x)\},$$
$$\mathscr{D} = \{D(B, x)\}.$$

In order to make $\mathscr{D}$ a subspace we remove the normalization restriction on the coefficients. The next theorem is of the nature of a characterization theorem but the necessary and the sufficient conditions are not the same.

**Theorem 9–6.** *If $f(x) - R(C^*, x)$ alternates $\nu(\mathscr{N} + R(C^*, x)\mathscr{D})$ times on $[0, 1]$, then $R(C^*, x)$ is a best approximation to $f(x)$. If $R(C^*, x)$ is a best approximation to $f(x)$ then $f(x) - R(C^*, x)$ alternates $\eta(\mathscr{N} + R(C^*, x)\mathscr{D})$ times on $[0, 1]$.*

The proof of this result follows rather closely the reasoning presented above.

*Proof.* If $f(x) - R(C^*, x)$ alternates $\nu$ times and

$$\|f - R(C, x)\| < \|f - R(C^*, x)\|$$

then $R(C, x) - R(C^*, x)$ has at least $\nu$ zeros. This implies that $N(A, x) - R(C^*, x)D(B, x)$ has $\nu$ zeros since $D(B, x) > 0$, but this contradicts the definition of $\nu$.

Suppose that $f(x) - R(C^*, x)$ does not alternate $\eta$ times. Let $\{x_i | i = 1, 2, \ldots, p\}$ divide $[0, 1]$ into subintervals so that $\| f(x) - R(C^*, x) \|$ is assumed in each subinterval with fixed sign. Now $p < \eta$ and hence there is an $R(\delta C, x)$ so that

$$N(\delta A, x_i) - R(C^*, x_i)D(\delta B, x_i) = 0, \qquad i = 1, 2, \ldots, p$$

and

$$\mathrm{sgn}\,[\,f(x) - R(C^*, x)] = -\,\mathrm{sgn}\,[R(C^*, x) - R(\delta C, x)]$$

at those points where $\| f(x) - R(C^*, x) \|$ is assumed. This implies that (9–4.3) is consistent and by Theorem 9–3 $R(C^*, x)$ is not a best approximation. This concludes the proof.

The following corollary is a restatement of Theorem 9–4.

**Corollary.** *Let $R(C^*, x)$ be a best approximation to $f(x)$. If $\delta(\mathcal{N} + R(C^*, x)\mathcal{D}) = \eta(\mathcal{N} + R(C^*, x)\mathcal{D})$ then $R(C^*, x)$ is unique.*

## 9–5  POLYNOMIAL RATIONAL FUNCTIONS

In this section we review some previously established results for the *polynomial rational functions.*†

$$R(C, x) = \frac{N(A, x)}{D(B, x)} = \frac{\sum_{i=0}^{n} a_i x^i}{\sum_{i=0}^{m} b_i x^i}, \tag{9–5.1}$$

when $D(B, x) > 0$ for $x \in [0, 1]$. This is the same approximating function studied in Section 3–8. We have from the results obtained there and in Chapter 7:

**Theorem 9–7.** *The polynomial rational function (9–5.1) is varisolvent. The degree is given explicitly by*

$$m(C) = \begin{cases} n + m - d + 1, & R(C, x) \not\equiv 0 \\ n + 1, & R(C, x) \equiv 0 \end{cases} \tag{9–5.2}$$

*where $d = \min\{p, q \mid a_{n-p} \neq 0, b_{m-q} \neq 0\}$.*

The existence of best approximations for every continuous function is established in Section 3–8 or may be deduced from the results of the first section of this chapter. $d$ is called the *defect* of the rational function.

---

† Note that the number of parameters in this special case is not $n + m - 1$, but rather $n + m + 1$. This is to conform with the usual conventions about the degree of polynomials.

We consider one other question in this section and that is the continuity (or lack of it) of the dependence of the best polynomial rational approximation on the function $f(x)$. The first result (Maehly and Witzgall, 1960) is

**Theorem 9–8.** *Assume that $R(C_f, x)$ is the best approximation to $f(x)$ on $[0, 1]$ and $m(C_f) = n + m + 1$. Then the best approximation $R(C_g, x)$ to $g(x)$ depends continuously on $g(x)$ in a neighborhood of $f(x)$, i.e. there are constants $K$ and $\delta_0 > 0$ such that $\|f(x) - g(x)\| \leq \delta_0$ implies*

$$\| R(C_f, x) - R(C_g, x) \| \leq K \| f(x) - g(x) \|. \qquad (9\text{–}5.3)$$

The proof of this result parallels closely that of Theorem 3–4.

*Proof.* Let $\{x_i | i = 1, 2, \ldots, m(C_f) + 1 = n + m + 2\}$ be points upon which $f(x) - R(C_f, x)$ alternates $m(C_f)$ times. Let $\delta C = C_g - C_f$,

$$\delta = \| f(x) - g(x) \|,$$

and let $d_f$ and $d_g$ denote the deviations of the best approximations to $f(x)$ and $g(x)$, respectively. One has

$$d_g \leq d_f + \delta$$

and if we assume, for concreteness, that $R(C_f, x_1) - f(x_1) < 0$ then, after some manipulation

$$(-1)^i [R(C_f, x_i) - R(C_g, x_i)] \geq -2\delta, \qquad i = 1, 2, \ldots, n + m + 2. \quad (9\text{–}5.4)$$

We have $D(B_g, x) \geq \epsilon > 0$ for $x \in [0, 1]$ and $\delta < \delta_0$, and hence with the notation of (9–4.7) and (9–4.8) these inequalities appear as

$$(-1)^{i+1} [\delta C \cdot \mathbf{g}(C_f, x_i)] \geq 2\delta\epsilon, \qquad i = 1, 2, \ldots, n + m + 2. \quad (9\text{–}5.5)$$

We have that $m + n + 2$ inequalities for $n + m + 1$ parameters and that any $n + m + 1$ of the vectors $\mathbf{g}(C_f, x_i)$ are linearly independent. This is equivalent to stating that the form $\delta C \cdot \mathbf{g}(C_f, x)$ is a linear approximating function formed from a Tchebycheff set (the functions given in (9–4.7)). An assertion is established in the proof of Theorem 3–4 which states that, in this case, (9–5.5) implies there is a $K$ such that

$$\| \delta C \cdot \mathbf{g}(C_f, x) \| \leq K \delta \epsilon.$$

This implies that

$$\| R(C_f, x) - R(C_g, x) \| \leq K \delta$$

which establishes the theorem.

This theorem states that in the normal, nondegenerate situation where $R(C, x)$ is of maximum degree, then the best approximation depends continuously on the function being approximated. In the abnormal or degenerate situation there is a different type of behavior present. Let us consider the example of Problem 3–18.

EXAMPLE 8.   $$R(C, x) = \frac{1}{b_0 + b_1 x}, \qquad x \in [-1, +1]$$

$$f(x) = x + \alpha.$$

We may show that the best approximation is

$$R(C^*, x) = \begin{cases} -\dfrac{\alpha^2}{\sqrt{1 + \alpha^2} - x}, & \alpha \neq 0 \\ 0, & \alpha = 0 \end{cases}$$

and has deviation $\sqrt{(1 + \alpha^2)} - \alpha$. The critical point set is $\{-1, +1\}$ for $\alpha = 0$ and $\{-1, \sqrt{(1 + \alpha^2)} - \alpha, +1\}$ for $\alpha \neq 0$. The error curve is shown in Fig. 9–5 for $\alpha = 0.0$ and $\alpha = 0.1$.

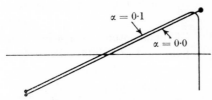

$\alpha = 0{\cdot}1$

$\alpha = 0{\cdot}0$

FIG. 9–5.   The error curves in Example 8 for $\alpha = 0.0, 0.1$.

There clearly is a discontinuity present in this example. We see that one of the extremal points disappears and that the convergence of the approximating function is not uniform. Indeed

$$\lim_{\alpha \to 0} R(C^*, x) = \begin{cases} 0, & x \neq +1 \\ 2, & x = +1. \end{cases}$$

On the other hand the deviation does converge to the correct limit as $\alpha$ tends to zero.

The phenomenon in Example 8 is present in more general situations as seen in the next lemma.

**Lemma 9–9.** *Let* $f(x) - R(C, x)$ *alternate* $k$ *times on* $[0, 1]$ *and let* $x_1$ *be the smallest extremal point and*

$$f(x_1) - R(C, x_1) = \|f - R(C)\| = \rho. \tag{9–5.6}$$

*Set* $a = f(0) - R(C, 0)$. *Given* $\epsilon > 0$ *then there is a continuous function* $f_\epsilon(x)$ *and* $\alpha, \beta$ *so that with*

$$R(D, x) = R(C, x) + \frac{x - \alpha}{x - \beta}$$

*we have*

$$\| R(D) - R(C) \| = a + \rho,  \tag{9-5.7}$$

$$\| f - f_\epsilon \| \leq \epsilon  \tag{9-5.8}$$

*and $R(D) - f_\epsilon$ alternates $k + 1$ times.*
Note that by assumption (9–5.6) we have $a > -\rho$.

*Proof.* The interval $[0, 1]$ is divided into two intervals $I_1$ and $I_2$ so that $x_1 \in I_1$ and $f(x) - R(C, x)$ alternates $k - 1$ times on $I_2$. Assume that $f(x) - R(C, x) = 0$ at the common end point of $I_1$ and $I_2$. We may assume that $2\epsilon < \rho + a$ and we denote by $z$ the largest value in $I_1$ such that

$$f(z) - R(C, z) = \rho - \tfrac{1}{2}\epsilon.$$

It is readily seen that there exist $\alpha$, $\beta$ so that

$$\frac{\alpha}{\beta} = \rho + a, \qquad \frac{z - \alpha}{z - \beta} = \tfrac{1}{2}\epsilon.$$

Note that $(x - \alpha)/(x - \beta)$ is monotonic decreasing and (9–5.7) is satisfied.
We define $f_\epsilon(x)$ as follows. In the interval $I_2$

$$f_\epsilon(x) = f(x) + \frac{x - \alpha}{x - \beta}.$$

Thus

$$f_\epsilon(x) - R(D, x) = f(x) - R(C, x), \qquad x \in I_2.$$

In the interval $I_1$ we require

$$f_\epsilon(0) = f(0), \qquad f_\epsilon(z) = f(z) + \epsilon$$

and $f_\epsilon(x)$ is defined in the remainder so as to be continuous, and to satisfy both (9–5.8) and

$$(f_\epsilon(x) - R(D, x)) \leq \rho.$$

It is clear that this can be done (see Fig. 9–6) and this function $f_\epsilon(x)$ satisfies (9–5.8) and $f_\epsilon(x) - R(D, x)$ alternates $k + 1$ times. Note that the lemma remains true if (9–5.6) is replaced by $f(x_1) - R(C, x_1) = -\rho$ and $a$ is replaced by $-a$.

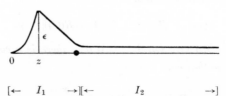

$$[\leftarrow \quad I_1 \quad \rightarrow][\leftarrow \qquad I_2 \qquad \rightarrow]$$

Fig. 9–6.  The graph of $f_\epsilon(x) - f(x)$ in the construction of Lemma 9–9.

To summarize the implications of this lemma and Theorem 9–8, let us denote by $T_{m,n}$ the operator which associates with $f(x)$ the best approximation to $f(x)$ by rationals of degree $m$ over $n$, i.e.

$$T_{m,n} : f(x) \to R(C_f, x)$$

where $R(C_f, x)$ is the best approximation to $f(x)$. We say that $f(x)$ on $R(C_f, x)$ is *normal* if $m(C_f) = n + m + 1$. We have as a direct consequence of Theorem 9–8 and Lemma 9–9:

**Corollary.** *The operator $T_{m,n}$ is continuous at $f(x)$ if and only if $f(x)$ is a normal point.*

*Proof.* The "if" part follows directly from Theorem 9–7. If $f(x)$ is not normal then $m(C_f) \leq n + m$ and hence, in Lemma 9–9 the rational function $R(D, x) = R(C_f, x) + (x - \alpha)/(x - \beta)$ has numerator and denominator of degree one more than $R(C_f, x)$. Since $f(x) - R(C_f, x)$ alternates $m(C_f)$ times, then $f_\epsilon(x) - R(D, x)$ alternates at least $m(D)$ times and $R(D, x)$ is a best approximation to $f_\epsilon(x)$ and, further, it is a rational of degree $m$ over $n$. Thus $T_{m,n}$ is not continuous at $f(x)$.

This result is due to Cheney and Loeb, 1964, and, in complete form, to Werner, 1964 and Loeb, 1965. A similar result for generalized rational functions is given by Cheney and Loeb, 1966.

In view of the close connection between the trigonometric and algebraic polynomials, it is natural to expect that results similar to the preceding are valid for trigonometrical rational functions. Thus let

$$R(C, \theta) = \frac{\sum_{i=0}^n a_i \cos i\theta + \sum_{i=1}^m a_{i+m} \sin i\theta}{\sum_{i=0}^m b_i \cos i\theta + \sum_{i=1}^m b_{i+m} \sin i\theta} = \frac{N(A, \theta)}{D(B, \theta)} \qquad (9\text{–}5.9)$$

where $-\pi \leq \theta \leq \pi$ and the points $-\pi$ and $\pi$ are identified. Just as for the ordinary rationals we require that $D(B, \theta) > 0$ and we may normalize the coefficients in the denominator as in (9–1.1). The following result has been established.

**Theorem 9–9.** *Let $f(\theta)$ be a periodic continuous function. Then we have:*

(a) *$f(\theta)$ possesses a best trigonometric rational approximation of the form (9–5.9) on $[-\pi, +\pi]$;*

(b) *$R(C, \theta)$ is a varisolvent function and the degree of varisolvence is*

$$m(C) = \begin{cases} 2(n + m - d) + 1, & R(C, \theta) \not\equiv 0 \\ 2n + 1, & R(C, \theta) \equiv 0 \end{cases}$$

*where $d = \min \{p, q|\ |a_{n-p}| + |a_{2n-p}| \neq 0, |b_{m-q}| + |b_{2m-q}| \neq 0\}$.*

While this theorem is very similar to Theorems 9–7 and 3–8, the proofs are considerably more complex. Some of the intermediate lemmas used in the proofs are presented in Problems 9–16, 9–17, 9–18. Part (a) of this theorem is due to Cheney and Loeb, 1964, and part (b) to Loeb, 1965. (Loeb actually establishes uniqueness and characterization theorems directly, but it follows from the results of Chapter 7 that $R(C, \theta)$ is then varisolvent).

## 9–6   COMPUTATION

The computational aspects of approximation by polynomial rational functions has received considerable attention in the literature. In this chapter we present several of these methods in varying detail. Our attention is directed exclusively at the computation of best Tchebycheff approximations and hence the methods of telescoping and sequence transformations considered in Chapter 6 are not considered here.

As in the case of linear Tchebycheff approximations there are *methods of ascent* of the *exchange* type. We consider these methods first. There are three basic difficulties to be overcome which may be labelled (a) *nonlinearity*, (b) *nonexistence*, and (c) *degeneracy*. The first of the difficulties is readily overcome. For the second difficulty we have two alternatives: the first is to avoid situations where best approximations do not exist and the second is to use stabilized best approximations. The final difficulty is relatively infrequent, and there are special computations which one may try in such situations.

It is useful to keep in mind that for many problems—particularly the accurate approximation of mathematical functions—there are two distinct phases to the solutions of the approximation problem. The first phase is when one is "far away" from the solution. Here the important attribute of a computational method is that it be sure-fire. This is particularly important in the approximation of physically measured data. That is to say, it will reach an approximation "close" to the best approximation no matter what complications are encountered along the way. However, once one gets close to the solution the computational method should be as efficient as possible. That is to say we should hope to be able to ignore nonlinearity, nonexistence and degeneracy and use a simple but efficient computation scheme. Such schemes are normally obtained by a perturbation of the various nonlinear equations along with the assumption of no existence or degeneracy problems.

There is yet another factor which may have a bearing on computation schemes and that is the computing power of the present larger computers. In a nutshell, these machines are so fast that it may not pay off to optimize the efficiency of the computation scheme for large classes of problems. That is to say one uses a method of the sure-fire type for the entire computation. The problems which tend to fall into this category are the most common approximation problems, namely low accuracy (four or five decimal places) approximations with a few (five or six) parameters. The reason for these remarks is that there is sometimes a tremendous overhead in the systems operations of a computer. It takes a certain amount of time to set up a problem, and input and output is relatively slow. The net result is that it is not unusual for the actual mathematical computations to require only 5 or 10 percent of the computer time used for the problem. It must be emphasized that these remarks apply only to some of the more powerful computers and particular operating systems.

It is common in the approximation of mathematical functions to make certain simplifying assumptions. These are normally that (a) there is no degeneracy, (b) the end points of the interval are extremal points, and, usually tacitly, (c) there are no existence problems encountered in the process. It is undoubtedly true that these assumptions are valid for at least 95 percent of the mathematical (as differentiated from physical data) approximation problems encountered. It is also true that one can easily concoct examples for which all of these assumptions are not valid. The following example shows that there are real problems with real difficulties.

EXAMPLE 9.           $R(c, x) = \dfrac{a_0}{b_0 + b_1 x}$,        $x \in [2, 3]$

$$f(x) = \Gamma(x).$$

The best approximation is

$$\frac{0.49669}{1 - 0.25086x}$$

and the deviation is 0.00747. The error curve is shown in Fig. 9–7. We note that the error curve almost alternates one extra time, which implies that the best approximation by

$$R(c, x) = \frac{a_0 + a_1 x}{b_0 + b_1 x + b_0 x^2} \tag{9–6.1}$$

is nearly degenerate. Indeed, the best approximation by the form (9–6.1) is degenerate on the interval [1.95, 3]. This near degeneracy shows up very clearly and unpleasantly in any computational scheme where considerable care has not been taken to account for special situations.

The gamma function is the source of at least three other special situations. The best rational approximations of degrees 0/4, 2/7 and 8/0 on [2, 3] all lead

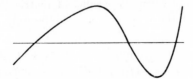

FIG.   9–7.   The error curve for the best approximation to $\Gamma(x)$ on [2, 3] by $a_0/(b_0 + b_1 x)$.

to error curves of this type. Another mathematical function which encounters these difficulties is the Fermi–Dirac integral:

$$F_{1/2}(x) = \int_0^\infty \frac{t^{1/2}\,dt}{e^{t-x} + 1}.$$

Cody and Thacher, 1966, approximate

$$f(x) = x^2 \left[ \frac{F_{1/2}(x)}{x\sqrt{x}} - \frac{2}{3} \right], \qquad 4 \leq x \leq 16$$

with a weight function

$$w(x) = \frac{1}{\sqrt{x}\,F_{1/2}(x)}$$

by rational functions of $1/x^2$. The best approximation of degree 3 over 3 is very nearly degenerate. The numerator has a zero at $x = (15.93994749)^{1/2}$ and the denominator has a zero at $x = (15.93994663)^{1/2}$.

Since all of the exchange methods require one to compute best approximations on a critical point set, let us examine this problem. For the moment we assume that there is no degeneracy. Since the error curve must alternate $n + m + 1$ times on a critical point set $\{x_i \mid x_i < x_{i+1}\}$, we have

$$f(x_i) - R(C, x_i) = (-1)^i d, \qquad i = 1, 2, \ldots, m(C) \qquad (9\text{–}6.2)$$

where $|d|$ is the deviation of the best approximation. This equation is often rewritten as

$$N(A, x_i) - [f(x_i) + (-1)^i d]D(B, x_i) = 0. \qquad (9\text{–}6.3)$$

This is a nonlinear system, for $d$ is an unknown as well as $(A, B)$. The normalization is often taken in (9–6.3) to be $b_0 = 1$ or $b_m = 1$ in which case (9–6.3) is no longer homogeneous. In actuality, there is a number of solutions of (9–6.3), and only one (or possibly none) of them corresponds to an approximation without poles in the range of $x$. Iterative methods may be used for (9–6.3) in some cases (Fraser and Hart, 1962), but in others it is difficult to ensure that the computations converge to the continuous solution of (9–6.2) rather than one of the discontinuous ones.

This difficulty may be avoided by noting that (9–6.3) is a modified eigenvalue problem for $d$. Since (9–6.3) is homogeneous in $(A, B)$, it can have a nontrivial solution only when the coefficient matrix (which depends on $d$) is singular. Thus, for the case $m = n = 1$, the only possible values of $d$ satisfy

$$\det \begin{vmatrix} 1 & x_1 & -[f(x_1) - d] & -x_1[f(x_1) - d] \\ 1 & x_2 & -[f(x_2) + d] & -x_2[f(x_2) + d] \\ 1 & x_3 & -[f(x_3) - d] & -x_3[f(x_3) - d] \\ 1 & x_4 & -[f(x_4) + d] & -x_4[f(x_4) + d] \end{vmatrix} = 0.$$

Thus $d$ is one of the roots of such a determinant equation which is a polynomial of degree two in $d$. The solution of this determinant equation provides a direct method for overcoming the first difficulty mentioned above, namely the distinction of the continuous approximations from the discontinuous ones. It is seen that a similar determinant is obtained for $m, n > 1$ and that the determinant is a polynomial of degree $m + 1$ in $d$.

## 9–7  COMPUTATION—THE REMES ALGORITHM

The Remes algorithm has been applied to the computation of polynomial rational approximations with considerable success. There are many possible variations of the algorithm and the one presented here is modeled after the one proposed by Werner, 1962. At the end of this section, we discuss briefly other variants of the Remes algorithm. At that point a "strategy" is also presented for the computation of rational approximations by the Remes algorithm. The objective is to devise a scheme which is efficient when efficiency is possible and yet which will work in *almost* all cases.

This version is derived from a perturbation of the system (9–6.3) and is basically Newton's method applied to this system. Such a method is very efficient in the "close-by" phase of the solution. In the "far away" phase of the computation the perturbation solutions may lead to difficulties (such as poles and nonexistence). In these cases the size of the perturbation is successively reduced until no difficulties are present in the new estimate of the solution.

The Remes algorithm consists of essentially two steps:

(a)  One obtains the set $S_k$ of abscissas of the extrema of the error curve $f(x) - R(C_k, x)$

(b)  One computes the best rational approximation $R(C_{k+1}, x)$ to $f(x)$ on $S_k$.

With an initial guess $R(C_0, x)$ this process is repeated until a best approximation is obtained. It is not necessary that the steps be carried out exactly. For a precise description of this algorithm see Section 6–8.

We distinguish 3 cases.

*Case 1* (Normal case)

The error curve has $n + m + 2$ or more uniquely determined local extrema such that the sign of $f(x) - R(C_k, x)$ alternates from extrema to extrema.

*Case 2* (Degeneracy)

The error curve has less than $n + m + 2$ local extrema upon which the sign of $f(x) - R(C_k, x)$ alternates.

*Case 3*

All remaining cases, i.e. local extrema, are not uniquely determined.

We consider Case 1 first. If there are more than $n + m + 2$ local extrema, the prescription of the Remes algorithm suggests that we choose a set of $n + m + 2$ points which has the largest possible minimum local extremum of the error curve consistent with alternation of sign.

The Remes algorithm indicates that we are to solve the equations (9–6.2) and

$$[f(x_i) - R(C^*, x_i)]' = 0, \qquad i = 1, 2, \ldots, n + m + 2. \qquad (9\text{-}7.1)$$

The solutions of (9–7.1) and (9–6.2) correspond to Steps (a) and (b) of the algorithm respectively. The equations (9–7.1) assume of course, that $f(x)$ is differentiable. If this is not the case, then other methods of locating local extrema are required. These methods are usually of a searching and comparing nature. There is an extra condition in the Remes algorithm which should not be overlooked. This is that the error curve attains its maximum at the $x_i$. This does not follow automatically from (9–6.3) and (9–7.1) and there are examples (such as Example 9) where one may have a solution of these equations and not have solved the approximation problem.

The basic philosophy of the perturbation approach is that the changes to be made at any one time are small. Later it is shown how to adjust the perturbations in case they are too large. Let the points of $S_k$ in Step (a) be denoted by $x_i$. We wish to determine

$$S_{k+1} = \{x_i + \delta x_i | (9\text{-}6.4) \text{ holds for } x_i + \delta x_i\}.$$

To locate these extrema we apply one iteration of Newton's method (which is equivalent to a perturbation method) to the system (9–7.1). This leads to

$$\delta x_i = - \frac{[f(x_i) - R(C_k, x_i)]'}{[f(x_i) - R(C_k, x_i)]''}. \qquad (9\text{-}7.2)$$

We remark again that this approach is not applicable if $f(x)$ is not smooth. If the derivatives of $f(x)$ are complicated, it may be more efficient to estimate the derivative in (9–7.2) by finite differences.

Let us now consider the second step of the algorithm and the perturbation of (9–6.3). We have $C_k$ and $S_{k+1}$ (which is not necessarily assumed to be obtained by (9–7.2)). We wish to determine $C_{k+1} = C_k + \delta C$ so that

$$N(A_k + \delta A, x_i) - [f(x_i) + (-1)^i (d_k + \delta d)] D(B_k + \delta B, x_i) = 0,$$

$$x_i \in S_{k+1},$$

where $d_{k+1} = d_k + \delta d$ is the deviation of $C_{k+1}$. In a perturbation method we expand everything in terms of the perturbation and set the sum of the resulting first order terms equal to zero. We obtain

$$N(\delta A, x_i) - [f(x_i) + (-1)^i d_k]D(\delta B, x_i) = (-1)^i \delta d D(B_k, x_i),$$
$$x_i \in S_{k+1}. \quad (9\text{–}7.3)$$

Note that $f(x_i) + (-1)^i d_k = R(C_k, x_i)$ and a variant of (9–7.3) is obtained. This is a homogeneous system which, nevertheless, has a nontrivial solution if $R(C_k, x)$ is not the best approximation. This follows from Theorem 9–3 and (9–4.3). The value of $\delta d$ (such that $d_{k+1} > d_k$) may be assigned arbitrarily in (9–7.3) and the system solved for $\delta C$. Later it is shown how to estimate $\delta d$.

In Case 2 the same approach is used. There is no modification required in (9–7.1). However (9–7.3) is undetermined even after one assigns a value to $\delta d$. Thus one must obtain a particular solution of (9–7.3). There are well-known techniques for this in the case of general linear systems. There is in addition a natural method in this special case which makes use of the fact that $N$ and $D$ are polynomials.

In (9–7.3) we replace $f(x_i) + (-1)^i d_k$ by $R(C_k, x_i)$ and multiply through by $D(B_k, x_i)$ to obtain

$$D(B_k, x_i)N(\delta A, x_i) - N(A_k, x_i)D(\delta B, x_i) = (-1)^i \delta D^2(B_k, x_i),$$
$$i = 1, 2, \ldots, m(C_k). \quad (9\text{–}7.4)$$

Set

$$\alpha_l = \sum_{p+q=l} (b_{pk}\delta a_q - a_{qk}\delta b_p)$$

and (9–7.1) becomes

$$\sum_{l=0}^{n+m} \alpha_l x_i{}^l = \delta D^2(B_k, x_i), \qquad i = 1, 2, \ldots, m(C_k). \quad (9\text{–}7.5)$$

We may arbitrarily set $\alpha_l = 0$ for $l = m(C_k) + 1, \ldots, n + m$ and solve (9–7.5) for the remaining values of $\alpha_l$. Once the $\alpha_l$ are known, one may compute $\delta A$ and $\delta B$.

Up to this point we have ignored the possibility that $C_{k+1}$ as computed from (9–7.3) or (9–7.4) may not be an acceptable approximation. If this is the case we use

$$C_{k+1} = C_k + \lambda \delta C$$

where $\lambda$ is an appropriately chosen positive number.

**Lemma 9–10.** *Let $f(x)$ be continuous on $[0, 1]$, $m(C_k) = n + m + 1$ and $S_{k+1}$ chosen according to the Remes algorithm. Then in Cases 1 and 2, there is a $\lambda > 0$ such that $R(C_k + \lambda \delta C)$ has a smaller deviation from $f(x)$ on $[0, 1]$ than $R(C_k, x)$.*

It is assumed in this lemma that $\delta C$ is computed from (9–7.3) or (9–7.4).

Note that it is not assumed that $S_{k+1}$ is chosen from (9–7.2). The proof is very similar to the second portion of the proof of Theorem 9–3 and only an outline is given.

*Proof.* With $\sigma_i = \pm(-1)^i$ we have from (9–7.3) that (9–4.3) is consistent for $\sigma_i \delta d > 0$, $D(B_k, x_i) > 0$. If the number of extremal points is $n + m + 2$ or less the choice of $\lambda_0$ in the proof of Theorem 9–3 applies directly. If this number is larger than $n + m + 2$, then the proof is still applicable. If (9–4.4) holds on $X_e$ then $R(C_k + \lambda C, x)$ must also be a better approximation in the remaining extremal points, otherwise $R(C, x)$ would not have Property Z. This concludes the outline of the proof.

If the perturbation technique is suitable for Step 1, i.e. if (9–7.2) can be used, then it is practical to combine two perturbation equations to obtain a system in which one need not assign $\delta d$ arbitrarily. We have

$$N(A_k, x_i) - [f(x_i) + (-1)^i d_k]D(B_k, x_i) = 0, \qquad x_i \in S_k,$$

$$N(A_k + \delta A, x_i + \delta x_i) - [f(x_i) + \delta x_i) + (-1)^i(d_k + \delta d)]$$
$$\times D(B_k + \delta B, x_i + \delta x_i) = 0, \qquad x_i + \delta x_i \in S_{k+1}$$

These equations lead to the following system (recall that the $\delta x_i$ are known from (9–7.2)).

$$N(\delta A, x_i) - [f(x_i) + (-1)^i d_k]D(\delta B, x_i) = (-1)^i \delta d D(B_k, x_i)$$
$$- \delta x_i \big(N'(A_k, x_i) - f'(x_i)D(B_k, x_i) - [f(x_i) + (-1)^i d_k]D'(B_k, x_i)\big).$$
$$(9\text{–}7.6)$$

There are many possible variants of this equation. One may replace $x_i$ by $x_i + \delta x_i$ and $[f(x_i) + (-1)d_k]$ by $R(C_k, x_i)$ in any term where it is deemed appropriate. Note that the quantities in the coefficient of $\delta x_i$ are used in the computation of $\delta x_i$.

We now consider Case 3 where local extrema are not uniquely determined. We propose to use here the exact analog of the procedure used in the proof of the characterization theorem for best approximations. That is to say we locate points $z_i$, $i = 1, 2, \ldots, m(C_k)$ such that

$$R(C_k, z_i) = f(z_i)$$

and the error curve alternates exactly once in each interval $[z_1, z_{i+2}]$ (we set $z_0 = 0$, $z_{m(C_{k+1})} = 1$). Let $x_1$ be an extremal point in $[0, z_1]$. We desire $C_{k+1} = C_k + \delta C$ to satisfy

$$f(x) - R(C_{k+1}, x) = f(x) - R(C_k, x), \qquad x = z_1, z_2, \ldots, z_{m(C_k)},$$
$$|f(x_1) - R(C_{k+1}, x_1)| < |f(x_1) - R(C_k, x)|.$$

We replace these equations, in the usual way, by perturbation equations to obtain

$$N(\delta A, z_i) - R(C_k, z_i)D(\delta B, z_i) = 0, \qquad i = 1, 2, \ldots, m(C_k)$$

$$N(\delta A, x_1) - R(C_k, x_k)D(\delta B, x_1) = -\delta d D(B_k, x_1). \tag{9-7.7}$$

If $R(C_k, x)$ is degenerate, i.e. $m(C_k) < m + n + 1$, then the same modification may be made here as in (9-7.3). It follows from the proof of Theorem 7-3 that Lemma 9-9 is valid for Case 3 if (9-7.7) is used to determine $\delta C$.

There is no *a priori* reason that this approach could not be used in every case. It certainly is applicable in all circumstances. There is the added complication, of course, of determining the zeros $z_i$ of the error curve. Another approach based on the zeros of the error is Maehly's second method, presented in the next section.

We are now in a position to give a complete description of a Remes type algorithm based entirely on perturbation equations. We show that if $f(x)$ is continuous on [0, 1], then this algorithm generates a sequence of approximations which converges to the best approximation. This very strong result is compromised slightly by the fact that one would not, in practice, be inclined to use the exact prescription of the algorithm due to its complexity.

**Remes Algorithm-Perturbation.** *Let $m_0$, $n_0$ and $f(x)$ be given. The algorithm contains two iterative procedures. The "outer" one is described as follows:*

(a) *Set $p = \min(n_0, m_0)$.*

(b) *Compute the best approximation to $f(x)$ on [0, 1] by a rational function of degree $(n_0 - p)$ over $(m_0 - p)$.*

(c) *Decrease $p$ by 1 and return to (b).*

*For each approximation to be found in (b) we use the usual Remes algorithm statements:*

(1) *Take $R(C_0, x)$ to be the best approximation of degree $(n_0 - p - 1)$ over $(m_0 - p - 1)$.*

(2) *Obtain the set $S_k$ of abscissas of the extrema of the error curve $f(x) - R(C_k, x)$.*

(3) *Compute $\delta C$ according to (9-7.3) for Case 1, (9-7.4) for Case 2 and (9-7.7) for Case 3.*

(4) *Determine $\lambda$ so that $R(C_{k+1}, x)$, $C_{k+1} = C_k + \lambda \delta C$ has the smallest possible deviation from $f(x)$ on [0, 1].*

(5) *Increase $k$ by 1 and return to (2).*

In order to understand what this procedure does, we outline the proof that it is effective. First note that the first approximation to be found in (b) is either a polynomial or the reciprocal of a polynomial. Polynomial approximations are easily obtained and since the only degenerate case of a reciprocal polynomial is the constant zero, we either have the normal (Case 1) situation or a trivial one. Hence we are assured that this procedure can be initiated.

At this point the following result, to be established in Problem 9–8, is needed.

**Lemma 9–11.** *Let $d_0$ be the deviation of the approximation to $f(x)$ on $[0, 1]$ by a rational function of degree $(n - 1)$ over $(m - 1)$. If $R(C, x)$ is of degree $n$ over $m$ with deviation $d < d_0$, then $R(C, x)$ is not degenerate, i.e. $m(C) = n + m + 1$.*

Thus when we increase $p$ by 1 and return to (b) there are only two possibilities. Either we already have the best approximation (in which case, it is degenerate) or we can improve upon the approximation. In the second case, the above lemma assures us that we will never encounter a degenerate situation again.

This means that in considering the inner iteration (Steps (2) through (5)) we need only be concerned with Case 1 and Case 3. By Lemma 9–9 it follows that $d_{k+1} < d_k$ and one needs only to show that $d_{k+1}$ depends continuously on $C_k$ in order to have established that this algorithm defines a descent mapping. The only possible source of discontinuity is the dependence on $C_k$ of the extremal points of the error curve $f(x) - R(C_k, x)$. This situation may be treated as in the proof of Theorem 6–3. Indeed, once it is determined that $m(C_k) = m + n + 1$ for all $k \geq 1$, the argument of Theorem 6–3 is applicable to prove the convergence of the Remes algorithm as prescribed in Chapter 6.

This completes the outline of the proof of the following result.

**Theorem 9–10.** *Let $f(x)$ be continuous on $[0, 1]$. Then the perturbation version of the Remes algorithm generates a sequence of rational approximations $R(C_k, x)$ which converges uniformly to the best rational approximation $R(C^*, x)$ to $f(x)$ on $[0, 1]$.*

In the situation where everything is normal and no difficulties are encountered, Werner was able to show that this algorithm converges quadratically. This is to say that $\|C_{k+1} - C^*\|$ is proportional to $\|C_k - C^*\|^2$. This requires that the third derivative of $f(x)$ be continuous. Then this perturbation method is a variant of Newton's method, which is also known to converge quadratically. This quadratic convergence has been observed experimentally.

A few of the many possible variations of the Remes algorithm have been published (Fraser and Hart, 1962, Stoer, 1964, Ralston, 1965, and Werner, 1962). Except for Werner, the main point of these algorithms is to be efficient when efficiency is possible and to ignore the other situations. Thus these algorithms are more likely to fail, but, as compensation, when they work they are efficient and simpler.

It is reasonable to attempt a strategy to combine the possibilities of efficiency with the sureness of the algorithm described above. The basic approach is to start with the assumption that no difficulties are present. This allows one to use initially the efficient variations of the Remes algorithm. However, during the computation, one makes periodic checks as to whether any difficulties have been encountered. If some evidence of difficulty is encountered, then the program modifies itself to make convergence more likely. Furthermore, at the end the error curve is carefully examined to ensure that a best approximation has been found. If it has not been found, then the program makes further modifications and attempts another calculation.

It is clear that a program which uses this strategy will not be simple. It is not unlikely that this strategy would be more practical if implemented by several separate programs, rather than attempting to include everything in one large one.

A general flow chart of one possible strategy of this nature is shown in Fig. 9–8. Many details of the logic of the computation have not been specified in this flow chart and this particular strategy has not been tested. Note in particular that no provisions have been included for Case 3. It seems likely that if difficulties of this type occur, one should use *Maehly's second method*, which is described in the next section.

The problem of convergence for almost degenerate best approximations is still unsolved at this time. The approach presented here (which is basically that of Werner) has not been fully explored, but Cody and Thacher, 1966, report considerable difficulty with the Fermi–Dirac integral and, in particular, that some machine codes using this approach did not work. They experimented with several possibilities and found the following scheme to be the most reliable.

If the best approximation $R^*_{n,m}$ to $f(x)$ by rationals of degree $n$ over $m$ is nearly degenerate, consider

$$g(a, x) = (x - a)f(x)$$

and attempt to approximate $g(a, x)$ by rationals $R_{n,m-1}$ of degree $n$ over $m - 1$ with the weight function $w(x) = 1/(x - a)$. The parameter $a$ is then varied (perhaps by a one-dimensional search procedure) to make the error curve

$$\frac{g(a, x) - R^*_{n\ m-1}}{x - a}$$

oscillate an extra time, i.e. until it almost alternates $n + m + 1$ times. The initial estimate for the Remes algorithm is then taken to be $R^*_{n,m-1}/(x - a)$.

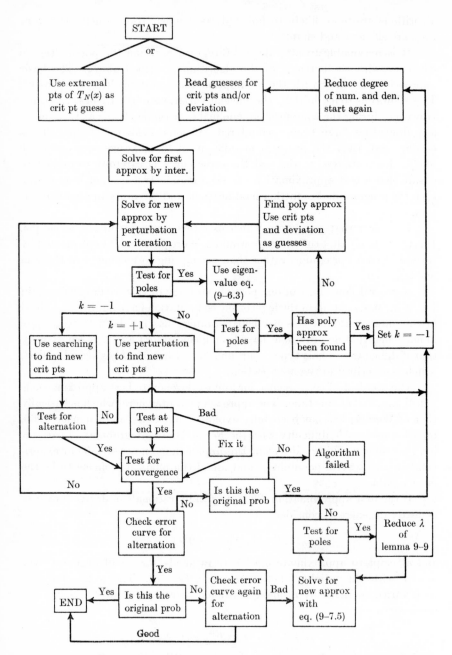

FIG. 9–8.   Outline of a possible strategy to combine efficiency and certainty in the use of the Remes algorithm.

The parameter $a$ is an estimate of the pole of the denominator of $R^*_{n,m}$. In particularly delicate situations, the value of $a$ must be obtained quite accurately.

## 9–8  COMPUTATION—OTHER METHODS

There are several other computational methods for rational approximation which have been used with considerable success. Indeed there are at least a dozen known methods for rational approximation (some of which do not give best Tchebycheff approximations). In this section three methods are presented which seem to have special merit and which are distinctly different in approach. These methods are: *Maehly's second method* (Maehly, 1963), *a descent algorithm* (Cheney and Loeb, 1962), *weighted linear method* (Loeb, 1959). All of these methods have been reported as giving practical computational efficiency. Convergence of the descent algorithm, unlike the others, has been established. A noteworthy feature of Maehly's second method is that it may be applied to any approximation problem.

The survey by Cheney and Southard, 1964, lists most of the methods for rational approximation that had been reported upon at the time of its publication.

A. *Maehly's Second Method.* The basic idea of this method is to adjust the zeros of $f(x) - R(A, x)$ so that a best Tchebycheff approximation is obtained. Thus, if $R(A, x)$ is close to being a best approximation, one expects to have

$$f(x) - R(A, x) = G(x) \prod_{k=1}^{n+m+1} (x - z_k) \tag{9-8.1}$$

where $G(x)$ is a positive function and the $z_k$ are the zeros of the error curve. It is clear that (9–8.1) does not hold in general and hence a fundamental assumption must be made in order to proceed with an analysis.

ASSUMPTION 1. *Let $R(A^*, x)$ be the best Tchebycheff approximation to $f(x)$. Then (9–8.1) is valid for all $R(A, x)$ sufficiently close to $R(A^*, x)$ with a unique determination of the $z_k$ and $G(x) > 0$.*

Thus this method demands that the approximation problem presents no difficulties other than nonlinearity. The method proceeds with two steps:

(a)  Given the values of the $z_k$, one determines the approximation $R(A_i, x)$. This is a straightforward rational interpolation problem, but if the $z_k$ are not close to the $z_k^*$, it may fail to have a solution.

(b)  Given the approximation $R(A_i, x)$, one computes the local extrema of the error curve and uses their values to obtain a new estimate of the zeros, $z_k$. One then returns to Step (a) to compute $R(A_{i+1}, x)$.

The crucial element of this method is the correction of the zeros $z_k$ in Step (b). For brevity we denote $f(x) - R(A_i, x)$ by $\epsilon(x, \bar{z})$, where $\bar{z}$ stands for the zeros $z_1, z_2, \ldots$ Let $x_i$, $i = 1, 2, \ldots, n + m + z$ be the local extrema of $\epsilon(x, \bar{z})$. If $\epsilon(x, \bar{z})$ does not alternate sufficiently often, we wish to choose correction $\delta z_i$ in the zeros so that

$$\epsilon(x_i, \bar{z} + \delta\bar{z}) = (-1)^{i+1}\lambda. \qquad (9\text{--}8.2)$$

One may take the logarithm of the absolute value of (9–8.2), expand in the first term of Taylor's series to obtain

$$\ln |\epsilon(x_i, \bar{z})| + \sum_{k=1}^{n+m+1} \left(\frac{\partial \ln G}{\partial z_k} - \frac{1}{x_i - z_k}\right)\delta z_k = \ln |\lambda|.$$

We now make an additional

ASSUMPTION 2. *The function $G(x)$ does not depend (very much) on the zeros $z_k$, i.e.*

$$\frac{\partial \ln G}{\partial z_k} = 0.$$

This then gives a linear system of equations

$$\sum_{k=1}^{n+m+1} \frac{\delta z_k}{x_i - z_k} = \ln |\epsilon(x_i, \bar{z})| - \ln |\lambda| \qquad (9\text{--}8.3)$$

for the corrections $\delta z_k$ and the new estimate $\lambda$ of the deviation.

There are several variants of this approach possible. The original presentation suggests that the $\ln |\lambda|$ term be eliminated from (9–8.3). One may omit the taking of the logarithm and obtain

$$\epsilon(x_i, \bar{z}) \sum_{k=1}^{n+m+1} \frac{\delta z_k}{x_i - z_k} = (-1)^{i+1}\lambda - \epsilon(x_i, \bar{z}). \qquad (9\text{--}8.4)$$

One may assume a correction $\delta\lambda$ in the deviation $\lambda$ and solve for $\delta\lambda$ rather than $\lambda$ itself in either (9–8.3) or (9–8.4).

The convergence of Maehly's second method is investigated by Dunham, 1965. That difficulties may arise is seen from the following analysis of the special case:

(a)  $R(A, x) = a$,      $x \in [-1, +1]$.
(b)  $f(x)$ odd, monotonic and differentiable with $f(1) = 1$.

There is only one interpolation point, $z$, and $x_1 = -1$, $x_2 = +1$.

$$\epsilon(x_1, z) = f(-1) - f(z) = -[1 + f(z)],$$

$$\epsilon(x_2, z) = f(1) - f(z).$$

The equations (9–8.3) become

$$\frac{\delta z}{-1 - z} = \ln |1 + f(z)| - \ln |\lambda|,$$

$$\frac{\delta z}{1 - z} = \ln |1 - f(z)| - \ln |\lambda|.$$

One may eliminate $\ln |\lambda|$ and expand $f(z)$ in its Taylor series to obtain

$$\delta z = -\tfrac{1}{2}(1 - z^2) \ln \left( \frac{1 + f(z)}{1 - f(z)} \right)$$

$$= -(1 - z^2)\big(f(z) + [f(z)]^3/3 + \cdots\big)$$

$$= -(1 - z^2)[zf^{(1)}(0) + z^3 f^{(3)}(0)/3! + \cdots]$$

$$= -zf^{(1)}(0) + O(z^3).$$

Thus

$$|z + \delta z| = |z| \, |1 - f^{(1)}(0) + O(z^2)|.$$

This implies that $|z + \delta z| > |z|$ for $z$ sufficiently small if $f^{(1)}(0) < 0$ or $f^{(1)}(0) > 2$, i.e. Maehly's second method diverges. Since $f(x)$ is odd and increasing the possibility $f^{(1)}(0) < 0$ is excluded. If $0 < f^{(1)}(0) < 2$, then the method converges and the cases $f'(0) = 0, f'(0) = 2$ depend on the behavior of the higher order terms. The convergence is faster than linear only if $f'(0) = 1$. A similar analysis is carried out for $n + m > 0$ by Dunham, 1966, and a similar situation exists there.

A modification of Maehly's second method is presented by Dunham, 1966, along with the results of a number of experiments comparing Maehly's method, the modification and the Remes algorithm. Dunham concludes that, for linear approximation, the Remes algorithm is superior to Maehly's second method in three respects: (a) its initial approximation is usually better (i.e. based on interpolation at the zeros of a Tchebycheff polynomial of appropriate degree), (b) the convergence is faster, and (c) the convergence is certain. For rational approximation, his experiments and the theoretical results of Section 9–7 again favor the Remes algorithm. However, there is a possibility that Maehly's second method may work well in those cases that present difficulty for the Remes algorithm.

Let us consider the essential elements of this method. They are (a) a reparameterization of the approximating function in terms of the zeros $z_k$ of the error curve, (b) the application of Newton's method for the leveling of the error curve. Note that the reparameterization does not depend either on the fact that one is using rational functions or on Assumption 1. The simplicity of the application of Newton's method depends on the assumption that $G(x)$ does not depend heavily on the parameters $z_k$.

It is not clear whether the two assumptions merely imply that Newton's method is particularly simple to apply in these cases, or whether they are essential for the convergence of Newton's method.

**B.** *A Descent Algorithm.* We wish to determine $C^* = (A^*, B^*)$ such that $R(C^*, x)$ is a best approximation, i.e.

$$\left\| f(x) - \frac{N(A^*, x)}{D(B^*, x)} \right\| = \Delta^*$$

is a minimum. For any estimate $C_k$ of $C^*$, we have

$$\left\| f(x) - \frac{N(A_k, x)}{D(B_k, x)} \right\| - \Delta^* \leq 0$$

or, if we assume $D(B_k, x) > 0$,

$$\left| f(x)D(B_k, x) - N(A_k, x) \right| - \Delta^* D(B_k, x) \leq 0.$$

We also have

$$\left| f(x)D(B_k, x) - N(A_k, x) \right| - \Delta_k D(B_k, x) \leq 0$$

where

$$\Delta_k = \| f(x) - R(C_k, x) \|.$$

Assume then that $C_k$ is known and define the auxiliary function

$$\delta_k(C) = \max_{x \in [0, 1]} \left\{ \left| f(x)D(B, x) - N(A, x) \right| - \Delta_k D(B, x) \right\}. \qquad (9\text{--}8.5)$$

The new estimate $C_{k+1}$ of $C^*$ is determined such that

$$\delta_k(C_{k+1}) \leq \delta_k(C) \qquad (9\text{--}8.6)$$

for all $C$. The determination of $C_{k+1}$ so as to minimize (9–8.5) is a *linear programming* problem and hence there is a variety of methods available to compute $C_{k+1}$.

The algorithm as stated here may be applied to a general rational function of the form (9–1.2).

There is a very satisfactory convergence result (Cheney and Loeb, 1962) for the case of polynomial rational functions.

**Theorem 9–11.** *For polynomial rational functions we have* $\delta_k(C_{k+1}) \leq 0$ *as determined by (9–8.6) if and only if* $C_{k+1} = C^*$, *and* $D(B_{k+1}, x) = 0$ *for* $x \in [0, 1]$ *implies that* $C_k = C^*$. *Furthermore,* $\Delta_{k+1} < \Delta_k$ *and*

$$\lim_{k \to \infty} \Delta_k = \Delta^*.$$

The proof of this theorem is omitted here, but it is of interest to discuss what happened to the difficulties present in the Remes algorithm. It is clear that they must have been transferred to the linear programming problem. Note that the theorem assures us that this problem will not become degenerate. Thus, if the best approximation to $f(x)$ is of less than maximal degree, the linear programming problem (9–8.6) to be solved gets closer and closer to a degenerate problem which will undoubtedly introduce some computational difficulties.

It is noted by Cheney and Loeb that this theorem may be extended to a quite general setting, including rational approximation with constraints. The details and exact conditions for this extension have not been given.

C. *Weighted Linear Method.* Rephrase the approximation problem to the minimization of

$$\left\| \frac{f(x)D(B, x) - N(A, x)}{D(B, x)} \right\|$$

In this approach $1/D(B, x)$ is regarded as a weight function and $C_k = (A_k, B_k)$ is determined to minimize

$$\max_{0 \le x \le 1} \frac{1}{D(B_{k-1}, x)} |f(x)D(B_k, x) - N(A, x)|. \qquad (9–8.7)$$

The determination of $C_k$ from (9–8.7) is a linear approximation problem which may be attacked by a variety of methods. Conditions under which this algorithm is convergent are unknown but Loeb, 1958, reports that it has been successfully employed.

## PROBLEMS

9–1. There is a variety of ways in which to normalize the rational function (9–1.2). These include

(a) $\displaystyle\sum_{i=1}^{n} a_i^2 + \sum_{i=1}^{m} b_i^2 = 1$

(b) $b_1 = 1.$

(c) $b_m = 1.$

(d) $\max |b_i| = 1.$

(e) $\max |a_i| = 1.$

Discuss which of these normalizations have a serious defect in (1) the polynomial case, (2) the general case. Which of these normalizations allow one to establish Lemma 9–1?

9–2. Investigate the existence question for the following approximating functions.

(a) $\displaystyle\frac{a_1 + a_2 e^x + a_3 e^{2x}}{b_1 + b_2 e^x}$ $\qquad x \in [-1, 1]$

(b) $\dfrac{a_1 + a_2 \cos x}{b_1 + b_2 e^x}$, $\qquad x \in [-\pi, \pi]$

(c) $\dfrac{a_1 + a_2 \cos x}{b_1 + b_2 x}$, $\qquad x \in [-\pi, \pi]$

(d) $\dfrac{a_1 + a_2 |x|}{b_1 + b_2 x}$, $\qquad x \in [-1, +1]$

(e) $\dfrac{a_1 + a_2 x}{b_1 x + b_2 \phi(x)}$, $\qquad x \in [\tfrac{1}{3}, 1]$

where $\phi(x)$ is defined in Example 4.

9–3. Determine which of the following nonlinear approximating functions satisfy condition E.

(a) $a + b e^{tx}$
(b) $a + b r^x$, $\qquad r > 0$
(c) $a \log (1 + bx) + c$, $\qquad x \in [0, 1], b > -1$
(d) $a + b \sin (tx)$
(e) $a + b(x - t)_+^3 + c(x - s)_+^3$, where $(y)_+^3 = \tfrac{1}{2}(y^3 + |y|^3)$

9–4. Consider approximation by (9–1.2) with the condition $D(B, x) > 0$ for $x \in [0, 1]$ replaced by $D(B, x) \geq \epsilon > 0$ for $x \in [0, 1]$. Establish that this set of functions is closed and that every continuous function possesses a best approximation.

9–5. State and prove the analog of Lemma 9–2 for functions defined on a compact metric space $X$.

9–6. Show that the dense nonzero property is equivalent to the condition: the set $\{d_i(x)\}_{i=1}^m$ is linearly independent on every open subset of $[0, 1]$.

9–7. Modify the definition of the dense nonzero property for functions defined on a finite point set. Give an example of a set of functions with this property. Is Lemma 9–3 valid with your definition? Discuss the usefulness of this approach.

9–8. Prove Lemma 9–11.

9–9. Consider the inconsistent system of inequalities

$$x > 0, \qquad y > 0$$
$$-2x - y - 5 > 0$$
$$4x + 2y + 1 > 0.$$

Show that this system has two distinct subsystems which are irreducibly inconsistent. Use these examples to show that one cannot define the term "maximal irreducibly inconsistent subsystem" of a system of linear inequalities in the natural way.

9–10. Derive the equations for Maehly's second method for the approximating function $a + b e^{tx}$.

The following problems are included primarily for reference purposes.

9–11. The abstract formulation of the stability of rational approximations is as follows. Let $X$ be an arbitrary set, $F$ and $G$ be bounded mappings with

$F : X \to E_n$ and $G : X \to E_n$, and $f$ be a bounded real function defined on $X$. The problem is to obtain $A^* \in E_n$, so that

$$\sup_X \left| \frac{F(x) \cdot A}{G(x) \cdot A} - f(x) \right| = d(A)$$

is minimized. The dot product notation is used.
Set

$$D_0 = \{ B \in E_n \,|\, B \cdot G(x) \geq 0 \text{ all } x \in X \text{ and } \| B \| = 1 \}$$
$$D_1 = \{ B \in E_n \,|\, B \cdot G(x) > 0 \text{ all } x \in X \text{ and } \| B \| = 1 \}$$
$$D_2 = \{ B \in E_n \,|\, B \cdot G(x) = 0 \text{ for some } x \in X \text{ and } B \cdot G(x) = 0$$
$$\Rightarrow B \cdot F(x) = 0 \}$$

$$\Omega = \{ F(x) - f(x)G(x) \,|\, x \in X \}$$
$$d_0(A) = \sup_X \left( \left| \frac{F(x) \cdot A}{G(x) \cdot A} - f(x) \right| \text{with } | \, A \cdot G \, (x) | \neq 0 \right)$$

*Theorem 1.* If $\Omega$ is $n$-dimensional and $A \cdot G(x) \geq \epsilon$ for all $x \in X$ is consistent for some $\epsilon > 0$ then $d_0(A)$ achieves a minimum on $D_1 \cup D_2$.

Consider the two systems of inequalities

(1)  $|(F(x) - f(x)G(x)) \cdot A| \leq MG(x) \cdot A, \| A \| = 1$
(2)  $|(F(x) - f(x)G(x)) \cdot A| < MG(x) \cdot A, \| A \| = 1$

*Theorem 2.* Assume that $\Omega$ is $n$-dimensional and $A \cdot G(x) \geq \epsilon$ for all $x \in X$ is consistent for some $\epsilon > 0$. There exists a smallest number $M_0 > 0$ for which (1) is consistent and a largest number $M^*$ for which (2) is inconsistent. We have $M^* \geq M_0$. If $M_0 \leq M \leq M^*$ then 0 belongs to the boundary of the convex hull of the set

$$\{ F(x) - (f(x) + M)G(x) \} \cup \{ -F(x) + (f(x) - M)G(x) \}, \qquad x \in X.$$

(Goldstein, 1963.)

9–12.  We may modify Definition 9–1 by replacing the conditions (a) and (b) by

(c)  $D(B, x) \neq 0$ for $x \in X_0$ dense in $[0, 1]$
(d)  $\lim_{y \to x} R(C, y)$ exists for $x$ such that $D(B^*, x) = 0$ and $y \in X_0$.

One may establish Theorem 9–1 with this modified definition. (Boehm, 1964.)

9–13.  Consider the system of strict linear inequalities

$$l_i(A) > \alpha_i, \qquad i = 1, 2, \ldots, p$$

where $l_i(A)$ is linear in $A = (a_1, a_2, \ldots, a_n)$, i.e. a linear functional.

(a)  This system is consistent if and only if, for any $p$ numbers $\lambda_i \geq 0$, not all zero, the relation

$$\sum_{i=1}^{p} \lambda_i l_i = 0$$

implies

$$\sum_{i=1}^{p} \lambda_i \alpha_i < 0.$$

(b)  Corollary. The system $l_i(A) > 0$ is inconsistent if and only if the zero-functional is in the convex hull of $\{l_i \mid i = 1, 2, \ldots, p\}$.
(Carver, 1922.)

9–14. With the hypothesis of the Corollary of Theorem 9–5 establish that there is an $a'' > 0$ so that

$$\|f(x) - R(C, x)\| \geq \|f(x) - R(C^*, x)\| + a'' \|R(C^*, x) - R(C, x)\|.$$

(Cheney, 1965.)

9–15. Let $P$ and $Q$ be the spaces of polynomials of degree $\leq n$ and $\leq m$, respectively. Let $r = p/q$ for $p \in P$ and $q \in Q$ with $q > 0$ on $[0, 1]$ and $r$ irreducible. Then $P + rQ$ is a Haar subspace of dimension $1 + \max (n + \text{degree of } q,\ m + \text{degree of } p)$. (Cheney, 1965.)

9–16. (See also Problem 9–17).

(a)  If $T$ is a trigonometric polynomial of degree $\leq n$ then $p = (1 + x^2)^n T \times (2 \tan^{-1} x)$ is an algebraic polynomial of degree $2n - k$ where $k$ is the multiplicity of $\pi$ as a root of $T$. If the coefficients of $T$ are real, so are those of $p$.

(b)  If $p$ is an algebraic polynomial of degree $\leq 2n$ then $T(\theta) = (\cos\frac{1}{2}\theta)^{2n} p(\tan \frac{1}{2}\theta)$ is a trigonometric polynomial of degree $\leq n$. If the coefficients of $p$ are real, so are those of $T$.

(c)  Let $T_1$ and $T_2$ be nonzero trigonometric polynomials with real coefficients such that $|T_1(\theta)| \leq |T_2(\theta)|$ for all $\theta$. If $T_2$ has a real zero then there exist nonzero real trigonometric polynomials $T_3$ and $T_4$ such that $T_1 T_4 = T_2 T_3$ and the degrees of $T_3$ and $T_4$ are less than the degrees of $T_1$ and $T_2$, respectively.

(Cheney and Loeb, 1964.)

9–17. (See also Problem 9–16.)

Let $\mathcal{T}_k$ be the set of trigonometric polynomials of degree exactly $k$.

(a)  $T \in \mathcal{T}_k$ if and only if

$$T(\theta) = e^{-ik\theta} p(e^{i\theta})$$

where $p$ is a polynomial of degree $2k$ such that

$$p(z) = z^{2k} \overline{p(1/\bar{z})}.$$

(b)  If $\theta$ is a zero of multiplicity $m$ of $T(\theta)$ then $e^{i\theta}$ is a zero of multiplicity $m$ of $p(z)$ defined in (a).

(c)  Suppose $T_1 \in \mathcal{T}_n$, $T_2 \in \mathcal{T}_m$ and $r = T_1/T_2$. Assume that $T_2$ has real zeros and any such zero of $T_2$ is also a zero of $T_1$ with multiplicity at least as great. Then $r = T_3/T_4$ where $T_3 \in \mathcal{T}_{n'}$, and $T_4 \in \mathcal{T}_{m'}$, $T_4(\theta) \neq 0$ for all real $\theta$. If $L$ is the total multiplicity of the zeros of $T_2$, then $L$ is even and $n' = n - L/2$, $m' = m - L/2$.

*Corollary.* Let $T(\theta)$ have $2k$ real roots $\theta_i$, then $T(\theta) = T_1(\theta) T_2(\theta)$ where $T_1(\theta_i) = 0, i = 1, 2, \ldots, 2k$ and $T_2(\theta) > 0$ for all $\theta$ and the degree of $T_1(\theta)$ is $k$.
(Rivlin, 1964.)

9–18.  Let $T_{n,m}$ be the set of rational trigonometric functions (9–5.9).  For any $R \in T_{n,m}$ let $v(R) + 1$ be the maximum order of all Tchebycheff systems over $[-\pi, \pi)$ obtained from the following $2(n + m + 1)$ functions:

$$1, \cos \theta, \ldots, \cos n\theta \qquad R, R \cos \theta, \ldots, R \cos m\theta$$
$$\sin \theta, \ldots, \sin n\theta \qquad R \sin \theta, \ldots, R \sin m\theta$$

Let $u(R) + 1$ be the maximum number of zeros in $[-\pi, \pi)$ possessed by any non-zero function

$$g(\theta) = a_0 + \sum_{i=1}^{n} (a_j \cos j\theta + a_{n+j} \sin j\theta) + R(\theta)[b_0 + \sum_{i=1}^{m} (b_j \cos j\theta + b_{m+j} \sin j\theta)].$$

(a)  If $R(C^*, \theta) \in T_{n,m}$ is a best approximation to $f(\theta)$ on $[-\pi, \pi)$ then $R(C^*, \theta) - f(\theta)$ alternates $v(R) + 2$ times on $[-\pi, \pi)$.

(b)  If $f(x) - R(C^*, \theta)$ alternates $u(R) + 2$ times on $[-\pi, \pi)$ then $R(C^*, \theta)$ is a best approximation to $f(\theta)$ on $[-\pi, \pi)$.

(c)  For any $R \in T_{n,m}$ we have $u(R) \geq v(R)$.  For any irreducible $R \in T_{n,m}$ we have $u(R) = v(R) = 2 \max [n + \text{degree} \quad D(B, \theta),$ $m + \text{degree } N(A, \theta)]$.

(d)  Let $R \in T_{n,m}$ be irreducible with numerator of degree $n$.  Then there exists a neighborhood of $R$ in $T_{n,m}$ which contains only irreducible rational functions with numerator of degree $n$.  (Loeb, 1965.)

9–19.  We consider least squares approximation in the setting of the end of Section 9–4.

(a)  If $f(x)$ is continuous on $[0, 1]$, then $f(x)$ possesses a best $L_p$-approximation by polynomial rational functions.

(b)  Let $R(C, x)$ be a generalized rational function and set

$$\mathscr{D}^+ = \{D(B, x) \mid D(B, x) > 0, x \in [0, 1]\}$$

If $\mathscr{D}^+$ contains two elements whose ratio is strictly monotone on $[0, 1]$ and if $\mathscr{N}$ contains an element whose support is dense in $[0, 1]$ then the orthogonal complement of $\{R(C, x) \mid R(C, x) = N(A, x)/ D(B, x)\}$ is zero.  Corollary:  The orthogonal complement of the polynomial rational functions is 0 whenever $n \geq 0$ and $m \geq 1$.

(c)  $R(C_0, x)$ is a best $L_2$-approximation to some continuous function $f(x)(\neq R(C_0, x))$ on $[0, 1]$ if and only if $R(C_0, x)$ has zero defect.

(d)  Let $R(C^*, x)$ be a local minimum of $\|f - R(C, x)\|_2$.  Then

$$\int (f - R(C^*))(N(A^*)D(B) + D(B^*)N(A)) \frac{dx}{[D(B^*)]^2} = 0$$

and

$$\int [N^2(A) + 2(f - 2R(C^*))N(A)D(B)$$
$$+ (3R^2(C^*) - 2fR(C^*))D^2(B)] \frac{dx}{[D(B^*)]^2} \geq 0$$

for all $N(A)$ and $D(B)$.  (Cheney and Goldstein, 1967.)

9–20.  Set

$$L_2(C) = \sum_{X} (f(x) - R(C, x))^2.$$

In order to minimize $L_2(C)$ we may minimize

$$L'_2(C_k) = \sum_X [f(x)D(B_k, x) - N(A_k, x)]^2 \frac{1}{D^2(B_{k-1}, x)}$$

to determine a sequence of approximations. If this sequence converges (say to $C^*$) then

$$\frac{\partial L_2(C^*)}{\partial a_i} = \frac{\partial L_2(C^*)}{\partial b_j} = 0, \qquad \text{all } i, j.$$

(Loeb, 1959.)

9–21. Consider an exchange algorithm for computing best Tchebycheff approximations by $F(A, x)$. For any $(n + 1)$-tuple of points we let

$$\mu : (x_1, \ldots, x_{n+1}) \to (a_1^*, \ldots, a_n^*)$$

denote the mapping of these points to the parameters of the best approximation on this $(n + 1)$-tuple. Further set

$$\eta(x_1, \ldots, x_{n+1}) = \max_{x_i} |f(x_i) - F(\mu(x_1, \ldots, x_{n+1}), x_i)|.$$

We assume that the initial approximant $A_0$ for the exchange algorithm is such that all succeeding approximations lie in a region where the following conditions are satisfied:

(a)   $\text{sgn}[f(x_i) - F(\mu, x_i)] = S_i$ is constant.

(b)   $\eta$ and $\mu$ are differentiable.

(c)   The following matrix has rank $n$

$$D_{ij} = \left[\frac{\partial F(\mu, x_i)}{\partial a_j}\right] \quad A = \mu(x_1, \ldots, x_{n+1}).$$

(d)   Let $\sigma_i(x_1, \ldots, x_{n+1})$ be such that

$$\sum_{i=1}^{n+1} \sigma_i D_{ij} = 0, \quad \sum_{i=1}^{n+1} \sigma_i S_i = 1.$$

Then $\sigma_i \neq 0$.

We may establish

(1)   $\dfrac{\partial \eta}{\partial x_j} = \sigma_j \left[\dfrac{df(x_j)}{dx} - \dfrac{dF(\mu, x_j)}{dx}\right].$

(2)   If $\dfrac{\partial \eta}{\partial x_j} = 0$ then

$$\frac{\partial \mu_m}{\partial x_j} = 0$$

where $\mu_m$ is the $m$th parameter of $\mu(x_1, \ldots, x_{n+1})$.

(3)   If $\dfrac{\partial \eta}{\partial x_i} = \dfrac{\partial \eta}{\partial x_j} = 0$ for $i \neq j$ then

$$\frac{\partial^2 \eta}{\partial x_i \partial x_j} = 0.$$

This last result implies that the exchange algorithm converges quadratically. (Curtis and Powell, 1966.)

# 10

# Spline Functions

## 10-1 INTRODUCTION

Spline functions are piecewise polynomials of degree $n$ that are connected together (at points called knots) so as to have $n - 1$ continuous derivations. They were first considered from a mathematical viewpoint by Schoenberg, 1946, and became the object of rather intensive research in the late 1950's. This research is continuing at a steady pace and is motivated by two facts.

First, spline functions have certain mathematical properties that might well place them at the center of future developments in some areas of applied mathematics and numerical analysis. These properties are briefly developed in Section 10–6. This material does not belong properly to the area of "approximation of functions", but it is felt that this aspect of spline functions must be included if the reader is to obtain an appreciation of their place in approximation theory and related areas.

Second, spline functions are the most successful approximating functions for practical applications so far discovered. The reader may be unaware of the fact that ordinary polynomials are inadequate in many situations. This is particularly the case when one approximates functions which arise from the physical world rather than from the mathematical world. Functions which express physical relationships are frequently of a disjointed or dis-associated nature. That is to say that their behavior in one region may be totally unrelated to their behavior in another region. Polynomials along with most other mathematical functions, have just the opposite property. Namely their behavior in any small region determines their behavior everywhere. Splines do not suffer this handicap since they are defined piecewise, yet, for $n \geq 3$, they represent nice, smooth curves in the physical world.

This is perhaps the first attempt to present in one place the theory of approximation by spline functions and the reader will soon find that there are many gaps in the material. The key to the successful use of splines is to have the location of the knots as variables. This makes them nonlinear approximating functions and they have a type of nonlinearity not encountered previously. After a section which presents some basic properties of splines, we consider the existence question for spline approximation. Fairly satis-factory results are obtained. The next section considers least squares approximation and the results are either trivial or nonexistent. In Section 10–5 we consider Tchebycheff approximation and obtain a characterization theorem of the alternation variety for best approximation with the *knots fixed*. The nonlinear theory is discussed briefly and it promises to be both challenging and interesting. The next section discusses the optimal approxi-mation of linear functionals. It is seen that spline functions—and generaliza-tions of the concept—play a central role.

The final section contains a description of a computational method for least squares approximation. Convergence proofs are not available for this method, but it has been tested extensively and has given good results. In view of the usefulness of spline approximations, it is worthwhile presenting this method even while the search continues for more efficient methods and for a better understanding of the computational problems of spline approxi-mation.

## 10–2  SPLINE FUNCTIONS AND THEIR BASIC PROPERTIES

Spline functions are defined in terms of a set

$$0 = \xi_0 < \xi_1 \cdots < \xi_k < \xi_{k+1} = 1 \tag{10-2.1}$$

of points called *knots*. The spline is a polynomial of degree $n$ between the knots and constrained to have the $n - 1$ continuous derivatives at the knots. The splines may be expressed in terms of the functions

$$(x - \xi)_+^n = \begin{cases} (x - \xi)^n, & x \geq \xi. \\ 0, & x \leq \xi \end{cases} \tag{10-2.2}$$

**Definition 10–1.** *A spline $S(A, \Xi, x)$ is a function of the form*

$$S(A, \Xi, x) = \sum_{i=1}^{k} a_i(x - \xi_i)_+^n + \pi(x) \tag{10-2.3}$$

*where $\pi(x)$ is a polynomial of degree $n$ with coefficients $a_i$, $i = k + 1$, . . . , $k + n + 1$. The parameter vector of coefficients is denoted by $A = (a_1, a_2, \ldots, a_{k+1+n})$ and the parameter vector of knots is denoted by $\Xi = (\xi_1, \xi_2, \ldots, \xi_k)$.*

The spline (10–2.3) is called a spline of *degree* $n$ with knots $\Xi$ (or alter-natively, an $n$-spline). The arguments of $S(A, \Xi, x)$ are often suppressed when no confusion can arise. This is particularly true with considerations involving a fixed set of knots.

There is another useful representation of $S(A, \Xi, x)$ of a Lagrangian nature in terms of the *cardinal splines* $C_i(\Xi, x)$. These splines are partially determined by the conditions

$$C_i(\Xi, \xi_j) = \delta_{ij}, \qquad i, j = 1, 2, \ldots, k\,. \tag{10–2.4}$$

This leaves $n + 1$ coefficients of $C_i$ undetermined which may be determined by requiring that certain derivatives of $C_i$ be zero at certain points. *In case n is odd*, we standardize the cardinal splines by the conditions

$$C_i^{(r)}(\Xi, \xi_1) = C_i^{(r)}(\Xi, \xi_k) = 0, \qquad r = \frac{n+1}{2}, \frac{n+3}{2}, \ldots, n. \tag{10–2.5}$$

Here the superscript $(r)$ denotes the $r$th derivative. Thus we have a second representation

$$S(A, \Xi, x) = \sum_{i=1}^{k} a_i C_i(\Xi, x) + \pi(x) \tag{10–2.6}$$

where $A$ again stands for the coefficients of $C_i$ and of the $n$th degree polynomial. This form is useful in certain situations where one can restrict consideration to those splines with $\pi(x) \equiv 0$. It is a consequence of Theorem 10–1 that these splines exist.

We note that $S(A, \Xi, x)$ involves $n + 2k + 1$ parameters, $n + k + 1$ of which are linear (the vector $A$) and $k$ of which (the knots) enter nonlinearly. Many analytical and practical situations are such that the knots $\Xi$ are fixed in some *a priori* manner. Once this is done, we have a linear approximating function and the results of preceding chapters are immediately applicable. However, much of the interest in splines arises from the ability to choose (or vary) the knots, even though this may be in an *ad hoc*, artificial or *a priori* manner.

Some particular splines are considered in classical analysis, but splines in general have not received much attention until recently. There are two particularly simple splines which are familiar, those of degree zero—the step functions, and those of degree one—the broken lines. Additional instances of the appearance of splines in classical areas are indicated in the following examples.

EXAMPLE 1. *Taylor's series with exact remainder.*
Consider the integral

$$\int_0^1 (x - t)^{(n-1)} f^{(n)}(t)\, dt.$$

One may integrate by parts $(n - 1)$ times, rearrange terms and establish the formula

$$f(x) = \sum_{k=0}^{n-1} \frac{1}{k!} f^{(k)}(0) x^k + \frac{1}{(n-1)!} \int_0^1 (x - t)_+^{n-1} f^{(n)}(t)\, dt. \tag{10–2.7}$$

EXAMPLE 2. *Peano's theorem* (*Peano, 1913*).

Consider a quadrature formula of the form

$$Q(f) = \sum_{j=1}^{k} \alpha_j f(\xi_j)$$

which is exact for polynomials of degree $n$ or less.

From (10–2.7) one finds that

$$Q(f) = \sum_{k=0}^{n-1} \frac{1}{(k+1)!} f^{(k)}(0) x^{k+1}$$

$$+ \frac{1}{(n-1)!} \int_0^1 \left[ \sum_{j=1}^{k} \alpha_j(\xi_j - t)_+^{n-1} \right] f^{(n)}(t)\, dt.$$

One may integrate $f(x)$ from (10–2.7) and subtract the preceding result to obtain

$$\int_0^1 f(x)\, dx - Q(f)$$

$$= \frac{1}{(n-1)!} \int_0^1 \left[ -\sum_{j=1}^{k} \alpha_j(\xi_j - t)_+^{n-1} + \int_0^1 (x - t)_+^{n-1}\, dx \right] f^{(n)}(t)\, dt.$$

This expression gives the error of the quadrature formula $Q$ in terms of a definite integral. Note that this remainder term may be written as

$$\frac{1}{(n-1)!} \int_0^1 [t^n + S(A, \Xi, t)] f^{(n)}(t)\, dt. \tag{10–2.8}$$

The particular spline function $S$ in (10–2.8) depends, of course, on the coefficients $\alpha_j$ and points $\xi_j$ of the quadrature formula.

EXAMPLE 3. *Representation of divided differences.*

Divided differences are defined by

$$f(x_1, x_2) = \frac{f(x_2) - f(x_1)}{x_2 - x_1},$$

$$f(x_1, x_2, \ldots, x_k) = \frac{f(x_2, \ldots, x_k) - f(x_1, x_2, \ldots, x_{k-1})}{x_k - x_1}.$$

The expression $f(x_1, x_2, \ldots, x_k)$ is called the *divided difference of $f$ of order* $k - 1$. We note that the divided difference depends linearly on $f(x)$ and that the divided difference of order $n + 1$ is zero for any polynomial of degree $n$. One may apply the divided difference to (10–2.7) and obtain, for $k \geq n$,

$$f(\xi_1, \xi_2, \ldots, \xi_k) = \frac{1}{(n-1)!} \int_0^1 M_{n-1}(t\ \xi_1, \xi_2, \ldots, \xi_k) f^{(n)}(t)\, dt$$

where $M_{n-1}(t, \Xi)$ is the $k$th divided difference of $(x - t)_+^{n-1}$ as a function of $x$. One may show that $M_{n-1}(t, \Xi)$ is an $(n - 1)$-spline and, when $k = n$, $M_{n-1}(t, \Xi)$ is called the *fundamental spline* function of the knots $\Xi$. The fundamental spline is nonnegative and is zero outside the interval $[\xi_1, \xi_k]$.

EXAMPLE 4. *Uniform probability distributions.*

Consider random variables with probability density function

$$f(t) = \begin{cases} \frac{1}{2} & \text{if } |t| \leq 1 \\ 0 & \text{if } |t| > 1. \end{cases}$$

If $x_1, x_2, \ldots, x_k$ are such independent random variables then

$$x_1 + x_2 + \cdots + x_k$$

is a random variable with probability density function

$$f(t) = S(A, \Xi, t)$$

where $\Xi = \{\pm k, \pm k - 2, \pm k - 4, \ldots\}$.

We now turn to the fundamental problem of the existence of a solution of the equations

$$S(A, \Xi, x_j) = y_j. \tag{10–2.9}$$

This type of interpolation problem—or solvence problem—plays a central role in the development of properties of approximating functions. There are $n + 2k + 1$ parameters in (10–2.9) and thus one would hope that, at least in some circumstances, the range of $j$ could be taken to be from 1 to $n + 2k + 1$. Just what these circumstances might be are unknown at this time. We can, however, give a satisfactory result concerning interpolation at $n + k + 1$ points. We begin with a basic result due to Schoenberg and Whitney, 1953.

**Theorem 10–1.** *For $n > 0$ the determinant*

$$|(x_i - \xi_j)_+^n|, \qquad i, j = 1, 2, \ldots, k, \tag{10–2.10}$$

*is positive if and only if the following inequalities are satisfied*

$$x_{i-n-1} < \xi_i < x_i, \qquad i = 1, 2, \ldots, k. \tag{10–2.11}$$

*Proof.* The proof is by induction on the degree $n$. The case $n = 0$ is to be established in Problem 10–1. Assume then that the theorem is established for the determinants $|(x_i - \xi_j)_+^n|$. The key tool of the proof is the following identity (see Polya and Szegö, 1925, Problem 68 and Problem 10–10).

$$|(x_i - \xi_j)_+^n|$$
$$= \int \int \cdots \int_{0 \leq t_1 < t_2 < \cdots < t_k \leq 1} |(x_i - t_p)_+^0| \, |(t_q - \xi_j)_+^{n-1}| dt_1 \cdots dt_k. \tag{10–2.12}$$

This is not the most general form of this identity, but it suffices here. It is clear that (10–2.12) is nonnegative and can actually be positive only when $|(x_i - t_p)^0_+|$ and $|(t_q - \xi_j)^{n-1}_+|$ are simultaneously positive on a region in the $\{t_i\}$ space of positive measure. The induction hypothesis implies these determinants are positive only if

$$x_{j-1} < t_j < x_j, \qquad j = 1, 2, \ldots, k,$$

and

$$t_{j-n} < \xi_j < t_j, \qquad j = 1, 2, \ldots, k.$$

The requirement that the $t_j$ satisfying these relations form a set of positive measure is seen to be exactly (10–2.11). This concludes the induction step and the proof.

There is a number of corollaries of this result which are of considerable importance. The first concerns the system of equations (10–2.9).

**Corollary 1.** *The system (10–2.9) has a solution for arbitrary values*

$$y_j, \qquad j = 1, 2, \ldots, n + k + 1$$

*if and only if*

$$x_i < \xi_i < x_{i+n+1}, \qquad i = 1, 2, \ldots, k. \qquad (10\text{–}2.13)$$

*In this case the solution is unique.*

This result follows from Theorem 10–1 by noting that, in the interval $[x_1, x_{n+k+1}]$, $S(A, \Xi, x)$ is identical with

$$\sum_{j=1}^{n+k+1} \alpha_j (x - \zeta_j)^n_+$$

where $\zeta_1 < \zeta_2 \cdots < \zeta_{n+1} < x_1$ and $\zeta_{n+j+1} = \xi_j$. Since (10–2.4) is a linear system of equations, it has a solution for arbitrary $\{y_j\}$ if and only if the coefficient determinant is nonzero. Theorem 10–1 is then immediately applicable and the inequalities (10–2.11) become reindexed due to the "artificial" knots introduced.

The next corollary is of interest because it bridges, in a natural manner, the gap between two well-known and often used results. The first of these is that one can interpolate $n + 1$ arbitrary values $y_j$ at $n + 1$ distinct points $\{x_j\}$ by a polynomial of degree $n$. The second is that one can interpolate these same values by a broken line.

**Corollary 2.** *Given $x_1 < x_2 < \cdots < x_m$, consider splines with $k$ knots among the $x_i$, $i = 2, 3, \ldots, m - 1$ and of degree $n = m - k - 1$. Then equation (10–2.9) has a unique solution for arbitrary values $y_j$, $j = 1, 2, \ldots, m$.*

In Section 10–6 it is natural to consider splines of the form

$$\pi_n(x) + \sum_{j=1}^{k} a_j (x - \xi_j)^{2n-1}_+,$$

with the additional requirements that the spline be a polynomial of degree $n$ for $x > \xi_k$ as well as for $x < \xi_1$. These are called the *natural splines* of degree $2n - 1$. That the following is a corollary of Theorem 10–1 is to be established in Problem 10–5.

**Corollary 3.**   *Given* $x_1 < x_2 \cdots < x_k$ *there is a natural spline function (unique for* $n < k$*) of degree* $2n - 1$ *with knots* $x_j, j = 1, 2, \ldots, k$*, satisfying* (10–2.9) *for arbitrary values* $y_j, j = 1, 2, \ldots, k$.

For the sake of completeness we note the following

**Corollary 4.**   *The cardinal splines, defined by* (10–2.4)*, exist if* $k \geq (n + 1)/2$.

## 10–3   EXISTENCE THEOREMS FOR NONLINEAR SPLINE APPROXIMATION

If we regard the knots as fixed, then there is no difficulty in establishing the existence of best spline approximations from the results of Chapter 1. In this section we consider the case of variable knots and there we encounter certain difficulties. This is due to the fact that the splines do not form a closed set of functions. Thus a sequence of splines $S(A_k, \Xi_k, x)$ may have some knots coalescing in such a way that the limiting function does not have the required continuity of derivatives at the knots. Simple examples of this are shown in Fig. 10–1 for the case of splines of degree 1. It is seen that the limiting function can be (a) a step function, (b) a "delta" function or (c) a "dipole" distribution.

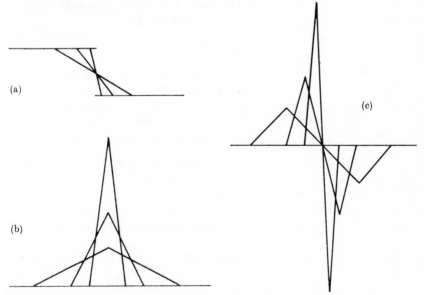

FIG. 10–1.   Sequences of splines of degree 1 which converge to a discontinuous function (a) or to distributions (b), (c).

We do not pause to make precise the definition† of distribution as we are able to avoid this concept during the proofs. However, this concept does facilitate a heuristic understanding of why these limiting functions do not need to be considered in the existence problem.

Let $d(x)$ symbolically denote a distribution which is the sum of a finite number of delta functions and multipole distributions. In this section we use the notation

$$\|f(x)\|_p = \left[ \int_0^1 [f(x)]^p \, dx \right]^{1/p}.$$

We now assert, heuristically, that if $C(x)$ is continuous then

$$\|C(x) + d(x)\|_p \geq \|C(x)\|_p.$$

Let $I_\epsilon$ be a collection of intervals of total length $\epsilon$ so that $d(x) = 0$ outside $I_\epsilon$ and set $I = [0, 1] - I_\epsilon$. Then we have

$$\|C(x) + d(x)\|_p^p = \int_I [C(x)]^p \, dx + \int_{I_\epsilon} [C(x) + d(x)]^p \, dx.$$

Now

$$\left[ \int_{I_\epsilon} [C(x) + d(x)]^p \, dx \right]^{1/p} \leq \left[ \int_{I_\epsilon} [C(x)]^p \, dx \right]^{1/p} + \left[ \int_{I_\epsilon} [d(x)]^p \, dx \right]^{1/p}$$

and the first term on the right tends to zero as $\epsilon$ tends to zero and the second term is $\|d(x)\|_p$. Since $\epsilon$ is arbitrary we conclude that

$$\|C(x) + d(x)\|_p = \|C(x)\|_p + \|d(x)\|_p.$$

Thus, in terms of approximating functions on an interval, we can only worsen the approximation by adding a distribution to it.

For many nonlinear approximating functions it is necessary to extend the definition of the approximating function in order to obtain an existence theorem. This is the case for splines and the required extension is

**Definition 10–2.** *A function $S^e(A, \Xi, x)$ is said to be an extended spline of degree $n$ with $k$ knots if there are intervals $(\xi_i, \xi_{i+1})$, $i = 0, 1, 2, \dots, l$ with $l \leq k$, $\xi_0 = 0$, $\xi_{l+1} = 1$ so that*
(a) *$S^e(A, \Xi, x)$ is a polynomial of degree $n$ in each interval,*
(b) *$S^e(A, \Xi, x)$ has $n - p_j$ continuous derivatives at $\xi_j, j = 1, 2, \dots, l$,*

(c)
$$\sum_{j=1}^{l} p_j \leq k. \qquad (10\text{–}3.1)$$

---

† It is seen from the heuristic analysis below that a definition different from the usual one is required.

We adopt the convention that $f(x)$ is differentiable of order 0 or $-1$ at $x_0$ if $f(x)$ is continuous or has a simple jump discontinuity at $x_0$, respectively.

A knot of an extended spline is said to be of multiplicity $p$, or simply a $p$-*tuple knot* if the spline has a continuous $(n - p)$th derivative at the knot. An ordinary (or 1-tuple) knot may be called a *simple knot*.

We first establish that a uniformly bounded (in norm) sequence of extended splines of degree $n$ with $k$ knots contains a subsequence which converges pointwise to an extended spline except possibly at $k$ points. This is, in fact, a corollary of Theorem 8–4. However, a direct proof of this for splines is essentially more elementary than the proof of Theorem 8–4. The basic tool of the proof is to expand the splines in a Taylor series (with remainder) and then use Gauss elimination to establish the required relations.

**Lemma 10–1.** *Let $\{S^e(A_m, \Xi_m, x)\}$ be a sequence of extended splines of degree $n$ with $k$ knots. Assume that, for some $1 \leq p \leq \infty$,*

$$\|S^e(A_m, \Xi_m, x)\|_p \leq K < \infty$$

*for all $m$. Then there is a subsequence $\{S^e(A_m, \Xi_m, x)\}$ and an extended spline $S^*(x)$ of degree $m$ with $k$ knots so that*

$$\lim_{m \to \infty} S^e(A_m, \Xi_m, x) = S^*(x)$$

*except for possibly $k$ values of $x$.*

*Proof.* We establish the result first for splines with distinct knots, then show that every extended spline is the limit of splines with distinct knots. From this we quickly obtain the lemma. We require the preliminary

*Assertion.* Let $\Delta^m = (\delta_1^m, \delta_2^m, \ldots, \delta_t^m)$. *Suppose that* $\Delta^m \to 0$ *as* $m \to \infty$ *and that*

$$\sum_{i=1}^{t} a_i^m (\delta_i^m)^l$$

*is bounded for each $l = 0, 1, \ldots, t - 1$. Let $a_i^m(1) = a_i^m$ and*

$$a_i^m(r) = a_i^m(r - 1) \prod_{q=1}^{r-1} (\delta_i^m - \delta_q^m)$$

*or $1 < r \leq i$. Then, for each $l = 0, 1, \ldots, t - r$,*

$$\sum_{i=r}^{t} a_i^m(r)(\delta_i^m)^l \tag{10–3.2}$$

*is bounded.*

There is nothing to prove if $r = 1$. For simplicity of notation the superscripts $m$ are omitted. If (10–3.2) is bounded for $l = 0, 1, \ldots, t - r$, then

$$\sum_{i=r}^{t} a_i(r)(\delta_i - \delta_{r-1})^{q-l}$$

is bounded for $0 \leq l \leq q \leq t - r$. It follows that if we set

$$F = \sum_{l=0}^{q} \left[ \binom{q}{l} (\delta_{r-1} - \delta_r)^l \sum_{i=r}^{t} (\delta_i - \delta_{r-1})^{q-l} a_i(r) \right]$$

then $F$ is bounded. But for $1 \leq q \leq t - r$,

$$F = \sum_{i=r}^{t} a_i(r) \sum_{l=0}^{q} \binom{q}{l} (\delta_i - \delta_{r-1})^{q-l} (\delta_{r-1} - \delta_r)^l$$

$$= \sum_{i=r}^{t} a_i(r)(\delta_i - \delta_r)^q = \sum_{i=r+1}^{t} a_i(r+1)(\delta_i - \delta_r)^{q-1}$$

$$= \sum_{l=0}^{q-1} \binom{q-1}{l} \left[ \sum_{i=r+1}^{t} a_i(r+1)(\delta_i)^l \right] (-\delta_r)^{q-1-l}.$$

The assertion follows immediately by induction on $q$, then on $r$.

Let the $\xi_{jm}$ be distinct for each fixed $m$ and choose a subsequence so that

$$\lim_{m \to \infty} \xi_{jm}$$

exists for each $j$. We denote by $\Xi^* = \{\xi_1^*, \ldots, \xi_l^*\}$ the set of distinct limits obtained. The $\{\xi_{jm}\}$ are partitioned into $l$ groups according to

$$\xi_{jm} = \xi_q^* + \delta_{jq}^m$$

and $\delta_{jq}^m \to 0$, i.e. the knots are grouped according to their corresponding limits. We now establish the

*Assertion. Assume that* $\xi_{jm} \to \xi^*, j = 1, 2, \ldots, q \leq n + 1$ *and the* $\{\xi_{jm}\}$ *are distinct for each fixed $m$. If, for any $1 \leq p \leq \infty$,*

$$\left\| \sum_{j=1}^{q} a_j^m (x - \xi_{jm})_+^n \right\|_p \leq K < \infty$$

*then for any $\epsilon > 0$ there is a subsequence $\{a_j^m, \xi_{jm}\}$ and numbers $b_i$ so that*

$$\lim_{m \to \infty} \max_{|x - \xi^*| \geq \epsilon} \left| \sum_{j=1}^{q} a_j^m (x - \xi_{jm})_+^n - \sum_{i=0}^{q-1} b_i (x - \xi^*)_+^{n-i} \right| = 0.$$

Again for simplicity of notation the indices $m$ are omitted. We have the Taylor series expansion

$$(x - \xi_j)_+^n = \sum_{l=0}^{n} (\xi_j - \xi^*)^l \binom{n}{l} (x - \xi^*)_+^{n-l} + R(\xi_j, x)$$

where

$$R(\xi_j, x) = 0$$

for $|x - \xi^*| > |\xi_j - \xi^*|$. Set $\delta_j = (\xi_j - \xi^*)$ and obtain

$$\sum_{j=1}^{q} a_j (x - \xi_j)_+^n = \sum_{l=0}^{n} \left[ \sum_{j=1}^{q} a_j (\delta_j)^l \right] \binom{n}{l} (x - \xi^*)_+^{n-l} + R_1(x)$$

where $R_1(x) = 0$ for $|x - \xi^*| > \max(|\delta_1|, |\delta_2|, \ldots, |\delta_q|)$. The functions $(x - \xi^*)_+^{n-l}$ are linearly independent for $l = 0, 1, 2, \ldots, n$ and hence the coefficients

$$\binom{n}{l} \sum_{j=1}^{q} a_j(\delta_j)^l, \qquad l = 0, 1, \ldots, n$$

are bounded as $m \to \infty$. We may choose a subsequence $\{a_j, \delta_j\}$ so that each coefficient converges and we denote the limits by $b_l$, e.g.

$$\lim_{m \to \infty} \sum_{j=1}^{q} a_j(\delta_j)^l = b_l, \qquad l = 0, 1, 2, \ldots, n.$$

We may take linear combinations of these relations as determined by Gauss elimination of the numbers $a_j$ from the first $q$ relations. The multipliers are all powers of $\delta_i$'s and one obtains, for $l \geq q$

$$a_q(q)(\delta_q)^l \to b_l + O(\Delta),$$

where the notation of the first assertion is used. The first assertion implies that $a_q(q)(\delta_q)^{q-1}$ is bounded and thus for $l \geq q$ we have $b_l = 0$. Since

$$\lim R_1(x) = 0$$

for $x \neq \xi^*$, the assertion is established.

This assertion immediately establishes the lemma in the case that the knots are distinct.

Given distinct $\delta_j^m, j = 1, 2, \ldots, q$ there are $a_j^m$ so that

$$\binom{n}{l} \sum_{j=1}^{q} a_j^m(\delta_j^m)^l = b_l$$

for any set $b_l, l = 0, 1, \ldots, q - 1$. Given a term

$$\sum_{l=0}^{q-1} b_l(x - \xi_i^*)_+^{n-l}$$

we choose $q$ distinct knots $\xi_{jm} = \xi_i^* + \delta_j^m$. Given $\epsilon > 0$ we let $\delta_j^m \to 0$ as $m \to \infty$ and observe that,

$$\lim_{m \to \infty} \max_{|x - \xi_i^*| \geq \epsilon} \left| \sum_{j=1}^{q} a_j^m(x - \xi_{jm})_+^n - \sum_{l=0}^{q-1} b_l(x - \xi_i^*)_+^{n-l} \right| = 0.$$

We may write any extended spline with $l$ distinct knots as

$$S^e(A_m, \Xi_m, x) = \sum_{j=1}^{l} \sum_{q=0}^{p_j-1} a_{jq}^m(x - \xi_{jm})_+^{n-q}$$

for appropriately chosen coefficients $a_{jq}^m$. Denote by $\Xi^*$ the set of limits of a convergent subsequence of $\{\Xi_m\}$. Given $\epsilon > 0$ there are coefficients $b_{jq}^m$ and distinct numbers $\delta_q^m$ with $\delta_q^m \to 0$ as $m \to \infty$ so that

$$\lim_{\substack{m \to \infty \\ |x - \xi_i{}^*| \geq \epsilon \\ \text{all } i}} \max \left| \sum_{q=0}^{p_j-1} a_{jq}^m (x - \xi_{jm})_+^{n-q} - \sum_{q=1}^{p_j} b_{jq}^m (x - \xi_{jm} - \delta_q^m)_+^n \right| = 0.$$

The splines

$$\sum_{j=1}^{l} \sum_{q=1}^{p_j} b_{jq}^m (x - \xi_{jm} - \delta_q^m)_+^n$$

are uniformly bounded and have $k$ distinct knots. Hence there is a spline $S^*(x)$ of degree $n$ with $k$ knots which is the pointwise limit of a subsequence of these splines except possibly for $x = \xi_i^*$. It is clear that for the corresponding subsequence of $\{S^e(A_m, \Xi_m, x)\}$ we have

$$\lim_{m \to \infty} S^e(A_m, \Xi_m, x) = S^*(x).$$

This establishes the lemma.

**Theorem 10–2.** *Let $f(x) \in L_p[-1, 1]$, $1 \leq p \leq \infty$. Then there exists an extended spline $S^e(A^*, \Xi^*, x)$ so that*

$$\|f(x) - S^e(A^*, \Xi^*, x)\|_p \leq \|f(x) - S^e(A, \Xi, x)\|_p$$

*among all extended splines of degree $n$ and with $k$ knots.*

*Proof.* There exists a sequence $S^e(A_m, \Xi_m, x)$ of extended splines of degree $n$ and with $k$ knots so that

$$\lim_{m \to \infty} \|f - S^e(A_m, \Xi_m)\|_p = \inf_{A, \Xi} \|f - S^e(A, \Xi)\|_p.$$

It is clear that this sequence is uniformly bounded in norm. From Lemma 10–1 we may choose a subsequence which converges pointwise (except possibly at the knots) to an extended spline $S^*(x) = S^e(A^*, \Xi^*, x)$ of degree $n$ with $k$ knots. $S^*(x)$ might be undefined at the knots and we define it there so as to be continuous from the right (except at 1 where it is taken to be continuous from the left).

We require a slightly different argument for $p = \infty$, which we leave for the moment. For $1 \leq p < \infty$ let $\eta > 0$ be given and define

$$I_\epsilon = [-1, 1] - \sum_{j=1}^{l} (\xi_j^* - \epsilon, \xi_j^* + \epsilon).$$

We have

$$\|f - S_m\|_p^p - \|f - S^*\|_p^p = \int_{I_\epsilon} [|f - S_m|^p - |f - S^*|^p] \, dx \qquad (10\text{–}3.3)$$

$$+ \sum_{j=1}^{l} \left[ \int_{\xi_j - \epsilon}^{\xi_j + \epsilon} |f - S_m|^p \, dx - \int_{\xi_j - \epsilon}^{\xi_j + \epsilon} |f - S^*|^p \, dx \right].$$

Since $S_m$ converges uniformly to $S^*$ on $I_\epsilon$ there is an $m_1(\epsilon) < \infty$ so that for $m_1(\epsilon) \leq m$ the integral over $I_\epsilon$ in (10–3.3) is less than $\eta/3$ in absolute value. Since $|f|^p$ and $|S^*|^p$ are integrable, there is an $\epsilon_1 > 0$ so that for $\epsilon < \epsilon_1$ the sum of the rightmost integrals in (10–3.3) is less than $\eta/3$ in absolute value.

We have for $m \geq m_1(\epsilon)$, $\epsilon \leq \epsilon_1$

$$\|f - S_m\|_p^p \geq \|f - S^*\|_p^p - \eta + \sum_{j=1}^{l} \left[ \int_{\xi_j - \epsilon}^{\xi_j + \epsilon} |f - S_m|^p \, dx \right].$$

Since $\eta$ is arbitrary and the sum on the right is nonnegative we see that

$$\lim_{m \to \infty} \|f - S_m\|_p \geq \|f - S^*\|_p.$$

Thus $S^e(A^*, \Xi^*, x)$ is the required best approximation and the proof is complete for $1 \leq p < \infty$.

For $p = \infty$ we proceed in the same way to obtain $S^*$. Then we have

$$\|f - S_m\|_\infty = \max \{\max_{I_\epsilon} |f - S_m| ;$$

$$\max |f(x) - S_m(x)| \text{ for } x \in [\xi_j - \epsilon, \, \xi_j + \epsilon], \, j = 1, 2, \ldots, l\}$$

$$\geq \max_{I_\epsilon} |f - S_m|.$$

However,

$$\lim_{m \to \infty} \max_{I} |f - S_m| = \max_{I_\epsilon} |f - S^*|$$

and

$$\lim_{\epsilon \to 0} \max_{I_\epsilon} |f - S^*| = \sup_{x \in [-1, 1]} |f - S^*| = \|f - S^*\|_\infty,$$

which implies that

$$\lim_{m \to \infty} \|f - S_m\|_\infty \geq \|f - S^*\|_\infty.$$

This concludes the proof.

It is interesting to wonder if there is a continuous function $f(x)$ with a best Tchebycheff approximation by extended splines which is actually discontinuous. One might expect there to be no such function. That this expectation is wrong is seen from the following example.

EXAMPLE. Consider Tchebycheff approximation by splines of degree 1 with 2 knots, e.g. broken lines with at most two breaks. The extended splines of degree 1 with 2 knots contain in addition all piecewise continuous lines with one discontinuity. The continuous function $f(x)$ is also piecewise linear and is defined by Fig. 10–2.

It is readily seen that a best Tchebycheff approximation to $f(x)$ is the discontinuous extended spline shown by the dashed line. It is clear that one can choose $f(x)$ to be arbitrarily smooth in this example.

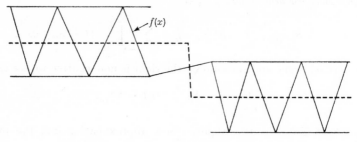

FIG. 10-2. The piecewise linear function $f(x)$.

The above example does show that a smooth function may have a discontinuous best approximation. However, that function has other best approximations, all of which are continuous. This leads to the following question: *Does there exist a continuous function $f(x)$ all of whose best Tchebycheff approximations by extended splines are discontinuous?* Equally interesting is the similar question: *Does there exist an $f(x)$ with $p$ continuous derivatives, $p \leq n - 1$, all of whose best Tchebycheff approximations by extended splines of degree $n$ have a discontinuous $p$th derivative?*

We show that the answer to the first question is no except in the obvious case of $n = 0$. The second question is more difficult and the complete answer is not known. We show for $p = 1$ and $n \geq 2$ that the answer is also no, but for $p = 2$ and $n = 3$ the answer is yes.

The basic idea is that if many knots coalesce in a best approximation, one may be able to "spread" them without affecting the maximum error. This is attempted by means of a *local modification* of the spline. It is clear that if spreading the knots affects the spline globally, then the maximum error is affected for some function too.

We start with a preliminary computation. For simplicity of notation, we examine the possibility of modifying an extended spline $S_0(x)$ with a knot at $x = 0$. Thus we consider

$$S_0(x) = \begin{cases} 0 & x < 0 \\ \sum_{j=q}^{n} \alpha_j x^j, & |\alpha_q| \neq 0, \quad x \geq 0 \end{cases}$$

which is an extended spline with an $(n - q + 1)$-tuple knot at 0. That is to say it has a discontinuous $q$th derivative at 0. Let $S(x)$ be a prospective local modification with simple knots $\eta_1 < \eta_2 < \cdots < \eta_p$ and another knot $\delta > \eta_p$. We derive conditions which $S(x)$ must satisfy in order that, for a given $\epsilon$,

$$S(x) \equiv S_0(x), \qquad |x| > \epsilon.$$

The total multiplicity of the knots of $S(x)$ must be $n - q + 1$ so the multiplicity of knot $\delta$ must be

$$r = n - q + 1 - p$$

The condition that $\delta$ is an $r$-tuple knot is that

$$\frac{d^m S(x)}{dx^m}\bigg|_{x=\delta} = \frac{d^m S_0(x)}{dx^m}\bigg|_{x=\delta}, \qquad m = 0, 1, 2, \ldots, (n - r).$$

These equations become

$$\sum_{j=1}^{p} a_j(\delta - \eta_j)^{n-m} = \sum_{j=q}^{n} \alpha_j \delta^{j-m} \frac{j(j-1)\cdots(j-m+1)}{n(n-1)\cdots(n-m+1)} \qquad (10\text{--}3.4)$$

for $m = 0, 1, \ldots, p + q - 1$. If one can determine knots $-\epsilon \leq \eta_j$ and $\delta \leq \epsilon$ and coefficients $a_j$ to satisfy (10–3.4) then

$$S(x) = \begin{cases} \sum_{j=1}^{p} a_j(x - \eta_j)_+^n & x \leq \delta \\ S_0(x) & x \leq \delta \end{cases} \qquad (10\text{--}3.5)$$

is a local modification of $S_0(x)$ with an $(n - q - p + 1)$-tuple knot at $\delta$.

Let $S^*(x)$ be an approximation to $f(x)$. If the local modification to $S^*(x)$ is to be such that the maximum of $|f(x) - S^*(x)|$ is not affected, then an additional constraint is placed on $S(x)$. Assume $f(x)$ has $s$ continuous derivatives at $x = 0$. Then

$$f(x) = \sum_{i=0}^{} f_i x^i + o(x^s).$$

The error $f(x) - S^*(x)$ has the form, for $s \geq q$

$$\sum_{i=0}^{q-1} (f_i - a_i^*)x^i + \sum_{i=q}^{s} (f_i - \alpha_i^*)x^i + o(x^s), \qquad x \geq 0$$

$$\sum_{i=0}^{q-1} (f_i - a_i^*)x^i + \sum_{i=q}^{s} (f_i - \beta_i^*)x^i + o(x^s), \qquad x \leq 0$$

where $\alpha_q^* \neq \beta_q^*$. There are two cases to consider if $x = 0$ is an extreme point of the error curve. This is according to whether the discontinuity in the $q$th derivative is in the same direction as the second derivative of the error curve or not. That is to say Case 1 is for $\alpha_q^* > \beta_q^*$ and a maximum or $\alpha_q^* < \beta_q^*$ and a minimum. Case 2 consists of the other two possibilities.

In Case 1 we must make a local modification with $S(x) - S^*(x) \geq 0$ in some neighborhood of $x = 0$. In Case 2 we must make a local modification with $S(x) - S^*(x) \leq 0$ in some neighborhood of $x = 0$. If these extra conditions are satisfied then $|f(x) - S(x)| \leq |f(x) - S^*(x)|$ in the neighborhood of $x = 0$. This means that we must be able to satisfy (10–3.4) with the sign of $S(x) - S_0(x)$ specified at $x = 0$.

The first result applies to the case $q = 0$, i.e. when $S^*(x)$ is discontinuous.

**Lemma 10–2.** *Let $S^*(x)$ be given with $q = 0$ and $n \geq 1$ and let $\epsilon > 0$ be given. Then there exist splines of degree $n$ with $k$ knots, $S_1(x)$ and $S_2(x)$, such that*

(a) *$S_1(x)$ and $S_2(x)$ each have two knots $-\epsilon < \eta_1 < \delta < \epsilon$ and $\eta_1$ is simple, $\delta$ is $n$-tuple.*

(b) *$S_1(x) \equiv S_2(x) \equiv S^*(x)$ except in $[-\epsilon, \epsilon]$.*
(c) *$S_1(x) - S^*(x) \geq 0$ in $[-\delta/2, \delta/2]$.*
(d) *$S_2(x) - S^*(x) \leq 0$ in $[-\delta/2, \delta/2]$.*

*Proof.* We may assume that $S^*(x) = S'(x) + S_0(x)$ where $S_0(x)$ is of the form of the preliminary computations. We need to satisfy (10–3.4) for $m = 0$ and $p = 1$, i.e.

$$a_1(\delta - \eta_1)^n = S_0(\delta).$$

Choose $\delta < \epsilon$ sufficiently small that the terms $x^s$ for $s \geq 1$ are negligible. Suppose $S_0(\delta) > 0$. Then for $S_1'(x)$ choose the knot $\eta_1$ to be $-\delta$ and set

$$a_1 = S_0(\delta)/(2\delta)^n > 0.$$

For $S_1'(x)$ choose the knot $\eta_2$ to be $\delta/2$ and set

$$a_1 = S_0(\delta)/(\delta/2)^n > 0.$$

The splines $S_1'(x)$ and $S_2'$ are defined by (10–3.5). Set $S_1(x) = S'(x) + S_1'(x)$ and $S_2(x) = S'(x) + S_2'(x)$ and the requirements of the lemma are satisfied.

Suppose, on the other hand, that $S_0(\delta) < 0$. Then choose the knot $\delta/2$ for $S_1'(x)$ and $-\delta$ for $S_2'(x)$ and again the requirements are satisfied.

For the next lemma we assume a spline of the form considered in the preliminary computation.

**Lemma 10–3.** *Let $S_0(x)$ be given with $q = 1$ and $n \geq 2$ and let $\epsilon > 0$ be given. Then there exists a spline $S_1(x)$ of degree $n$, such that*

(a) *$S_1(x)$ has two knots $-\epsilon < \eta_1 < 0 < \delta < \epsilon$ and $\eta_1$ is simple and $\delta$ is $(n - 1)$-tuple.*
(b) *$S_1(x) \equiv S_0(x)$ except in $[-\epsilon, \epsilon]$.*
(c) *$\operatorname{sgn}[S_0(\delta)][S_1(x) - S_0(x)] > 0$ in $[\eta_1, \delta]$.*

*Proof.* We need to satisfy (10–3.4) for $m = 0, 1$ and $p = 1$. The equations become

$$a_1(\delta - \eta_1)^n = \alpha_1\delta + o(\delta^2)$$

$$a_1(\delta - \eta_1)^{n-1} = \frac{\alpha_1 + o(\delta)}{n}.$$

Choose $\delta < \epsilon/n$ so small that the $o(\delta^2)$, $o(\delta)$ terms do not affect the sign of $S_0(x)$ in $[0, \delta]$. Eliminate $a_1$ to obtain

$$-\epsilon < \eta_1 = (1 - n)\delta + o(\delta^2) < 0.$$

We solve for $a_1$ and see that $a_1$ has the same sign as $\alpha_1$, i.e. as $S_0(\delta)$. The modification $S_1(x)$ is defined by (10–3.5) and clearly satisfies the requirements of the lemma.

These two results on local modifications allow us to establish

**Theorem 10–3.** *Let $f(x)$ have $p$ continuous derivatives in $[0, 1]$. Then $f(x)$ possesses a best Tchebycheff approximation by extended splines of degree $n$ which also has $p$ continuous derivatives for the following combinations of $n$ and $p$:*

(a) $p = 0$ ($f(x)$ continuous),      $n \geq 1$.
(b) $p = 1$ ($f(x)$ differentiable),      $n \geq 2$.

*Proof.* Consider the case $p = 0$. It follows from Theorem 10–2 that $f(x)$ possesses a best Tchebycheff approximation, say $S^*(x)$, by extended splines of degree $n$ with $k$ knots. Suppose $S^*(x)$ is discontinuous at some point $x_0$. If $x_0$ is not an extremal point of $|f(x) - S^*(x)|$, then either local modifications in Lemma 10–2 may be used to obtain a continuous $S(x)$ so that $\|f(x) - S(x)\|_\infty \leq \|f(x) - S^*(x)\|_\infty$. If $x_0$ is an extremal point of $f(x) - S^*(x)$ then the jump in $S^*(x)$ is positive at a maximum or negative at a minimum. In either case one of the modifications of Lemma 10–2 may be used to obtain a continuous $S(x)$ which is also a best approximation.

Consider the case $p = 1$. Again we obtain $S^*(x)$ from Theorem 10–2 and Lemma 10–3 may be applied to remove discontinuities in the derivative at points $x_0$ which are not extremal points of $|f(x) - S^*(x)|$. Note that $x_0$ cannot be an interior point of a set of extremal points nor can it be the limit of 2 sequences of extremal points, one with points to the left of $x_0$ and one with points to the right of $x_0$. This would imply that $f(x)$ has a discontinuous derivative at $x_0$.

If $x_0$ is a maximum of $f(x) - S^*(x)$ then the jump in the derivative of $S^*(x)$ is positive. Thus the modification $S_1(x)$ from Lemma 10–3 has $S_1(x) - S^*(x) > 0$ in a neighborhood of $x_0$. This implies that $f(x) - S^*(x) > f(x) - S_1(x)$ near $x_0$.

If $x_0$ is a minimum of $f(x) - S^*(x)$ then the jump in the derivative of $S^*(x)$ is negative. Thus the modification $S_1(x)$ from Lemma 10–3 has $S_1(x) - S^*(x) < 0$ in a neighborhood of $x_0$. This implies that $f(x) - S^*(x) < f(x) - S_1(x)$ near $x_0$. Both of these local modifications do not increase $\|f(x) - S^*(x)\|_\infty$ and the theorem is established.

For $p = 0$ and 1 this result is the best that one could hope for. The natural conjecture that one makes from Theorem 10–3 is false. In Theorem 10–4 an example is exhibited which shows that the combination ($p = 2, n = 3$) does not allow one to smooth the second derivative of best approximations arbitrarily. One can heuristically explain this by simply counting parameters. If $q = 2$, then one must use 2 knots ($p = 2$) in (10–3.4). This implies that $n - r$ is 3, which, for cubic splines, means that $\delta$ is, in fact, not a knot at all. Then it is unreasonable to expect the effect of the modification to be localized. Indeed, it follows that the only solution to (10–3.4) is $S_0(x)$ itself, i.e. $\eta_1 = \eta_2 = 0$.

The case ($p = 2, n \geq 4$) is not so simple, as this counting analysis does not apply. The following analysis shows that the spreading of knots by local modifications as in (10–3.5) does not work. Suppose an ($n - q + 1$)-tuple knot at 0 is replaced by 2 simple knots $\eta_1$ and $\eta_2$ and an ($n - q - 1$)-tuple knot at $\delta$. Set $\rho_i = (\delta - \eta_i)$ and the system (10–3.4) appears as

$$a_1 \rho_1^3 + a_2 \rho_2^3 = \alpha_1 \delta^2 + O(\delta^3) = f$$

$$a_1 \rho_1^2 + a_2 \rho_2^2 = \frac{2\alpha_2 \delta}{n} + O(\delta^2) = d$$

$$a_1 \rho_1 + a_2 \rho_2 = \frac{2\alpha_2}{n(n-1)} + O(\delta) = c$$

$$a_1 + a_2 = \frac{6\alpha_3}{n(n-1)(n-2)} + O(\delta) = b.$$

This type of system is studied in Chapter 8. Set

$$e_1 = \frac{a^2 - cf}{bd - c^2}$$

$$e_2 = \frac{bf - dc}{bd - c^2}$$

then it follows from Lemma 8–6 that the solutions $\rho_1$ and $\rho_2$ are the roots of

$$z^2 - e_2 z - e_1 = 0.$$

A calculation shows that for $\delta$ sufficiently small

$$e_1 = \frac{-(n-1)(n-2)}{2} \delta^2, \quad e_2 = (n-1)\delta$$

and the solutions are

$$\rho_i = \frac{(n-1)\delta}{2}\left(1 \pm \sqrt{[1 - 2(n-2)/(n-1)]}\right)$$

This gives imaginary values for $n \geq 4$. Thus for $n = 6$ we obtain

$$\eta_i = \frac{\delta(-3 \pm \sqrt{-15})}{2}$$

**Theorem 10–4.** *There is an infinitely differentiable function $f(x)$ whose unique best Tchebycheff approximation by extended cubic splines with two knots has a discontinuous second derivative.*

*Proof.* We consider, for simplicity of notation, the interval $[-1, +1]$ and the extended cubic spline

$$S^*(x) = \begin{cases} 0 & x \leq 0 \\ x^2 & x \geq 0 \end{cases}$$

which has a double knot at $x = 0$. The function $f(x)$ is defined so that (a) $f(0) = 0$, (b) $f(x) - S^*(x)$ alternates three times with deviation 1 in each of the six intervals $I_{k+4} = [k/3, (k+1)/3]$, $k = -3, -2, \ldots, 2$, (c) $f(x)$ is infinitely differentiable in $[-1, +1]$. It is clear that such a function exists and we show that $S^*(x)$ is the unique best Tchebycheff approximation to $f(x)$ by extended cubic splines with two knots. Let

$$S(A, \Xi, x) = a_1(x - \xi_1)^3_+ + a_2(x - \xi_2)^3_+ + \sum_{i=0}^{3} b_i x^i \qquad (10\text{–}3.6)$$

be an approximation with a continuous second derivative to $f(x)$. Note that the best Tchebycheff approximation to $f(x)$ by cubics is uniquely determined on each of the intervals $I_k$. Thus $S(A, \Xi, x)$ cannot be a better approximation than $S^*(x)$ and simultaneously have $\xi_1 \in I_1$, $\xi_2 \in I_6$. Assume that $\xi_1 \notin I_1$ (the alternative possibility may be handled by the change of variable $x' = -x$). This implies that $b_i = 0$, $i = 0, 1, 2, 3$.

Now $S(A, \Xi, x)$ must equal $x^2$ in one of the intervals $I_4, I_5, I_6$ since we have either (a) one of these intervals contains no knot or (b) the knots are at $\frac{1}{3}$ and $\frac{2}{3}$. The second possibility (b) implies that $S(A, \Xi, x) \equiv x^2$ in $[0, 1]$. For the possibility (a) take $x_0$ a point in one such interval. We have

$$S(A, \Xi, x_0) = x_0^2, \qquad \frac{d^2 S(A, \Xi, x_0)}{dx^2} = 2,$$

$$\frac{dS(A, \Xi, x_0)}{dx} = 2x_0, \qquad \frac{d^3 S(A, \Xi, x_0)}{dx^3} = 0.$$

From the fourth relation we find $a_1 = -a_2$ and, setting $\rho_1 = (x - \xi_1)_+$, $\rho_2 = (x - \xi_2)_+$, $c = 1/a_1$, we have after manipulation that

$$\rho_1 - \rho_2 = \frac{c}{3}, \quad \rho_1 + \rho_2 = 2x_0, \quad \rho_1\rho_2 = x_0^2.$$

A solution is not possible with either $\rho_1 = 0$ or $\rho_2 = 0$ and if we solve for $\rho_1$, $\rho_2$ from the first two relations and substitute into the third we obtain

$$x_0^2 - \frac{c^2}{36} = x_0^2$$

or $c = 0$. This is impossible and hence $S(A, \Xi, x)$ cannot be a best Tchebycheff approximation and be of the form (10–3.6). This concludes the proof.

## 10–4  $L_2$-APPROXIMATION BY SPLINES

There are two distinct cases to be considered, namely approximation with the knots fixed in some *a priori* way, and approximation with variable knots. In the first case we have a linear approximation problem and the standard analysis of Chapter 2 may be applied. All that remains in this case is to work out the various details. In the second case we can establish neither uniqueness nor characterization theorems. Theorem 10–2 gives an existence theorem in terms of extended splines. This case is, however, of great importance.

In the case of fixed knots $\Xi$, the problem is to determine coefficients $A^*$ such that

$$\int_0^1 [f(x) - S(A^*, \Xi, x)]^2 \, dx \tag{10–4.1}$$

is minimum. The Corollary of Theorem 1–4 states that the solution exists and Theorem 1–2 implies that it is unique. The coefficients $A^*$ are characterized by the fact that they are the solution to the normal equations (2–2.3). It is often useful, both in theory and practice, to have an orthonormal basis when considering least squares approximation. Such a basis exists for the splines and we denote by $O_j(\Xi, x)$ the $j$th *orthonormal spline*. Specifically, for $j \leq n$,

$$O_j(\Xi, x) = P_j(x) = \text{Legendre polynomial of degree } j \text{ on } [0, 1]$$

and for $j \geq n + 1$,

$$O_j(\Xi, x) = \pi(x) + \sum_{i=1}^{j-n} \alpha_i(x - \xi_i)_+^n$$

where $\pi(x)$ is the appropriate polynomial of degree $n$. Thus we have

$$\int_0^1 O_j(\Xi, x)O_k(\Xi, x) \, dx = \delta_{jk}.$$

Since

$$S(A^*, \Xi, x) = \sum_{j=0}^{n+k} a_j^* O_j(\Xi, x),$$

it follows that the coefficients $a_j^*$ of the best approximation to $f(x)$ are determined by

$$a_j^* = \int_0^1 f(x) O_j(\Xi, x) \, dx. \tag{10–4.2}$$

The existence question for $L_2$-spline approximation is settled by Theorem 10–2. If one allows the knots to coalesce and accepts the extended splines, then one obtains an existence theorem. If one does not accept extended splines then, of course, one does not have an existence theorem.

For reference purposes we recall Theorem 8–2 and note the following corollary.

**Corollary (Theorem 8–2).** *Set*

$$E_{n,k}(f) = \| f(x) - S(A^*, \Xi^*, x) \|_2$$

*where $S(A^*, \Xi^*, x)$ is a best $L_2$-approximation to $f(x)$ by splines of degree $n$ with $k$ variable knots. Then either $E_{n,k}(f) = 0$ or*

$$E_{n,k+1}(f) < E_{n,k}(f). \tag{10–4.3}$$

With the aid of this Corollary we can show that there is no general uniqueness theorem for nonlinear least squares spline approximation. This is stated precisely in the following result due to de Boor.

**Theorem 10–5.** *For any pair of values of $n$ and $k$ there is a function $f(x)$ continuous on $[-1, 1]$ which possesses two distinct best $L_2$-spline approximations of degree $n$ with* (a) *$k$ variable knots or* (b) *$k + 1$ variable knots.*

*Proof.* The proof is based on the Corollary of Theorem 8–2 and symmetry arguments. We first establish the

*Assertion. If $n$ is even and $f(x)$ is an even function on $[-1, 1]$ with a best $L_2$-approximation $S(A^*, \Xi^*, x)$ then $S(A', \Xi', x)$ is also a best $L_2$-approximation if $A' = A^*$ and $\Xi' = -\Xi^*$.*

It follows directly from (10–4.2) that the coefficients are zero of the odd powers of $x$ in the polynomial part of $S(A^*, \Xi^*, x)$, i.e.

$$a_i^* = 0, \qquad i = 1, 3, 5, \ldots, n - 1$$

One may then verify that

$$\int_0^1 [f(x) - S(A^*, \Xi^*, x)]^2 \, dx = \int_0^1 [f(x) - S(A', \Xi', x)]^2 \, dx$$

and the assertion is established.

By a similar argument one establishes the

*Assertion. If $n$ is odd and $f(x)$ is an odd function of $[-1, 1]$ with a best $L_2$-approximation $S(A^*, \Xi^*, x)$ then $S(A', \Xi', x)$ is also a best $L_2$-approximation if $A' = A^*$ and $\Xi' = -\Xi^*$.*

Consider approximation by splines of degree $n$ with $k$ knots where $k$ is odd. If $k$ is even we consider splines with $k + 1$ knots and obtain conclusion (b) of the theorem. Choose a function (not a spline) $f(x)$ continuous and odd or even on $[-1, 1]$ according to whether $n$ is odd or even. If $f(x)$ possesses a unique best $L_2$-approximation $S(A^*, \Xi^*, x)$ then it is clear from the previous assertions that $\Xi^* = -\Xi^*$ which implies that zero is a knot in $\Xi^*$.

Further, 0 is a knot of odd multiplicity $q$ (one would normally expect it to be a simple knot, i.e. $q = 1$). Then in some neighborhood of 0 we have

$$\frac{d^{n+1-q}S(A^*, \Xi^*, x)}{dx^{n+1-q}} = \frac{n!c}{(n + 1 - q)!} (x)_+^{n+1-q} + \pi(x)$$

where $\pi(x)$ is a polynomial of degree $n - q + 1$ and $c$ is a constant.

It follows from the previous assertion that $S(A^*, \Xi^*, x)$ is an odd or even function according to whether $n$ is odd or even. This implies that the derivatives of $S(A^*, \Xi^*, x)$ are odd or even, but this is possible in some neighborhood of 0 only if $c = 0$. That is to say, only if $S(A^*, \Xi^*, x)$ actually has only $k - 1$ knots. In this case we have then that

$$E_{n,k-1}(f) = E_{n,k}(f)$$

which contradicts the Corollary of Theorem 8–2. Thus the assumption that $f(x)$ has a unique best $L_2$-approximation is untenable and the proof is complete.

Note that we have with the same proof the fact that Theorem 10–5 is valid for $L_p$-approximation for any $1 < p < \infty$.

Consider the problem of minimizing (10–4.1) as a function of $A$ and $\Xi$. A standard procedure for attacking such a problem is to locate a set of parameters where the derivative of this quantity is zero. Since this integral does not always have a unique minimum, and it appears likely that the set of minima might not be connected, this standard procedure sometimes fails. On the other hand, it succeeds often enough to make its study worthwhile. If we differentiate (10–4.1) with respect to the linear parameters we obtain

$$a_j^* = \int_0^1 f(x)O_j(\Xi^*, x)\,dx, \qquad j = 0, 1, 2, \ldots, n + k.$$

When (10–4.1) is differentiated with respect to $\xi_j$ we obtain for $j = 1, 2, \ldots, k$

$$\sum_{i=1}^{k} a_{n+i}^* \int_0^1 O_{n+i}(\Xi^*, x)(x - \xi_j^*)_+^{n-1}\,dx = \int_0^1 f(x)(x - \xi_j^*)_+^{n-1}\,dx.$$

This gives $n + 2k + 1$ equations for the parameters $A^*$ and $\Xi^*$. There has been no study of how to solve this system of equations for the knots $\Xi^*$.

## 10–5   TCHEBYCHEFF APPROXIMATION BY SPLINES

There are the two cases of fixed and variable knots to be considered. We first consider the set $\Xi$ of knots to be fixed. This gives a linear approximating function and it is already known that a best Tchebycheff approximation exists for every continuous function $f(x)$.

If the set of $n + k + 1$ functions $x^i$, $i = 0, 1, \ldots, n$; $(x - \xi_j)^n_+$, $j = 1, 2, \ldots, k$ were a Tchebycheff set, then one could apply directly the results of Chapter 3. That this is not the case is quickly seen from simple examples or Theorem 10–1. The subject matter of Chapter 12 is, to a large extent, the discussion of Tchebycheff approximation without Tchebycheff sets. Thus that body of results can be applied directly. On the other hand, we can obtain more specific results for this specific approximating function than are implied by the general analysis in Chapter 12. This is done here. The relationship between the specific results of this section and the general framework of Chapter 12 is not developed here.

The crucial question in linear Tchebycheff approximation is the possible location and number of zeros of the approximating function. This question is partially answered for splines by Theorem 10–1.

We begin with three lemmas concerning possible relationships of two sets of points in the interval $[0, 1]$. Although these lemmas are independent of splines, one should keep in mind that the objective is to determine situations where (10–2.13) is satisfied so that we may apply Theorem 10–1. The points labeled $\xi_i$ play the role of knots later and the points $x_i$ or $y_i$ are points to enter into the interpolation equation (10–2.9).

All of the points sets are indexed in their natural order, e.g. $x_i < x_{i+1}$, $\xi_i < \xi_{i+1}$, etc. Furthermore we often use the notation $\xi_0 = 0$, $\xi_{k+1} = 1$ (where $\xi_k$ is the largest of the $\xi_i$).

**Lemma 10–4.** *Let* $\{\xi_i \mid i = 1, 2, \ldots, k\}$ *and* $\{x_i \mid i = 1, 2, \ldots, n + p + 1\}$, $p \leq k$ *be such that each interval* $[\xi_j, \xi_{j+s+1}]$ *contains at most* $n + s$ *of the points* $x_i$. *Then there is a set* $\{y_i \mid i = 1, 2, \ldots, n + k + 1\}$ *which satisfies*

$$y_i < \xi_i < y_{i+n+1}, \qquad i = 1, 2, \ldots, k \qquad (10–5.1)$$

*and such that* $\{x_i\} \subset \{y_i\}$.

*Proof.* The proof is by two inductions. The first is an induction on $n$ with $p = 0$ and the second is on $p$ with $n$ arbitrary but fixed.

For $n = p = 0$ we take

$$y_i = \frac{(\xi_i + \xi_{i+1})}{2}, \qquad i = 0, 2, \ldots, k.$$

Assume then that the lemma is established for $p = 0$ and $n \leq N$. By this induction hypothesis there is a set $\{y_i' \mid i = 1, 2, \ldots, N + k + 1\}$ so that $x_j \in \{y_i'\}$ for $j \leq N$ and

$$y_i' < \xi_i < y_{i+N+1}'.$$

There are 3 cases possible (a) $y_m' < x_{N+1} < y_{m+1}'$ for some $m$, (b) $y_{N+k+1}' < x_{N+1}$ and (c) $y_m' = x_N$ for some $m$. In case (a) take

$$y_i = y_i' \quad \text{for} \quad i \leq m$$

$$y_{m+1} = x_{N+1}$$

$$y_i = y_{i-1}' \quad \text{for} \quad i = m + 2, \ldots, N + k + 2.$$

In case (b) take

$$y_i = y_i' \quad \text{for} \quad i \leq N + k + 1$$

$$y_{N+k+2} = x_{N+1}.$$

In case (c) take

$$y_i = y_i' \quad \text{for} \quad i \leq m - 1$$

$$y_m = (y_{m-1}' + y_m')/2$$

$$y_i = y_{i-1}' \quad \text{for} \quad i = m + 1, \ldots, N + k + 2.$$

It is readily verified that the sets $\{y_i\}$ thus specified satisfy the requirements of the lemma.

Consider then, that the lemma is established for sets of $n + p$ points. Let $x_1, \ldots, x_{n+p}$ lie in the interval $[\xi_j, \xi_{j+q+1}]$ where $q \geq p$. Then, by the induction hypothesis, there is a set $\{y_i'\}$ of $n + k + 1$ points satisfying (10–5.1) and such that $\{x_i \mid i = 1, 2, \ldots, n + p\} \subset \{y_i'\}$. We must now consider cases. In order to simplify the notation, we consider only the situation of $j = 0$. It is clear that the reasoning is independent of such a renumbering of the indices.

*Case 1*

$$x_{n+p} < y_m' < x_{n+p+1} < y_{m+1}'.$$

We now assert that one of the sets

$$Y_1 = \{y_1', \ldots, y_{m-1}', \ x_{n+p+1}, \ y_{m+1}', \ldots, y_{n+k+1}'\},$$

$$Y_2 = \{y_1', \ldots, y_m', \ x_{n+p+1}, \ y_{m+2}', \ldots, y_{n+k+1}'\}$$

fulfills the requirements of the lemma. Note we are stating that one can obtain an appropriate set $\{y_i\}$ by replacing one of $y_m'$ and $y_{m+1}'$ by $x_{n+p+1}$. All of the points of $Y_1$ and $Y_2$ satisfy (10–5.1) except possibly $x_{n+p+1}$. The conditions on $x_{n+p+1}$ are, respectively

$$x_{n+p+1} < \xi_m, \quad x_{n+p+1} > \xi_{m-n-1}, \qquad \text{set } Y_1,$$

$$x_{n+p+1} < \xi_{m+1}, \quad x_{n+p+1} > \xi_{m-n}, \qquad \text{set } Y_2.$$

$$(10\text{–}5.2)$$

Now the second and third inequalities are automatically satisfied and, since $\xi_{m-n} < \xi_m$, one of the other two must be satisfied. Whichever one is satisfied implies that the corresponding set fulfills the requirements of the lemma.

*Case 2.* Case 1 does not hold but

$$y'_m = x_{n+p} < \xi_q < x_{n+p+1} < y'_{m+1}.$$

Clearly $x_{n+p+1} < \xi_{m+1}$ and, since $\xi_{n-m-1} < y'_m$, we have $\xi_{n-m} \le \xi_q < x_{n+p+1}$ so that the set $Y_2$ defined for Case 1 fulfills the requirements of the lemma.

*Case 3*

$$\xi_q < y'_m = x_{n+p} < x_{n+p+1} < y'_{m+1} < \xi_{q+1}.$$

It is clear that one can replace $y'_{m+1}$ by $x_{n+p+1}$.

*Case 4*

$$\xi_q < y'_m = x_{n+p} < x_{n+p+1} < \xi_{q+1} < y'_{m+1}.$$

This includes the possibility that $\xi_q = \xi_k$ and hence $\xi_{q+1} = 1$ and $y'_{m+1}$ is irrelevant. Let $r$ denote the number of $y_i$ that are successively equal to $x_j$ immediately preceding $x_{n+p}$, e.g.

$$y'_m = x_{n+p}, \quad y'_{m-1} = x_{n+p-1}, \ldots, y'_{m-r} = x_{n+p-r}, \quad y'_{m-r-1} > x_{n+p-r-1}.$$

We then consider the set

$$Y_3 = \{y'_1, \ldots, y'_{m-r-2}, \quad y'_{m-r} = x_{n+p-r},$$
$$\ldots, y'_m = x_{n+p}, \quad x_{n+p+1}, \quad y'_{m+1}, \ldots, y'_{n+k+1}\}.$$

We now assert that either $Y_2$ or $Y_3$ fulfills the requirements of the lemma. We have either

$$x_{n+p+1} < \xi_{m+1}, \quad x_{n+p+1} > \xi_{m-n}$$

or

$$x_{n+p+1} < \xi_m, \quad x_{n+p+1} > \xi_{m-n-1}.$$

If the first pair of inequalities is satisfied then $Y_2$ fulfills the requirements of the lemma. Suppose these inequalities are not satisfied, i.e. $x_{n+p+1} < \xi_{m-n}$. Then the second pair is satisfied and this implies that $Y_3$ fulfills the requirements of the lemma. The association between $\{x_i\}$ and $Y_3$ to the left of $x_{n+p+1} = y_m$ is $x_{n+p-s} = y_{m-s+1}$. The points of $Y_3$ are to satisfy

$$\xi_{i-n-1} < y_i < \xi_i.$$

Since $\xi_{i-n} < y'_{i+1} = y_i < \xi_{i+1}$, the left side of this inequality is automatically satisfied. Thus we need only show that

$$y_{m-s} = x_{n+p-s+1} < \xi_{m-s}, \qquad s = 0, 1, \ldots, r+1.$$

Since $x_{n+p-r+1} < x_{n+p+1} < \xi_{m-n}$, this inequality is satisfied for $s \le n$.

6

Suppose then that $y_{m-s} > \xi_{m-s}$ for $s > n$, then the interval $[\xi_{m-s}, \xi_{m-n}]$ contains the points $x_{n+p-s+1}, \ldots, x_{n+p+1}$. This contradicts the assumption on the set $\{x_i\}$. Thus $y_{m-s} < \xi_{m-s}$ for all $s$ and the set $Y_3$ fulfills the requirements of the lemma. This concludes the induction step and the proof.

**Corollary.** *Let $\{\xi_i\}$ and $\{y_i\}$ contain $k$ and $n + k + 1$ points, respectively. Then*

$$[\xi_j, \xi_{j+s+1}] \text{ contains at most } n + s \text{ points } y_i, \qquad j = 0, 1, 2, \ldots, k. \tag{10-5.3}$$

*implies*

$$y_i < \xi_i < y_{i+n+1}, \qquad i = 1, 2, \ldots, k. \tag{10-5.4}$$

That (10-5.3) implies (10-5.4) is a special case of Lemma 10-4.

**Lemma 10-5.** *Let $\{\xi_i \mid i = 1, 2, \ldots, k\}$ and $\{y_i \mid i = 1, 2, \ldots, n + k\}$ be such that the interval $[\xi_j, \xi_{j+s+1}]$ contains at most $n + s$ points $y_i$. Then*

$$y_i < \xi_i < y_{i+n}, \qquad i = 1, 2, \ldots, k. \tag{10-5.5}$$

*Proof.* The proof is by induction on $k$. For $k = 1$ we see that (10-5.3) (which is a hypothesis of this lemma) implies that $[\xi_0, \xi_1]$ and $[\xi_1, \xi_2]$ each contain at most $n$ points $y_i$. Since there are $n + 1$ such points we have immediately

$$y_1 < \xi_1, \quad \xi_1 < y_{n+1}.$$

This is (10-5.5).

Assume now that there are $n + k$ points $y_i$ and the lemma has been established for $k - 1$ points $\xi_i$ and $n + k - 1$ points $y_i$. The interval $[\xi_0, \xi_k]$ contains at most $n + k - 1$ of the $y_i$ and hence $\xi_k < y_{n+k}$. Thus the interval $(0, y_{n+k})$ contains only $n + k - 1$ of the $y_i$. We ignore $\xi_k$ for the moment and set $\eta_i = \xi_i, i = 0, 1, 2, \ldots, k - 1$ and $\eta_k = y_{n+k}$. Then the interval $[\eta_j, \eta_{j+s+1}]$ contains at most $n + s$ of the $y_i$ (we do not count $y_{n+k}$). The induction hypothesis implies then that

$$y_i < \xi_i = \eta_i < y_{i+n}, \qquad i = 1, 2, \ldots, k - 1.$$

We already have $\xi_k < y_{n+k}$ and if $y_k > \xi_k$, then $[\xi_k, \xi_{k+1}]$ contains $y_k, \ldots, y_{n+k}$ which is $n + 1$ of the points $y_i$. This contradicts (10-5.3) and thus $y_k < \xi_k$ and (10-5.5) is established.

**Lemma 10-6.** *Let $\{\xi_i \mid i = 1, 2, \ldots, k\}$ and $\{x_i \mid i = 1, 2, \ldots, n + p + 1\}$, $p \leq k$, be such that (10-5.3) holds. Then there is a set $\{\eta_i \mid i = 1, 2, \ldots, p\}$ $\subset \{\xi_i\}$ so that (10-5.3) holds for the set $\{\eta_i\}$ replacing $\{\xi_i\}$ and $\{x_i\}$ replacing $\{y_i\}$.*

*Proof.* The proof is by induction on $k - p$. For $k - p = 0$ the statement is a tautology. We consider the case $k - p = 1$. It follows from Lemma 10-4 that there is a set $\{y_i\} = \{x_i\} \cup \{z\}$ of $n + k + 1$ points so that (10-5.3) is satisfied for the sets $\{\xi_i\}$ and $\{y_i\}$. Assume that $z \in [\xi_m, \xi_{m+1}]$. We wish to delete one of the points of $\{\xi_i\}$ to obtain the set $\{\eta_i\}$. In order to determine which one to delete, we establish the

*Assertion. One of the following statements is valid:*

$[\xi_{m-s}, \xi_{m+1}]$ *contains at most* $n + s - 1$ *points* $x_i$ *for each* $s$.    (10–5.6)

$[\xi_m, \xi_{m+s+1}]$ *contains at most* $n + s - 1$ *points* $x_i$ *for each* $s$.    (10–5.7)

If neither (10–5.6) nor (10–5.7) is valid then there are $s_1, s_2$ so that $[\xi_{m-s_1}, \xi_{m+1}]$ contains $n + s_1$ points $x_i$ and $[\xi_m, \xi_{m+s_2+1}]$ contains $n + s_2$ points $x_i$. The interval $[\xi_m, \xi_{m+1}]$ contains at most $n$ of the $y_i$ and since $z \in [\xi_m, \xi_{m+1}]$, this interval contains at most $n - 1$ of the $x_i$. This implies that the interval $[\xi_{m-s_1}, \xi_{m+s_2+1}]$ contains at least $(n - 1) + (s_1 + 1) + (s_2 + 1) = n + s_1 + s_2 + 1$ points. This contradicts (10–5.3) and establishes the assertion.

We delete a point from $\{\xi_i\}$ according to the following rules: (a) if $m = 0$, delete $\xi_1$, (b) if $m = k$, delete $\xi_k$, (c) if (10–5.6) is valid for $m > 0$, delete $\xi_m$, (d) if (10–5.7) is valid for $m < k$, delete $\xi_{m+1}$. These rules imply

$$\eta_i = \xi_1, \qquad i \le m - 1,$$

$$\eta_i = \xi_{i+1}, \qquad i \ge m + 1,$$

and $\eta_m = \xi_m$ or $\eta_m = \xi_{m+1}$ according to whether $\xi_{m+1}$ or $\xi_m$ is deleted.

It is now verified that $[\eta_j, \eta_{j+s+1}]$ contains at most $n + s$ of the points $x_i$. First assume that $\xi_m$ is the point deleted from $\{\xi_i\}$. If $j \ge m$ or $j + s + 1 \le m - 1$ then (10–5.3) holds as a direct consequence of the hypothesis as $\xi_m$ is not involved. If $j \le m - 1$ and $j + s + 1 \ge m$, then the interval $[\eta_j, \eta_{j+s+1}]$ is the interval $[\xi_j, \xi_{j+s+2}]$ which contains at most $n + s + 1$ of the points $y_i$. One of these is, however, the point $z$, so that $[\eta_j, \eta_{j+s+1}]$ contains at most $n + s$ of the points $x_i$. If it is $\xi_{m+1}$ rather than $\xi_m$ which is deleted, a similar analysis follows for the cases (a) $j \ge m + 1$, (b) $j + s + 1 \le m$ and (c) $j \le m, j + s + 1 \ge m + 1$. This concludes the case $k - p = 1$ of the induction.

Assume then that the lemma is established for $k - p = r - 1, r \ge 2$ and consider the case of $k - p = r$. We apply the established lemma to the set $\{\xi_i \mid i = 1, 2, \ldots, k - 1\}$ and $\{x_i\}$. From this we find a set $\{\eta_i' \mid i = 1, 2, \ldots, p\} \subset \{\xi_i \mid i = 1, 2, \ldots, k - 1\}$ so that $[\eta_j', \eta_{j+s+1}']$ contains at most $n + s$ of the $x_i$.

Let $\xi_i' = \eta_i', i = 1, 2, \ldots, p$ and $\xi_{p+1}' = \xi_k$. Then (10–5.3) is clearly satisfied for the sets $\{\xi_i'\}$ and $\{x_i\}$ because $\{\xi_i'\}$ contains $\{\eta_i'\}$ as a subset. The two sets $\{\xi_i' \mid i = 1, 2, \ldots, p + 1\}$ and $\{x_i \mid i = 1, 2, \ldots, n + p + 1\}$ satisfy the assumption of the first step of the induction argument if one takes $k' = p + 1$. That construction shows that a point may be deleted from

$\{\xi_i'\}$ and still retain condition (10–5.3). The resulting set is the set $\{\eta_i\}$ required in the lemma and this concludes the proof.

The next theorem establishes a property of splines which is the analog of the property of the assignment of simple zeros established in Problem 3–10 for Tchebycheff sets. Here, this property exists only when the knots $\Xi$ are in a certain relation to the points $x_i$ where sign changes are desired. This particular property is used in an essential way in the proof of the characterization theorem.

**Theorem 10–6.** *Let* $\Xi = \{\xi_i \mid i = 1, 2, \ldots, k\}$ *be knots and let* $n + k$ *points* $\{x_i\}$ *interior to* $[0, 1]$ *be given so that* (10–5.3) *holds. Then there is a spline* $S(A, \Xi, x)$ *of degree* $n$ *which changes sign at the* $x_i$ *and has no other zeros in* $[0, 1]$.

*Proof.* By Lemma 10–4 we may find a point $z$ so that the set $\{y_i\} = \{x_i\} \cup \{z\}$ satisfies (10–5.1). It follows from Theorem 10–1 that a unique solution $A$ exists to the equations

$$S(A, \Xi, x_i) = 0, \qquad i = 1, 2, \ldots, n + k,$$
$$S(A, \Xi, z) = 1.$$

We now show that $S(A, \Xi, x)$ cannot have another zero $x_0$. From Lemma 10–5 we see that $x_i < \xi_i < x_{i+n}$ and hence the set $\{y_i\} = \{x_i\} \cup \{x_0\}$ satisfies (10–5.1). Theorem 10–1 implies that $S(A, \Xi, x) \equiv 0$ since it has $n + k + 1$ zeros which satisfy (10–5.1). However, $S(A, \Xi, z) = 1$ and thus $x_0$ cannot exist.

If some point $x_p$ were a double zero, consider the spline which satisfies

$$S(A', \Xi, x_p) = \epsilon,$$
$$S(A', \Xi, x_i) = 0, \qquad i \neq p,$$
$$S(A', \Xi, z) = 1,$$

where $-\epsilon$ has the sign of $S(A, \Xi, x)$ for $x$ near $x_p$. For $\epsilon$ sufficiently small, $S(A', \Xi, x)$ has two simple zeros near $x_p$, say $z_1$ and $z_2$. Then the set $\{z_1\} \cup \{z_2\} \cup \{x_i \mid i \neq p\}$ satisfies (10–5.1) and hence $S(A', \Xi, x)$ is identically zero by the preceding argument. Since $S(A', \Xi, z) = 1$, this establishes that the $x_i$ are all simple zeros and $S(A, \Xi, x)$ changes sign at the $x_i$. This concludes the proof.

This result may be combined with Lemma 10–6 to obtain a somewhat stronger

**Corollary.** *Let* $\Xi$ *be* $k$ *knots and let* $n + p$ *points* $\{x_i\}$, $0 \leq p \leq k$, *interior to* $[0, 1]$ *be given so that* (10–5.3) *holds. Then there is a spline* $S(A, \Xi, x)$ *of degree* $n$ *which changes sign at the* $x_i$ *and has no other zeros in* $[0, 1]$.

We apply Lemma 10–6 to the sets $\Xi$ and $\{x_i\}$ to obtain a set

$H = \{\eta_i \mid i = 1, 2, \ldots, p\}$ so that (10–5.3) holds for $H$ and $\{x_i\}$. We may now apply Theorem 10–6 for the sets $H$ and $\{x_i\}$ to obtain a spline $S(A, H, x)$ which changes sign at the $x_i$ and has no other zeros. Since $H \subset \Xi$, the spline $S(A, H, x)$ is also a spline of degree $n$ with the $k$ knots $\Xi$.

With these more precise results on the nature of the zeros of splines, we can establish a characterization theorem for best Tchebycheff approximations (Rice, 1967).

**Theorem 10–7.**  *Let $f(x)$ be continuous on $[0, 1]$ and let $S(A, \Xi, x)$ be a spline function of degree $n$ and with $k$ fixed knots. Then a necessary and sufficient condition that $S(A^*, \Xi, x)$ be a best Tchebycheff approximation to $f(x)$ is that the error curve $f(x) - S(A^*, \Xi, x)$ alternates at least $n + p + 1$ times in some interval $[\xi_j, \xi_{j+p+1}]$.*

*Proof.* The mechanics of the proof of this result is similar to that of Theorem 3–1 and Theorem 12–5. It is, in fact, a corollary (after some computation) of Theorems 12–5 and 10–6. However, a direct approach is almost as short, so we outline the reasoning.

We consider the sufficiency first. If $f(x) - S(A^*, \Xi, x)$ alternates $n + p + 1$ times in $[\xi_j, \xi_{j+p+1}]$ and $S(A', \Xi, x)$ is a better approximation than $S(A^*, \Xi, x)$ then $S(A^* - A', \Xi, x)$ has $n + p + 1$ zeros in $[\xi_j, \xi_{j+p+1}]$. Let $p$ be the smallest value for which this is true. Then the Corollary of Lemma 10–4 implies that the conditions (10–2.13) are satisfied (with $k$ replaced by $p$) and Theorem 10–1 implies that $S(A^* - A', \Xi, x) = 0$ identically in $[\xi_j, \xi_{j+p+1}]$. This contradicts the assumption that $S(A', \Xi, x)$ is a better approximation.

We consider the necessity next. Since splines contain polynomials of degree $n$ as a special case, it follows at once that for the best approximation $S(A^*, \Xi, x)$ the error $S(A^*, \Xi, x) - f(x)$ alternates at least $n + 1$ times. Assume it alternatives $n + m + 1$ times on $[0, 1]$ with $m < k$ and without alternation $n + p + 1$ times on any subinterval $[\xi_j, \xi_{j+p+1}]$. Recall $0 = \xi_0$, $1 = \xi_{k+1}$. Then, as in the proof of Theorem 3–1, the interval $[0, 1]$ may be divided into $n + m + 2$ subintervals by $0 = x_0 < x_1 < \cdots < x_{n+m+2} = 1$ so that $S(A^*, \Xi, x) - f(x)$ alternates exactly once on any two adjacent subintervals and $S(A^*, \Xi, x_i) = f(x_i)$, $i = 1, 2, \ldots, n + m + 1$.

It follows from the Corollary of Theorem 10–6 that there is a spline $S(A', \Xi, x)$ of degree $n$ such that $S(A', \Xi, x)$ changes sign at the $x_i$ and has no other zeros. The constructions of Theorems 7–3 or 3–1 may be followed (in a much simplified form) to show that $S(A^* + \lambda A', \Xi, x)$ is a better approximation to $f(x)$ than $S(A^*, \Xi, x)$ for $\lambda$ appropriately chosen. This concludes the proof.

Since the basis functions of $S(A, \Xi, x)$ do not form a Tchebycheff set, there are continuous functions $f(x)$ which have several (infinitely many) best Tchebycheff approximations. On the other hand, it is shown in Chapter 12 that there are some things associated with the best approximations which are uniquely determined. One such thing is the set of critical point sets (see Definition 12–1 and 12–2 and Theorem 12–6). In the present specific case this may be stated as

**Theorem 10–8.** *If $S(A^*, \Xi, x)$ is a best Tchebycheff approximation to $f(x)$ such that $f(x) - S(A^*, \Xi, x)$ alternates $n + p + 1$ times in $[\xi_j, \xi_{j+p+1}]$, then for every best Tchebycheff approximation $S(A', \Xi, x)$, $f(x) - S(A', \Xi, x)$ alternates on the same points in $[\xi_j, \xi_{j+p+1}]$.*

This result may be further rephrased (see the Corollary of Theorem 12–6) as: *Let $S_1$ and $S_2$ be two best approximations to $f$. Then $f - S_1 = f - S_2$ at all the critical points.* Note that critical points are extremal points of $f - S$, but that some extremal points might not belong to a critical point set. The requirement, in this specific case, that a set $\{x_i\}$ be a critical point set (of $f - S$) is that the conditions of Theorem 10–7 be met. That is to say, the set $\{x_i\}$ contains $n + p + 2$ points and lies in $[\xi_j, \xi_{j+p+1}]$ for some $j$, and $f - S$ alternates $n + p + 1$ times on $\{x_i\}$.

We may use Theorem 10–1 and its consequences together with this result in order to establish the following form of a uniqueness theorem.

**Theorem 10–9.** *Let $S(A^*, \Xi, x)$ be a best Tchebycheff approximation to $f(x)$ such that $f(x) - S(A^*, \Xi, x)$ alternates $n + p + 1$ times on $[\xi_j, \xi_{j+p+1}]$, but does not alternate $n + q + 1$ times on any subinterval $[\xi_l, \xi_{l+q+1}]$ of this interval. Then $S(A^*, \Xi, x)$ is uniquely determined on the interval $[\xi_j, \xi_{j+p+1}]$.*

*Proof.* Let $\{x_i \mid i = 1, 2, \ldots, n + p + 2\}$ be the points of alternation in $[\xi_j, \xi_{j+p+1}]$. Then consider the $p$ knots $\xi_{j+1}, \ldots, \xi_{j+p}$ and the $n + p$ points $x_2, \ldots, x_{n+p+2}$, all of which are in the interior of this interval. We may apply Lemma 10–5 to these sets and obtain

$$x_{i+1} < \xi_{j+1} < x_{i+n'+1} = x_{i+n+2}.$$

This is a form of condition (10–5.1) for the applicability of Theorem 10–1 and it follows that the only spline of degree $n$ with knots $\xi_{j+1}, \ldots, \xi_{j+p}$ in the interval $[\xi_j, \xi_{j+p+1}]$ which is zero at these points $x_2, \ldots, x_{n+p+1}$ is the spline identically zero. It follows from Theorem 10–8 that the difference of any two best Tchebycheff approximations is zero at these points and hence identically zero in this interval. This concludes the proof.

In order to obtain some results on the characterization and uniqueness of Tchebycheff approximations by splines with variable knots, one needs information on two points: (a) The nature of the possible zeros of $S(A_1, \Xi_1, x) - S(A_2, \Xi_2, x)$ and (b) The solvability of the equations

$$S(A, \Xi, x_j) = S(A_0, \Xi_0, x_j) + \eta_j, \qquad j = 1, 2, \ldots, ?$$

for the coefficients $A$ and knots $\Xi$. At the present time this information is, in general, not available. In order to obtain a clue to what the theory will look like, there are two special cases that suggest themselves. These are splines of degree 1 and monosplines. The results for splines of degree 1 have not yet been worked out, but the problem does not appear to be completely intractable. In the remainder of this section we outline some results about monosplines.

A monospline of degree $n$ is a function of the form

$$M(A, \Xi, x) = x^n + S(A, \Xi, x) \qquad (10\text{–}5.8)$$

where $S(A, \Xi, x)$ is a spline of degree $n - 1$ with knots $\Xi$. Such a function appears in Peano's expression for the remainder term of quadrature formulae (10–2.8). A basic fact about monosplines is the following theorem announced by Schoenberg, 1958. A proof is given by Karlin and Schumaker, 1967.

**Theorem 10–10.** *Given $n + 2k$ points $x_i, x_i < x_{i+1}$ there exists a unique monospline $M^*$ of degree $n$ with knots such that*

$$M^*(A^*, \Xi^*, x_j) = 0, \qquad j = 1, 2, \ldots, m + 2k.$$

*Further, $M^*$ depends continuously on the set $\{x_i\}$.*

Assuming this result, Johnson, 1960, was able to establish the following interesting result.

**Theorem 10–11.** *For each choice of $n$ and $k$, there is a unique monospline $M^*$ of degree $n$ with knots, which deviates least from zero on $[-1, +1]$. For $n \geq 2$, $M^*$ is characterized as the unique monospline (of its type) which alternates $n + 2k$ times on $[-1, +1]$.*

It appears that the proof of this theorem depends on the fact that $M(A, \Xi, x)$ involves $x^n$ rather than some other function, say $f(x)$. Nevertheless, one may conjecture that these results are special cases of more general results along the following lines. We introduce a generalized concept of convexity.

**Definition 10–3.** *Let $F(A, x)$ depend on $n$ parameters $A$. The function $f(x)$ is said to be convex with respect to $F(A, x)$ if $f(x) - F(A, x)$ has at most $n$ zeros in $[0, 1]$ for any $F(A, x)$.*

This definition is apparently due to T. Popoviciu and E. F. Beckenbach. Considerable development of this concept (for $F(A, x)$ unisolvent) has been made by Beckenbach and Bing, 1945 (for $n = 2$) and Tornheim, 1950 (for general $n$).

One consequence of Theorem 10–10 is that $x^n$ is convex with respect to splines of degree $n - 1$ and with $k$ knots. It is likely that a result analogous to Theorem 10–9 with $x^n$ replaced by $f(x)$ may be valid for those $f(x)$ which are convex with respect to the splines of degree $n - 1$ and with $k$ knots.

For $n = 1$ (approximation by broken lines) one can directly establish the analog of Theorem 10–10 with $x^2$ replaced by any function $f(x)$ which is strictly convex. Other results on monosplines are indicated in Problems 10–3, 10–4.

## 10–6 SPLINES AND THE APPROXIMATION OF LINEAR FUNCTIONALS

Much of the recent work on spline functions has been concerned with their so-called minimal properties. That splines have these properties was established by Golomb and Weinberger in 1959, but, since they did not use the terminology of splines, these properties were re-established later. Very special cases were found earlier by Sard, 1949 and Holladay, 1957. The results established by Golomb and Weinberger are much broader than required here and we only outline the results pertinent to spline functions.

We begin by stating a rather general problem in Hilbert space concerning the estimation of the value of a linear functional.

PROBLEM. *Let $\mathscr{H}$ be a Hilbert space of real functions defined on $[0, 1]$ with inner product $(f, g)$. Let $f$ be an element of the subset $\mathscr{C}$ of $\mathscr{H}$ whose elements satisfy*

$$L_i(f) = \alpha_i, \qquad i = 1, 2, \ldots, k$$
$$(f, f) \le r^2 \tag{10–6.1}$$

*where the $L_i$ are known bounded linear functionals.*

(a) *Determine an element $f^*$ so that $\sup_{f \in \mathscr{C}} (f - f^*, f - f^*)$ is minimized.*

(b) *Given a linear functional $L$, determine the number $v^*$ so that*

$$\sup_{f \in \mathscr{C}} |v - L(f)|$$

*is minimized. Here $\mathscr{C}$ is the set (hypercircle) of elements of $\mathscr{H}$ which satisfy (10–6.1).*

Simply stated, the problem is to determine the best estimate of $L(f)$ given the information (10–6.1).

We may assume that the $L_i$ and $L$ are linearly independent, $\mathscr{C}$ is not empty and that

$$\sum_{i=1}^{n} |L_i(g)| + |L(g)| \le M \|g\|$$

for some constant $M$. We introduce the sets

$$\mathscr{L} = \{g \mid g \in \mathscr{H}, \quad L_i(g) = 0, \quad i = 1, 2, \ldots, k\}$$
$$\mathscr{L}_0 = \{g \mid g \in \mathscr{H}, \quad L_i(g) = L(g) = 0\}$$

and denote by $\mathscr{L}^\perp$ the orthogonal complement of $\mathscr{L}$. Let $f^*$ and $v^*$ be solutions of the problem.

**Lemma 10–7.**

(a) $f^* \in \mathcal{L}^\perp$ *is the center of the hypercircle* $\mathcal{C}$.

(b) $v^* = L(f^*)$

(c) $\sup_{f \in \mathcal{C}} |v^* - L(f)| = L(\bar{g})[r^2 - (f^*, f^*)]^{1/2}$

*where* $\bar{g} \in \mathcal{L}_0^\perp \cap \mathcal{L}$ *and* $(\bar{g}, \bar{g}) = 1$.

*Proof.* Let $f_0$ be the center $\mathcal{C}$ (i.e., the element of $\mathcal{C}$ of smallest norm). Note that $\mathcal{C}$ is in a hyperplane parallel to $\mathcal{L}$ and thus $f_0 \in \mathcal{L}^\perp$ (e.g., $g \in \mathcal{L} \Rightarrow f_0 + \alpha g \in \mathcal{C}$ for small $\alpha$ and $(f_0 + \alpha g, f_0 + \alpha g) = (f_0, f_0) + \alpha^2(g, g) + 2\alpha(f_0, g)$, and unless $(f_0, g) = 0$, $f_0$ cannot be of minimum norm). It is clear that the center $f_0$ is the element of $\mathcal{L}$ which minimizes $\sup_{f \in \mathcal{C}} (f - f^*, f - f^*)$. Hence $f_0 = f^*$.

(b), (c) Let $\bar{g}$ be the element of norm 1 which maximizes $|L(g)|$ among all $g$ in $\mathcal{L}$. Then $\bar{g} \in \mathcal{L}_0^\perp$. Any element of $\mathcal{C}$ is of the form

$$f = f^* + \frac{L(f) - L(f^*)}{L(\bar{g})} \bar{g} + h$$

where $h \in \mathcal{L}_0$. Note that $f^*$, $h$ and $\bar{g}$ are mutually orthogonal. See Fig. 10–3.

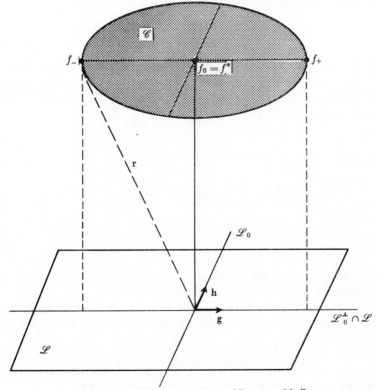

FIG. 10–3.  The construction of Lemma 10–7.

We may solve for $L(f)$ by computing

$$(f, f) = (f^*, f^*) + (h, h) + \left[\frac{L(f) - L(f^*)}{L(\bar{g})}\right]^2$$

or

$$[L(f) - L(f^*)]^2 \le [L(\bar{g})]^2[(f, f) - (f^*, f^*)]$$

or

$$|L(f) - L(f^*)| \le L(\bar{g})[r^2 - (f^*, f^*)]^{1/2}.$$

We note that equality holds here if $f = f_\pm = f^* \pm [r^2 - (f^*, f^*)]^{1/2}\bar{g}$.

We see, in fact, that $L(f)$ varies linearly between $f_+$ and $f_-$ (where it assumes its maximum and minimum values on $\mathscr{C}$, respectively) and the best estimate of $L(f)$ is the value of $L$ at the midpoint $f^*$ of this segment.

These results may be presented in a different form, one more tractable for computation, by the use of functional representers. Since the $L_i$ and $L$ are bounded, there exist elements $\phi_i$ and $\phi$ in $\mathscr{H}$ so that

$$L_i(f) = (f, \phi_i), \quad L(f) = (f, \phi).$$

These are the representing functions of $L_i$ and $L$. Then

$$\mathscr{L}^\perp = [\phi_1, \phi_2, \ldots, \phi_k],$$
$$\mathscr{L}_0^\perp = [\phi_1, \phi_2, \ldots, \phi_k, \phi],$$

where $[\ldots]$ denotes the subspace of $\mathscr{H}$ spanned by the elements $\ldots$.

If these representers are known, we can determine $f^*$ and $\bar{g}$ by the relations

$$f^* = \sum_{i=1}^{n} c_i\phi_i, \qquad \bar{g} = d\phi + \sum_{i=1}^{n} d_i\phi_i,$$

$$(f^*, \phi_j) = \sum_{i=1}^{n} c_i(\phi_i, \phi_j) = \alpha_j, \qquad j = 1, 2, \ldots, n$$

$$(\bar{g}, \phi_j) = d(\phi, \phi_j) + \sum_{i=1}^{n} d_i(\phi_i, \phi_j) = 0, \qquad j = 1, 2, \ldots, n \quad (10\text{-}6.2)$$

$$(\bar{g}, \phi) = d(\phi, \phi) + \sum_{i=1}^{n} d_i(\phi_i, \phi) \ne 0$$

$$\|\bar{g}\| = 1.$$

Note that $L(f^*)$ is a linear functional which we may denote by $L^*$, the best approximation to $L$ by a linear combination of the $L_i$.

We now rephrase the above results in a slightly different terminology. We say an element $g \in \mathscr{H}$ *interpolates* $f$ *with respect to the linear functionals* $L_i$ if $L_i(f) = L_i(g)$, $i = 1, 2, \ldots, n$. Set

$$W(f) = \{g \mid L_i(g) = L_i(f), \qquad i = 1, 2, \ldots, n\}$$

and let $P^\perp$ be the *projection operator* onto the subspace $\mathscr{L}^\perp$.

**Lemma 10–8.**

(a) $f^* = P^\perp f$ is the *unique element of* $\mathscr{L}^\perp$ *which interpolates* $f$ *with respect to the* $L_i$.

(b) $P^\perp f$ *is the element of minimum norm of* $W(f)$.

(c) $L^* = \sum\limits_{i=1}^{n} c_i L_i$ *is the best approximation to* $L$ *if* $L^* = LP^\perp$, *the representer of* $L^*$ *is* $P^\perp \phi = \phi^*$ *and*

$$|L(f) - L^*(f)| \leq \|\phi - \phi^*\| \, \|f - f^*\|.$$

These facts are restatements or direct consequences of the preceding analysis.

Part (a) of this Lemma is the "interpolation property of splines" often referred to in the literature, even though it is considerably weaker than Theorem 10–1 and its corollaries. The other two parts are the "minimal properties" and the "best approximation property" of splines and generalized splines.

If the representers $\phi_i$ and $\phi$ are known, then one may solve the problem under consideration by the relations (10–6.2). It is not always easy to find these representers, but if the *reproducing kernel* of $\mathscr{H}$ exists and is known, they may be found. The function $k(x, y)$ is the reproducing kernel if

(a) $k(x, y_0) \in \mathscr{H}$, and
(b) $f(x) = \big(k(x, y), f(y)\big)$

for every $f(x) \in \mathscr{H}$. Our main interest is in the following fact: if $L$ is a bounded linear functional with representer $\phi$ then

$$\phi(x) = (k(x, y), \phi(y)) = L_y k(x, y)$$

where $L_y$ indicates than $L$ acts on $k(x, y)$ as a function of $y$. Thus the representer $\phi(x)$ of any linear functional $L$ is simply $L_y k(x, y)$. Needless to say, reproducing kernels are difficult to obtain, but once they are found, they have the great advantage that the representer of any bounded linear functional may be directly computed.

We now give, without proof, the reproducing kernel for the Hilbert space associated with "generalized" splines. Let $M$ be an $n$th order differential operator in the normal form

$$\frac{d^n}{dx^n} + \sum_{i=1}^{n} a_i(x) \frac{d^{n-i}}{dx^{n-1}}$$

where each $a_i(x)$ is continuous in $[0, 1]$. Let $L_1, \ldots, L_k$ be linear functionals of the form

$$\sum_{i=1}^{n} \int_0^1 f^{(i)}(y) d\mu_i(y) \tag{10–6.3}$$

where $f^{(i)}$ is the $i$th derivative and $\mu_i(y)$ is of bounded variation. Denote by $\mathscr{H}^k$ the linear space

$$\mathscr{H}^k = \{f(x) \mid f^{(n-1)}(x) \text{ is absolutely continuous and } f^{(n)}$$

$$\text{is square integrable on } [0, 1]\}$$

and by $\mathscr{N}$ the subspace of $\mathscr{H}^k$,

$$\mathscr{N} = \{f(x) \mid Mf(x) = 0\}.$$

We have (de Boor and Lynch, 1966):

**Theorem 10–12.** *Let the $L_i$, $i = 1, 2, \ldots, n$ be linearly independent over $\mathscr{N}$. Then $\mathscr{H}^k$ is a Hilbert space with the inner product*

$$(f, g) = \sum_{i=1}^{n} L_i(f)L_i(g) + \int_0^1 [Mf(y)][Mg(y)] \, dy \qquad (10\text{–}6.4)$$

*and has the reproducing kernel*

$$k(x, y) = \sum_{i=1}^{n} c_i(x)c_i(y) + \int_0^1 G(x, t)G(y, t) \, dt \qquad (10\text{–}6.5)$$

*where $\{c_i(x)\}$ is the dual basis to $\{L_i\}$ in $\mathscr{N}$ and $G(x, y)$ is the Green's function for the problem:*

$$Mf(x) = g(x), \qquad L_i(f) = 0, \, i = 1, 2, \ldots, n.$$

The functions $c_i(x)$ satisfy

$$L_j\big(c_i(x)\big) = \begin{cases} 1, & i = j \\ 0, & i \neq j. \end{cases}$$

We may now relate this material with splines by choosing the special case

$$M = \frac{d^n}{dx^n}$$

in which case $\mathscr{N}$ is the subspace of polynomials of degree $n - 1$ and the Green's function involves the function $(x - y)_+^{n-1}$. If we take the linear functionals

$$L_i(f) = f(x_i), \qquad i = 1, 2, \ldots, n$$

where $0 \leq x_1 < x_2 < \cdots < x_n \leq 1$, then

$$k(x, y) = \sum_{i=1}^{n} \pi_i(x)\,\pi_i(y) + \frac{(-1)^n}{(2n-1)!}\bigg\{(x - y)_+^{2n-1}$$

$$+ \sum_{i,j=1}^{n} (x_i - x_j)_+^{2n-1}\pi_i(x)\pi_j(y)$$

$$- \sum_{i=1}^{n} [(x - x_i)_+^{2n-1}\pi_i(y) + (x_i - y)_+^{2n-1}\pi_i(x)]\bigg\} \qquad (10\text{–}6.6)$$

where

$$\pi_i(x) = \prod_{\substack{j=1 \\ j \neq i}}^{n} (x - x_j)/(x_i - x_j).$$

The reproducing kernel (10–6.6) is given explicitly by Golomb and Weinberger (1959). For any linear functional of the form (10–6.3) we have

$$L(f) = \sum_{i=1}^{n} L(\pi_i)f(x_i)$$

$$+ \frac{1}{(n-1)!} \int_0^1 L_x \left[ (x-y)_+^{2n-1} - \sum_{i=1}^{n} \pi_i(x)(x_i - y)_+^{2n-1} f^{(n)}(y) \right] dy.$$

We see from (10–6.6) that the representer of any linear functional $L(f) = f(\zeta)$ is a natural spline function of degree $2n - 1$ and knots $\{x_i\}$. Thus solving the problem stated at the beginning of this section, for this Hilbert space, naturally involves spline functions, and in particular the natural spline functions.

The generalized splines are defined by analogy from the Hilbert space $\mathcal{H}^k$ and (10–6.5). See Ahlberg, Nilson and Walsh, 1964, de Boor and Lynch, 1966, Karlin and Studden, 1966, Schoenberg, 1964.

## 10–7  COMPUTATIONAL METHODS

The representations of spline functions given in the first section are useful for analysis, but not so useful for computation. The representation (10–2.3) is extremely ill-conditioned. The representation (10–2.6) is not so ill-conditioned, but is awkward since one also must represent the cardinal splines $C_i(\Xi, x)$ in some other terms. We introduce two more representations which are useful for computational purposes.

The spline $S(A, \Xi, x)$ may be represented by $\Xi$ and the matrix $\{c_{ij} \mid i = 1, 2, \ldots, k + 1; \ j = 0, 1, \ldots, n\}$ where

$$S(A, \Xi, x) = \sum_{j=0}^{n} c_{ij}(x - \xi_{i-1})^n, \quad \text{for} \quad \xi_{i-1} \leq x \leq \xi_i. \quad (10\text{–}7.1)$$

The condition of this representation is exactly the same as the condition of polynomials on $[\xi_{i-1}, \xi_i]$ represented in terms of the powers of $(x - \xi_{i-1})$. Since one normally uses small values of $n$ (e.g. 2, 3 or 5), this results in a reasonably well-conditioned representation.

If the degree $n$ is odd, then the spline $S(A, \Xi, x)$ may be represented by $\Xi$ and the matrix $\{v_{ij} \mid i = 0, 1, \ldots, k + 1; \ j = 0, 1, \ldots, (n-1)/2\}$ where

$$v_{ij} = \frac{d^j S(A, \Xi, x)}{dx^j} \bigg|_{x = \xi_i} \quad (10\text{–}7.2)$$

The condition of this representation is exactly the same as the condition of polynomials on $[\xi_{i-1}, \xi_i]$ represented by values and $(n-1)/2$ derivatives at $\xi_{i-1}$ and $\xi_i$. Again for small values of $n$, this results in a reasonably well-conditioned representation.

There is a third representation which is useful in certain situations. That is to represent $S(A, \Xi, x)$ by $\Xi$ and

$$
\begin{cases}
\quad v_{io} & \text{for} \quad i = 0, 1, 2, \ldots, k+1 \\
v_{oj} \quad \text{and} \quad v_{k+1,j} & \text{for} \quad j = 1, 2, 3, \ldots, (n-1)/2
\end{cases} \qquad (10\text{-}7.3)
$$

where the $v_{ij}$ are defined by (10-7.2).

The representations (10-7.1) and (10-7.2) are redundant as (10-7.1) requires $(n+1)(k+1)$ parameters and (10-7.2) requires $(n-1)(k+2)/2$ parameters compared with the minimum $n + 2k + 1$ required by (10-7.3) or (10-2.3). The disadvantage of (10-7.3) is that it is laborious to evaluate $S(A, \Xi, x)$ at an arbitrary point $x$. The representation (10-7.2) is more work to evaluate than (10-7.1) by a factor of about 2 or 3. On the other hand (10-7.2) is more compact and always retains continuity and a continuous derivative in the presence of round off errors during computations. Of course, once one is not manipulating the splines, but rather using a specific spline for some purpose, one should almost certainly use the representation (10-7.1).

It is straightforward to pass between the representations (10-2.3), (10-7.1) and (10-7.2). Furthermore, it is straightforward to obtain the representation (10-7.3) from any of (10-2.3), (10-7.1) and (10-7.2). To pass from the representation (10-7.3) to (10-7.2) (and thence to the others) is the *spline interpolation problem*. It follows from Corollary 3 of Theorem 10-1 that (10-7.3) is a valid and uniquely determined representation. One may solve for the complete matrix $v_{ij}$ in (10-7.2) from the elements in (10-7.3) as follows. Set

$$
\Delta\xi_m = \xi_{m+1} - \xi_m
$$

$$
r = (n+1)/2
$$

$$
\gamma_{sj} = \sum_{t=0}^{r-1} \binom{t}{s}\binom{r-1+t-j}{t-j}.
$$

Then one may show that the matrix elements $v_{ij}$ in (10-7.2) satisfy the following system of equations.

$$
\sum_{j=0}^{r-1} \gamma_{sj}\left[ v_{i-1,j}(-\Delta\xi_{i-1})^{j-r-s} - v_{i+1,j}(\Delta\xi_i)^{j-r-s} \right.
$$

$$
\left. + \sum_{t=j}^{r-1} v_{ij} \binom{t}{j}\left( (\Delta\xi_i)^{t-r-j} - (-\Delta\xi_{i-1})^{t-r-j} \right) \right] = 0 \qquad (10\text{-}7.4)
$$

for $s = 0, 1, 2, \ldots, r-2$; $i = 1, 2, \ldots, k$. It is seen that the coefficient matrix in (10-7.4) is a *block tridiagonal* matrix of block size $(n-1)/2$ and of order $k(n - 1)/2$. In particular, for cubic splines it is a tridiagonal matrix of order $k$.

If the knots $\Xi$ are fixed then the computation of a best least squares approximation is a linear problem. One solves this problem by an orthogonalization procedure such as the modified Gram-Schmidt method. See the discussion in Section 12–10. It is essential in such procedures that the function to be orthogonalized be not nearly linearly dependent. One can obtain a basis for the spline functions with knots $\Xi$ from the system (10–7.4) which is "nearly orthogonal". One does this by imposing a pattern of sign oscillation in the $v_{io}$. Of course, the dot products in the orthogonalization must be computed more accurately than the other computations. This may be accomplished either with double precision accumulation of the dot products or with higher accuracy in all the computations of the dot product.

An algorithm for general spline approximation has been developed by de Boor and Rice, 1969. They attempt to solve the following problem: *Let $f(x)$ be defined on $[a, b]$ and $\epsilon > 0$ be given. Determine a spline of degree $n$ with as few knots as possible so that*

$$\left[ \int_b^a [f(x) - S(A, \Xi, x)]^2 \, dx \right]^{1/2} < \epsilon. \qquad (10\text{–}7.5)$$

In case $f(x)$ is specified only on a finite set of points in $[a, b]$ the integral in (10–7.5) is replaced by a quadrature formula (e.g. the trapezoidal rule). Likewise, if $x^i f(x)$ cannot be integrated in closed form then a quadrature formula must be used.

They attack this problem by successively solving the *least squares nonlinear spline approximation problem: Given $f(x)$ determine a spline $S(A^*, \Xi^*, x)$ of degree $n$ with $k$ knots so that*

$$\int_a^b [f(x) - S(A, \Xi, x)]^2 \, dx \qquad (10\text{–}7.6)$$

*is minimized.*

As the number $k$ of knots increases the value $E_{n,k}(f)$ decreases as seen in (10–4.3). Thus in theory one can increase $k$ until the condition (10–7.5) is satisfied. The algorithm for solving this latter problem is a method of descent type and hence one only obtains local minima of (10–7.6). It follows from Theorem 10–5 that there may be several local minima and, in fact, some of these do not correspond to best $L_2$-approximations.

A brief outline of the algorithm with $n = 3$ (de Boor and Rice, 1969) is given below. The representation (10–7.2) is used for splines during the computation. The integral in (10–7.6) is replaced by the trapezoidal rule and the first four orthogonal polynomials $O_j(\Xi, x)$ are obtained by applying the modified Gram-Schmidt process to the Legendre polynomials. Since the

$O_j(\Xi, x)$, $0 \leq j \leq 3$ are independent of $\Xi$, the function $f(x)$ is immediately replaced by

$$f(x) - \sum_{j=0}^{3} a_j^* O_j(x).$$

The remaining $O_{3+j}(\Xi, x)$, $j = 1, 2, \ldots, k$ are determined so that $O_{j+3}(\Xi, x)$ involves only the $j$ left-most knots. This makes it possible to economize on computations later. Specifically, when a knot, say $\xi_m$, is changed one needs only modify the $O_{j+3}(\Xi, x)$ for $j \geq m$.

Given an initial set of knots, they are improved cyclically in order to minimize (10–7.6). The cycle starts with the right-most knot and, working to the left, each knot is varied so as to reduce (10–7.6) as a function of this single knot. This cyclic process is continued until some criterion of convergence is met.

The variation of a particular knot $\xi_m$ is made with a discrete Newton method. A temporary orthogonal basis for the splines not involving $\xi_m$ is obtained.

This basis is used along with one orthogonal basis function $\psi_m(x)$ involving $\xi_m$ and hence only this last basis function changes during the discrete Newton method. Furthermore, one can replace the problem of minimizing (10–7.6) by that of maximizing

$$e(\xi_m) = - \int_a^b f(x)\psi_m(x)\, dx. \qquad (10\text{–}7.7)$$

It is substantially less computation to evaluate (10–7.7) than (10–7.6). The variation of $\xi_m$ is again terminated on various grounds, e.g.

(a) lack of sufficient change in $e(\xi_m)$,
(b) lack of sufficient change in $\xi_m$,
(c) $\xi_m$ approaches one of the neighboring knots $\xi_{m-1}$ or $\xi_{m+1}$ too closely,
(d) $\xi_m$ fails to satisfy a separation condition involving the number of knots versus the number of points in the trapezoidal rule near the ends of the interval of approximation,
(e) $\xi_m$ has been changed too many times.

Another feature is the approach to the nearly orthogonal splines used in the modified Gram-Schmidt. At the start of a cycle of knots variation, the original basis for orthogonalization is chosen (using 10–7.4) so that each spline has one more oscillation than the previous ones. Subsequently, when changes in the knots make it necessary to recompute some or all of the orthonormal basis of splines, the $v_{ij}$ values are chosen so as to make the new nearly orthogonal splines interpolate the most recent corresponding orthonormal spline at the new knots. This is, in particular, used when the last orthonormal spline is to be recomputed during the optimization of a particular knot.

This approach, along with the use of the modified Gram-Schmidt process and higher precision computation of dot products, seems to alleviate many of the difficulties attendant on computing least squares approximations using orthogonalization.

Under normal circumstances, additional knots are introduced one at a time and are cyclically optimized until the condition (10–7.5) is satisfied. A point is determined where the maximum error occurs for $k$ knots and the $(k + 1)$th knot is introduced midway between the two knots which bracket this point. The algorithm may also be terminated before (10–7.5) is satisfied in case the value of $E_{n,k}(f)$ does decrease significantly for several (say 3) successive values of $k$. Experience shows that this normally indicates that the additional knots merely serve to approximate random noise in the function $f(x)$.

The problem which de Boor and Rice attempt to solve cannot be solved by an algorithm. Thus the applicability of this algorithm is limited. This theoretical limitation is manifested in several ways. First, there is the problem of ascertaining when convergence has taken place. This problem appears on three levels, namely, for the whole algorithm, for the least squares nonlinear spline approximation problem and for the adjustment of knots within this latter problem. The decision that convergence has taken place is made on the basis of *ad hoc* numerical tests which are not infallible.

These decisions are delicate in view of the need to achieve some computational efficiency. These tests are based on experience with a certain class of functions $f(x)$ and might be completely inadequate for other classes. If one is to use such an algorithm extensively for a certain class of functions, it may well pay to experiment with modifications in these tests in order to achieve better efficiency with minimum risk.

Note that spline approximations with small values of $n$ are not likely to be useful for high accuracy approximations to mathematically defined functions. If $f(x)$ is very smooth then the degree of approximation with small values of $n$ is much slower than that of polynomial and rational approximations. See Birkhoff and de Boor, 1964, and Meir and Sharma, 1966, for pertinent results on spline interpolation. See Chapter 5 for results on polynomial approximation and Walsh, 1935, 1964, 1965, for results on rational approximation.

Spline approximations are extremely useful for low to medium accuracy (2 to 5 significant digits) approximations of functions of more or less arbitrary nature. Such functions occur frequently in the representation of relations in the physical world. An example of the possibilities with spline functions is shown in Fig. 10–4. It is literally impossible at the present time to obtain such a 3 significant digit approximation using polynomial or rational approximations.

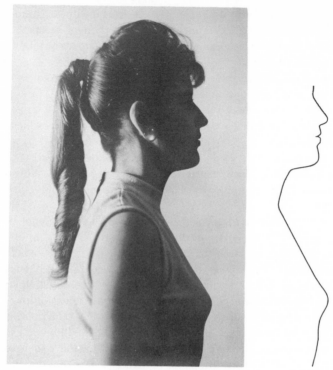

FIG. 10–4. A cubic spline approximation to a girl's profile with 16 knots.

## PROBLEMS

10–1. Show that the determinant

$$|(x_i - \xi_j)_+^0|, \qquad i, j = 1, 2, \ldots, k$$

is positive if and only if

$$x_{i-1} < \xi_i \leq x_i, \qquad i = 1, 2, \ldots, k.$$

10–2. Consider the least squares approximation of $f(x)$ on $[0, 1]$ by a spline $S(A, \Xi, x)$ of degree 1 with $k$ knots. Let $S(A, \Xi, x)$ be given by $a_{0j} + a_{1j}x$ for $x \in [\xi_{j-1}, \xi_j], j = 1, 2, \ldots, k + 1$. Show that the coefficients are given by

$$a_{0j} = \frac{1}{(\xi_j - \xi_{j-1})^3} [4(\xi_j^2 + \xi_j\xi_{j-1} + \xi_{j-1}^2)F_j - 6(\xi_j + \xi_{j-1})G_j],$$

$$a_{1j} = \frac{6}{(\xi_j - \xi_{j-1})^3} [2G_j - (\xi_j + \xi_{j-1})F_j],$$

where

$$F_j = \int_{\xi_{j-1}}^{\xi_j} f(x)\, dx, \qquad G_j = \int_{\xi_{j-1}}^{\xi_j} xf(x)\, dx.$$

(Stone, 1961.)

10–3.  The deviations $d_{n,k}$ of the monosplines of least deviation (from Theorem 10–7) for $n = 1, 2, 3, 4$, and $k$ knots are:

$$\frac{1}{k + 1} = d_{1k},$$

$$\frac{1}{2(k + 1)^2} = d_{2k},$$

$$\frac{1}{4(\sqrt{(3k)}/2 + 1)^3} = d_{3k},$$

$$\frac{1}{8(k/(\sqrt{2}) + 1)^4} = d_{4k}.$$

Further show that

$$\frac{1}{(k + 1)^n 2^{n-1}} \leq d_{nk} \leq \frac{n!}{3\pi^{m-2}(k + 1)^n}.$$

It is conjectured that

$$d_{nk} = \frac{1}{2^n \left(1 + k \sqrt{\dfrac{n}{2^{n-1}}}\right)^n}.$$

(Johnson, 1960.)

10–4.  Let $S(A, \Xi, x)$ be a spline of degree $n$. Define the order of a zero of $S(x)$ in the usual way for polynomials except at a knot $\xi_j$ and order $n$. If $S(x)$ is defined by $A(x - \xi_j)^n$, $x < \xi_j$; $B(x - \xi_j)^n$, $x > \xi_j$ we say $S(x)$ has a zero of order $n$ at $\xi_j$ if $AB > 0$, and of order $n + 1$ otherwise. Furthermore if $S(x) \equiv 0$ on some interval $[\alpha, \beta]$, we say that $S(x)$ has a zero of the order determined if $[\alpha, \beta]$ is taken to be one point. Let $Z(f)$ denote the number of zeros (counting multiplicities) of the function $f$. (a) Then $Z(S') \geq Z(S) - 1$ where $S'$ is the derivative of $S$, (b) $Z(S) \leq n + k$, (c) similar results hold for monosplines. (Johnson, 1960.)

10–5.  Let the data $\{(x_i, y_i) \mid i = 1, 2, \ldots, n\}$ be given and set, for any function $f(x)$,

$$Ef = \sum_{i=1}^{n} (f(x_i) - y_i)^2, \qquad If = \frac{1}{(m!)^2} \int [f^{(m)}(x)]^2 \, dx.$$

Let $S_0(x)$ be the natural spline of degree $2m - 1$ which interpolates the data. Given $\epsilon > 0$ the minimum of

$$\epsilon If + Ef$$

for all functions with $f^{(m)}$ square integrable is uniquely assumed by a natural spline $S_t(x)$ of degree $2m - 1$ with knots $x_i$. Likewise, given $a \leq IS_0(x)$, the minimum of $Ef$, among all functions with $If \leq a$, is uniquely assumed by a natural spline $S_a(x)$ of degree $2m - 1$. Furthermore, the two sets of splines $\{S_t(x) \mid 0 \leq \epsilon \leq \infty\}$ and $\{S_a(x) \mid 0 \leq a \leq IS_0(x)\}$ are identical. (Schoenberg, 1964.)

7A

10–6. Develop the theory of *trigonometric splines* associated with the differential operator

$$M = D(D^2 + 1^2)(D^2 + 2^2) \ldots (D^2 + m^2).$$

If the splines are required to be periodic, then they are piecewise trigonometric polynomials with continuous $(2m - 1)$th derivative. Show, for example, that every trigonometric spline $T(A, \Xi, x)$ of degree $m$ with knots $\Xi$ is of the form

$$T(A, \Xi, x) = \frac{1}{\pi} \sum_{i=1}^{n} c_i \Phi_m(x - \zeta_i) + \tau_m(x)$$

where

$$\Phi_m(t) = \frac{2^m}{(2m)!} \frac{\pi - t}{2} (1 - \cos t)^m, \qquad 0 \le t < 2\pi;$$

the constants $c_i$ satisfy

$$\sum_{i=1}^{n} c_i = 0, \ \sum_{i=1}^{n} c_i \cos r\xi_i = 0, \ \sum_{i=1}^{n} c_i \sin r\xi_i = 0, \qquad r = 1, 2, \ldots, m$$

and $\tau_m(x)$ is a trigonometric polynomial of degree $m$. (Schoenberg, 1964a.)

10–7. In the context of Section 10–6 with $M = d^n/dx^n$ consider the linear functionals

$$L_i(f) = f(x_i), \qquad i = 1, 2, \ldots, m - 1,$$
$$L_{m+i}(f) = f^{(i)}(1) - f^{(i)}(0), \qquad i = 0, 2, \ldots, n,$$

where $x_0 = 0$, $x_m = 1$. The reproducing kernel is

$$k(x, y) = \sum_{i=1}^{n} \pi_i(x)\pi_i(y) + (I - P_x^\perp)(I - P_y^\perp)[(-1)^m(y - x)_+^{2n-1}/(2n - 1)]$$

where $P_x^\perp$, $P_y^\perp$ are the projection operators acting on functions of $x$ and $y$, respectively. The polynomials $\pi_i(x)$ may be computed from the conditions $L_i(\pi_j) = \delta_{ij}$, $L_{m+i}(\pi_j) = \delta_{j,i+2}$, $i + 2, j \le n$. An explicit expression similar to (10–5.6) may be obtained, but it is somewhat more complicated. This gives rise to the *periodic splines*.
(de Boor and Lynch, 1966.)

10–8. Let $\Pi : 0 = x_0 < x_1 < \cdots < x_k = 1$ be a partition of $[0, 1]$ and set $|\Pi| = \max (x_i - x_{i-1}) \, i = 1, 2, \ldots$. Given $f(x)$ define $S_\Pi(x)$ as the natural cubic spline with knots $\Pi$ which interpolates $f(x)$ on $\Pi$. Assume $f^{(4)}(x)$ is continuous on $[0, 1]$ and define $M_\Pi = |\Pi|/\min (x_i - x_{i-1})$ as the mesh ratio bound and $N_\Pi = \max [(x_i - x_{i-1})/(x_{i+1} - x_i), (x_{i+1} - x_i)/(x_i - x_{i-1})] \, i = 1, 2, \ldots, k - 1$.

(a)  There exist constants $K_r(M_\Pi)$ depending on $M_\Pi$ above such that

$$\max_{x \in [0, 1]} |f^{(r)}(x) - S_\Pi^{(r)}(x)| \le K_r |\Pi|^{4-r} \max_{x \in [0, 1]} |f^{(4)}(x)|, r = 0, 1,$$

(b)  Let $\Pi_k$ be a sequence of partitions such that $|\Pi_k| \to 0$ and either (i) $M_{\Pi_k} \le M$ or (ii) $N_{\Pi_k} \le N$. Then if $f^{(3)}(x)$ is absolutely continuous on $[0, 1]$

$$|f^{(3)}(x) - S_{\Pi_k}^{(3)}(x)| \to 0 \text{ uniformly on } [0, 1] \text{ as } k \to \infty.$$

(Birkhoff and de Boor, 1964.)

**10–9.** For $k \geq 1$, let

$$0 = x_{k,0} < x_{n,1} < \cdots < x_{k,k} = 1$$

be a partition of $[0, 1]$ and let

$$h_{k,i} = x_{k,i+1} - x_{k,i}$$
$$h_k = \max_i h_{k,i}$$
$$q_k = \max_{i,j} (h_{k,i}/h_{k,j}).$$

For $f(x)$ continuous and periodic on $[0, 1]$ let $S_k(x)$ be the cubic spline (periodic on $[0, 1]$) with knots $\{x_{k,i}\}$ such that

$$S_k(x_{k,i}) = f(x_{k,i}), \qquad i = 0, 1, \ldots, k.$$

Let $\omega(f, h)$ denote the modulus of continuity of $f$ with length $h$. Then

(a)   $\|f - S_k\|_\infty \leq (1 + q_k^2)\omega(f, h_k).$

If $f \in C^1$ then

(b)   $\|f^{(r)} - S_k^{(r)}\|_\infty \leq 76\, h_k^{1-r}\omega(f', h_k), \qquad r = 0, 1.$

If $f \in C^2$ then

(c)   $\|f^{(r)} - S_k^{(r)}\|_\infty \leq 5h_k^{2-r}\omega(f'', h_k), \qquad r = 0, 1, 2.$

If $f \in C^3$ then

(d)   $\|f^{(r)} - S_k^{(r)}\|_\infty \leq [1 + q_k(1 + q_k)^2]h_k^{3-r}(f''', h_k), \qquad r = 0, 1, 2, 3.$

(Meir and Sharma, 1966.)

**10–10.** Establish the identity (10–2.12). Hint: Expand both sides completely, denote by $\alpha$ and $\gamma$ permutations of $[1, 2, \ldots, k]$, and obtain

$$\sum_\alpha (-1)^\alpha \prod_{j=1}^k (x_j - \xi_{a(j)})_+^n = n \sum_\alpha (-1)^\alpha \int \cdots \int_{0 \leq t_1 < \cdots < t_k \leq 1}$$
$$\sum_\gamma \prod_{j=1}^k (x_j - t_{\gamma(j)})_+^0 (t_{\gamma(j)} - \xi_{\alpha(j)})_+^{n-1}.$$

Note $\displaystyle \int_{0 \leq t_1 < \cdots <} \cdots \int_{t_k \leq 1} \sum_\gamma \prod_{j=1}^k (x_j - t_{\gamma(j)})_+^0 (t_{\gamma(j)} - \xi_{\alpha(j)})_+^{n-1}$

$$= \prod_{j=1}^k \int_0^1 (x_j - t_j)_+^0 (t_j - \xi_{\alpha(j)})_+^{n-1} dt_j.$$

(Polya–Szego, 1925.)

# 11

# Geometric Theory of Nonlinear Approximation

---

## 11–1 INTRODUCTION

The goal of this chapter is to place nonlinear approximation problems into a geometric framework from which we can obtain additional insight concerning these problems. This goal is not achieved in several important respects. However, let us first consider what is presented here. There is a relatively short description of the relation between approximation and projection on manifolds. Then follows the bulk of the chapter which is concerned with developing machinery for studying submanifolds of Minkowski space and the application to projections onto submanifolds. Finally there is a study of certain important nonlinear approximation problems and the conclusion is drawn that more general geometric concepts are required for an adequate geometric treatment of these problems.

There are at least three points at which this theory falls short. First, it is set in *finite dimensional spaces*. This means that the results are pertinent only to functions defined on finite point sets. Second, it applies in the main only to *Minkowski* (*strictly convex*) spaces and hence the important problems of Tchebycheff and $L_1$-approximations are excluded. Finally, even for finite dimensional Minkowski space there is much more that needs to be done.

The projection problem is as follows: *Given a subset $\mathscr{F}$ of the space $B^m$, and a point $b$, determine a point $P(b) \in \mathscr{F}$ closest to $b$.* The three main subproblems here (as in approximation) are those of existence, uniqueness and characterization. In the present case, the existence question is rather directly related to whether $\mathscr{F}$ is a closed set or not. The characterization results are not of great depth in the geometric theory. It is certain that more refined characterization results are both possible and desirable.

The question of uniqueness receives the most attention and there are three principal results. The first is the fundamental result that the only *Motzkin sets* (also called Tchebycheff sets) in a smooth Minkowski space are the *convex sets*. The second result (which follows rather directly from this) states that there is no possibility of a *global uniqueness theorem* for a nonlinear problem in a smooth space. The third result states that if the manifold $\mathscr{F}$ has bounded curvature, then there is a local uniqueness theorem for projections onto $\mathscr{F}$, i.e. there is a neighborhood of $\mathscr{F}$ such that every point of this neighborhood has a unique projection onto $\mathscr{F}$. It is for this third result that the machinery for manifolds in a Minkowski space is required. In particular, a concept of curvature is introduced which is both reasonable from the geometric view and sufficient for this result.

The final two sections concern non-manifold problems. Varisolvent functions are considered in some detail and it is seen that a geometric theory which deals with these objects must allow objects which are neither convex nor closed nor manifolds. The theory of manifolds is still pertinent for these problems, but an additional level of generality or complexity is required to treat these problems in a unified way.

## 11-2 APPROXIMATION AND PROJECTION

A statement of the approximation problem is given in Section 1-2. We reformulate it here. We have a domain $X$ and a set $B$ of real functions $b(x)$ defined on $X$. There is a norm function $\| \ \|$ defined on $B$ and $B$ is a Banach space. Further, we have an approximation function $F(A, x)$ depending on the parameters $A \in P$, where $P$ is the domain of the parameters. The statement of the approximation problem is

APPROXIMATION PROBLEM. *Given $b \in B$ determine the parameters $A^* \in P$ such that*

$$\|F(A^*) - b\| \leq \|F(A) - b\|$$

*for all $A \in P$.*

So far in this book, we have taken $X$ to be either an interval or a finite subset of an interval and we have primarily considered $B$ to be the set of continuous functions.

We now formulate a closely related problem. Consider an arbitrary Banach space $B$ and a subset $\mathscr{F} \subset B$.

**Definition 11-1.** *Given $b \in B$, the point $f^* \in \mathscr{F}$ is said to be a projection of $b$ onto $\mathscr{F}$ if the distance*

$$\|\mathscr{F} - b\| = \inf_{f \in \mathscr{F}} \|f - b\|$$

*of $b$ from $\mathscr{F}$ is assumed at $f^*$, i.e. $\|b - f^*\| = \|b - \mathscr{F}\|$.*

We now state the

PROJECTION PROBLEM. *Given $b \in B$ and $\mathscr{F}$, determine the projections $f^*$ of $b$ onto $\mathscr{F}$.*

The *projection operator* $\mathbf{P}_{\mathscr{F}}$ associates with each point $b \in B$ the set

$$\mathbf{P}_{\mathscr{F}}(b) = \{f \mid f \in \mathscr{F}, \quad \|b - f\| = \|b - \mathscr{F}\|\}.$$

The relationship between these two problems is straightforward. Associated with the approximating function $F(A, x)$ we have in $B$ the set

$$F = \{F(A, x) \mid A \in P\}. \tag{11–2.1}$$

Thus the best approximations to $b(x)$ are precisely the projections of $b$ onto $F$. There are, of course, projection problems which have no interpretation in terms of the approximation of functions.

We will use the identification (11–2.1) throughout this chapter and will, from time to time, use $\mathscr{F}$ and $F(A, x)$ interchangeably. Thus we may ascribe analytic properties to $\mathscr{F}$ or geometrical properties to $F(A, x)$. For example, we may say that $\mathscr{F}$ is unisolvent (meaning that $F(A, x)$ is unisolvent) or that $F(A, x)$ is connected (meaning that $\mathscr{F}$ is connected). At times we consider the set $\mathscr{F}$ independently of its embedding in $B$. However, we always have in the background that $\mathscr{F}$ is a subset of $B$ and, in particular, that the topology of $\mathscr{F}$ is induced by the topology of $B$. That is to say that neighborhoods in $\mathscr{F}$ must be the intersection of $\mathscr{F}$ with neighborhoods in $B$.

A large portion of this chapter is concerned with the case where $X$ is finite: i.e. $X = \{x_i \mid i = 1, 2, \ldots, m\}$. In this case we take as our representation of $B$ the real vector space

$$B^m = \{(b(x_1), b(x_2), \ldots, b(x_m)) \mid |b(x_i)| < \infty\}.$$

The projection problem interpretation is pertinent to approximation with constraints. For example, we may state the

LINEAR APPROXIMATION PROBLEM WITH CONSTRAINTS. *Given* $b \in B$, *a set*

$$\{\phi_i \mid i = 1, 2, \ldots, n\}$$

*and a set* $H \subset E^n$, *determine coefficients* $A^* = \{a_i^*\} \in H$ *so that*

$$\left\| \sum_{i=1}^{n} a_i^* \phi_i - b \right\| \leq \left\| \sum_{i=1}^{n} a_i \phi_i - b \right\|$$

*for all* $A \in H$.

One can, of course, state a similar nonlinear problem. We can also interpret this problem as a projection problem in $E^n$ as well as one in $B$. Consider a fixed element $b \in B$ and set

$$\rho^* = \inf_{A \in E^n} \|L(A, x) - b(x)\|$$

where, as usual, $L(A, x) = \Sigma a_i \phi_i(x)$. The sets

$$S(\rho) = \{A \mid \|L(A, x) - b(x)\| \leq \rho\}$$

are convex in $E^n$ for $\rho \geq \rho^*$ and define a "distance" of any element of $E^n$ from the set $S(\rho^*)$. This particular distance function need not define a metric in $E^n$, or even measure the distance between all pairs of points. We can, by simple analogy with Definition 11-1, define the projections of $S(\rho^*)$ onto $H$. The projections are then the best constrained approximations to $b(x)$.

It is worth noting that the second interpretation (as a projection in $E^n$) is not always possible for nonlinear approximation problems (with or without constraints). That is to say that the parameter domain $P$ cannot always be identified with $E^n$ (or any subset of $E^k$, $k \geq n$).

## 11-3  UNISOLVENT AND LOCALLY UNISOLVENT FUNCTIONS AS MANIFOLDS

We recall the definition of a manifold (Auslander and MacKensie, 1960).

**Definition 11-2.**  *A set $\mathcal{M}$ is a manifold if there is an atlas (a collection) of charts $\{(W_\alpha, \eta_\alpha) \mid \alpha \in I\}$ where $W_\alpha$ is an open subset of $E^n$, $\eta_\alpha : W_\alpha \to \mathcal{M}$ is a homeomorphism of $W_\alpha$ onto an open subset $U_\alpha$ of $\mathcal{M}$ such that:*

(a)  *if $f \in \mathcal{M}$ then there is an $\alpha$ in the index set $I$ so that $f \in U_\alpha$,*
(b)  *if $U_\alpha \cup U_\beta = U$ is not empty, then $\eta_\beta^{-1} \eta_\alpha$ is a homeomorphism of $\eta_\alpha^{-1}(U)$ onto $\eta_\beta^{-1}(U)$.†*

This is a precise way of saying that every point of $\mathcal{M}$ has a neighborhood which is just like a Euclidean neighborhood. If $\mathcal{M}$ is connected, then $n$ must be the same for every chart and we say that $\mathcal{M}$ is a manifold of dimension $n$. Since there is a coordinate system in $E^n$, the mappings $\eta_\alpha$ induce coordinates in the neighborhood $U_\alpha$. Thus the pair $(\eta_\alpha, U_\alpha)$ may be called a coordinate neighborhood in $\mathcal{M}$. There is a well defined hierarchy of smoothness and continuity classes $K$ for functions defined in $E^n$ (e.g. continuous, continuous $k$th derivative, analytic, etc.). We may use the coordinate neighborhoods $(\eta_\alpha, U_\alpha)$ to define the smoothness of $\mathcal{M}$. Let $K$ be such a class, then $\mathcal{M}$ is said to be of continuity class $K$ if every function $\eta_\beta^{-1} \eta_\alpha$: $\eta_\alpha^{-1}(U_\alpha \cap U_\beta) \to \eta_\beta^{-1}(U_\alpha \cap U_\beta)$ is of continuity class $K$. In particular we can speak of a *differentiable manifold* of class $C^k$ if $\eta_\beta^{-1} \eta_\alpha$ has $k$ continuous partial derivatives.

The main result of this section is

**Theorem 11-1.**  *If $\mathcal{F}$ is locally unisolvent of degree $n$, then $\mathcal{F}$ is a manifold of dimension $n$.*

---

† A third condition is also to be satisfied, but if the atlas satisfies (a) and (b) then it is known that there is another atlas, containing all the charts of this atlas, which satisfies this third condition.

Recall from Definition 7–7 that this is equivalent to $F$ being varisolvent of constant degree and implies that $X$ is a compact interval.

*Proof.* Choose $n$ distinct points $x_i$, $i = 1, 2, \ldots, n$ in $X$ and define the mapping $\phi$ from $\mathscr{F}$ to $E^n$ by

$$\phi : F(A^\circ, x) \in \mathscr{F} \to \big(F(A^\circ, x_1), F(A^\circ, x_2), \ldots, F(A^\circ, x_n)\big).$$

Set, for $f \in \mathscr{F}$,

$$W(f, \delta) = \{v \mid v \in E^n, \quad \|v - \phi(f)\|_{E^n} < \delta\}$$

and for $v \in W(f, \delta)$ define $\eta = \phi^{-1}$. It follows from Property Z that $\phi$ is one-to-one and hence $\eta$ is well defined. It follows from local solvence that $\phi$ is continuous and from Lemma 3–4 that $\phi^{-1}$ is continuous. Hence the mapping $\eta : W(f, \delta) \to \mathscr{F}$ is a homeomorphism. It is clear that

$$f \in U(f, \delta) = \eta[W(f, \delta)]$$

for any $\delta > 0$. If

$$U = \eta[W(f_1, \delta_1)] \cap \eta[W(f_2, \delta_2)]$$

is not empty then $\eta^{-1}\eta$ is the identity function on $U$ and hence homeomorphic. This concludes the proof.

**Corollary.** *If $\mathscr{F}$ is unisolvent, then $\mathscr{F}$ is homeomorphic to $E^n$.*

Note that both Theorem 11–1 and its Corollary are independent of any embedding of $\mathscr{F}$ in any Banach space $B$.

The following two examples illustrates two facts: (1) that $\mathscr{F}$ may be homeomorphic to $E^n$ without being unisolvent and (2) that $\mathscr{F}$ may be locally unisolvent without being homeomorphic to $E^n$.

EXAMPLE 1.    $X = [-1, +1]$,

$$\mathscr{F} = \left\{ \frac{a}{1 + ax} \mid -1 < a < +1 \right\}.$$

EXAMPLE. 2.    $X = [-1, +1]$,

$$\mathscr{F} = \left\{ \frac{a}{1 + ax} \mid -1 < a < -\tfrac{1}{2}, \tfrac{1}{2} < a < 1 \right\}.$$

If $X$ is a finite set, then $\mathscr{F}$ may be identified with an $n$-dimensional submanifold of $B^m$. Thus the study of approximation on finite sets by locally unisolvent functions is closely related to the study of projections in $B^m$ onto submanifolds. We note, however, that locally unisolvent manifolds are of a very special nature. For example, in $B^3$, the one-dimensional linear manifold

$$\mathscr{M} = \{(x_1, x_2, x_3) \mid x_1 = x_2, x_3 = 1\}$$

is not locally unisolvent.

## 11-4 MINKOWSKI GEOMETRY

We consider the $m$-dimensional vector space $V^m$ (i.e. the linear $m$-dimensional space). One may define a variety of metrics $\rho(v_1, v_2)$ on $V^m$ and we have

**Definition 11–3.** *The space $V^m$ with metric $\rho$ is Minkowskian (a strictly convex Banach space) if $\rho(v_1, v_2)$ is a function $\| \ \|$ of $v_1 - v_2$ alone such that*

(a) $\|v\| \geq 0$, and $\|v\| = 0 \Leftrightarrow v = 0$,
(b) $\|\alpha v\| = |\alpha| \, \|v\|$, $\alpha$ = real number,
(c) $\|v_1 + v_2\| \leq \|v_1\| + \|v_2\|$, equality only if $v_1 = \alpha v_2$ for some number $\alpha$.

There is a more intrinsic geometrical definition of a Minkowski space, namely, the metric satisfies (i) the metric topology on each line of $V^m$ is equivalent to the natural topology of the line, (ii) the linear midpoint $v_3 = \frac{1}{2}(v_1 + v_2)$ of $v_1$ and $v_2$ is also the metric midpoint of $v_1$ and $v_2$ (i.e. $\rho(v_1, v_3) = \rho(v_3, v_2) = \frac{1}{2}\rho(v_1, v_2)$). These two geometrical assumptions imply the conditions of Definition 11–3. A comparison with Chapter 1 shows that we are, in fact, considering geometry in finite dimensional normed linear spaces with strictly convex unit spheres and we call this Minkowski geometry.

To illustrate some of the more obvious difficulties with Minkowski geometry we mention a few facts.

A. Arc length is not invariant under rotations. Let $L_1^2$, and $L_\infty^2$ denote two-dimensional $L_1$ and $L_\infty$ space, respectively. The circumferences of the unit spheres in $L_1^2$ and $L_\infty^2$ are 8. If the unit spheres are rigidly rotated 45° (by Euclidean rotation) their circumferences become $4\sqrt{2}$.

B. Curvature is not invariant under rotation.

C. A useful measure of angle is difficult to make (and indeed, the meaning of rotation is not so clear).

D. Perpendicularity is not symmetric.

A particularly important geometrical object in the Minkowski (or any Banach) space $B^m$ is the *unit ball*

$$\mathscr{S}(0, 1) = \{b \mid \|b\| < 1\}.$$

In general the *ball* with center $b$ and radius $\rho$ is denoted by $\mathscr{S}(b, \rho)$. The closure of $\mathscr{S}(b, \rho)$ is the *closed ball* $\overline{\mathscr{S}}(b, \rho)$. If $b_1$ and $b_2$ are distinct points then the set of points of the form $(1 - \lambda)b_1 + \lambda b_2$ form for

$$-\infty < \lambda < \infty \quad \text{the } \textit{line } l(b_1, b_2) \text{ through } b_1 \text{ and } b_2,$$
$$0 \leq \lambda < \infty \quad \text{the } \textit{ray } r(b_1, b_2) \text{ from } b_1 \text{ through } b_2,$$
$$0 \leq \lambda \leq 1 \quad \text{the } \textit{segment } s(b_1, b_2) \text{ from } b_1 \text{ to } b_2.$$

A *flat* is the translate of a subspace and a *hyperplane* is an $(m - 1)$-dimensional flat. The hyperplane $H$ is a *hyperplane of support* of $\overline{\mathscr{S}}(b_0, \rho)$ if

$\partial \mathscr{S}(b_0, \rho) \cap H$ is not empty but $\mathscr{S}(b_0, \rho) \cap H$ is empty. If $\overline{\mathscr{S}}(b_0, \rho)$ possesses a unique hyperplane $H$ of support at a point $b \in \partial \mathscr{S}(b_0, \rho)$, then $H$ is a *tangent plane* of $\overline{\mathscr{S}}(b_0, \rho)$ at $b$.

We may classify such spaces in an interesting way by properties of $\mathscr{S}$. Condition (c) of Definition 11–3 implies that $\mathscr{S}$ is convex. If $\overline{\mathscr{S}}$ is strictly convex, then we say that $B^m$ is *strictly convex* (*strictly normed*). We say that $\mathscr{S}$ (or $B^m$) is *uniformly convex* if given $b_1, b_2 \in \mathscr{S}$ with $\|b_1 - b_2\| = \delta$ then $\frac{1}{2}\|b_1 - b_2\| \leq 1 - \epsilon(\delta)$. It is immediate that uniform and strict convexity are equivalent in finite dimensional spaces, however the distinction becomes real when we consider infinite dimensional spaces. That is to say that arguments based on strict convexity in finite dimensional spaces generally require the assumption of uniform convexity in infinite dimensional spaces.

The closure of $\mathscr{S}$ is denoted by $\overline{\mathscr{S}}$. Recall that a *plane of support* of $\overline{\mathscr{S}}$ is a hyperplane which contains at least one point of $\overline{\mathscr{S}}$, but which does not separate any two points of $\overline{\mathscr{S}}$. If $\|b\| = 1$ and there is exactly one plane of support of $\mathscr{S}$ containing $b$, we call this the *tangent plane* of $\overline{\mathscr{S}}$ at $b$. If every plane of support of $\overline{\mathscr{S}}$ is a tangent plane, we say that $\overline{\mathscr{S}}$ (and $B^m$) is *smooth*.

The *unit sphere* of $B^m$ is the boundary of $\mathscr{S}$,

$$\partial \mathscr{S} = \{b \,|\, \|b\| = 1\}.$$

This is an $(m-1)$-dimensional submanifold of $B^m$ and we ascribe to $\partial \mathscr{S}$ the descriptors of $\mathscr{S}$, e.g. we may say that the unit sphere is strictly convex, smooth, etc. Similarly we may us these descriptors for a convex set $\mathscr{R}$ (and $\partial \mathscr{R}$) other than $\mathscr{S}$.

So far we have considered familiar aspects of the geometry of a finite dimensional Banach space. We now wish to introduce a concept of perpendicular in $B^m$. Such a concept is already implicit in our definition of projection. We have

**Definition 11–4.** *Let $l_1$ and $l_2$ be two lines in $B^m$ which intersect at $b_0$. $l_1$ is perpendicular to $l_2$ (written $l_1 \perp l_2$) if $b_0$ is the projection of any $b \in l_1$ onto $l_2$. If $l_1 \perp l_2$ then $l_2$ is said to be transversal to $l_1$.*

It is clear that if $\mathscr{M}$ is a linear manifold, then $l_1 \perp \mathscr{M}$ means that $l_1$ is perpendicular to every line in $\mathscr{M}$. This definition implies that perpendicularity is not symmetric in $B^m$. Indeed, it is known that for $m > 2$, that complete symmetry of perpendicularity implies that $B^m$ is a Hilbert space. Recall that geometry in Hilbert spaces is the substance of classical and modern differential geometry.

Another geometrical object of interest in $B^m$ is the *limit sphere*. We use the notation

$$\mathscr{R}(a, b) = \{c \,|\, \|a - c\| = \|a - b\|\} = \partial \mathscr{S}(a, \|a - b\|)$$

which is the sphere with center $a$ passing through $b$.

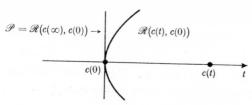

$$\mathscr{P} = \mathscr{R}(c(\infty), c(0)) \rightarrow \quad \mathscr{R}(c(t), c(0))$$

$c(0)$      $c(t)$    $t$

Fig. 11–1. The definition of limit spheres.

We consider a point $c(t)$ which varies along a given straight line, and the set $\mathscr{P}$ defined by

$$\mathscr{P} = \lim_{t \to \infty} \mathscr{R}(c(t), c(0))$$

is called a limit sphere. See Fig. 11–1. It is to be shown in Problem 11–1 that a limit set $\mathscr{P}$ exists. It is implied by Fig. 11–1 that the limit spheres are flat, but this is not always the case. We have

**Theorem 11–2.** *Every limit sphere in $B^m$ is a hyperplane if and only if $B^m$ is smooth.*

*Proof.* For any point $b$ on the boundary of a sphere $\mathscr{R} = \{a \mid \|c - a\| = v\}$ we consider the set of planes of support of $\mathscr{R}$ at $b$. This set is convex and we call its boundary the *tangent cone* of $\mathscr{R}$ at $b$. The first point of the proof is the

*Assertion. Every sphere $\mathscr{R}(c(t), c(0))$ has the same tangent cone.*

This follows immediately from the observation that the spheres $\mathscr{R}$ are homothetic, but we carry out the details. Let $\mathscr{R}_i$ denote $\mathscr{R}(c(t_i), c(0))$, $c_i$ denote $c(t_i)$, etc. It follows directly from the triangle inequality that $t_2 > t_1$ implies that $\mathscr{R}_1$ is inside $\mathscr{R}_2$ (e.g. the ball of which $R_2$ is the boundary contains $R_1$) except for the point $c(0)$. Thus every plane of support of $\mathscr{R}_2$ at $c(0)$ is a plane of support of $\mathscr{R}_1$.

To establish the converse, let $T$ be a plane of support of $\mathscr{R}_1$ and assume that $e_2 \in T$ is inside $\mathscr{R}_2$. Let $d_2$ be the point in $\mathscr{R}_2$ on the line through $c_2$ and $e_2$. Consider

$$d_1 = c_1 + \frac{t_1}{t_2}(d_2 - c_2),$$

$$e_1 = c_1 + \frac{t_1}{t_2}(e_2 - c_2),$$

A direct calculation shows that $d_1 \in \mathscr{R}_1$ and $e_1$ is inside $\mathscr{R}_1$. However,

$$e_2 = c_0 + (e_2 - c_0)$$

$$c_2 = c_0 + \frac{t_2}{t_1}(c_1 - c_0)$$

which implies that

$$e_1 = c_0 + \frac{t_1}{t_2}(e_2 - c_0)$$

and $e_1$ is in the plane of support $T$. This is a contradiction and establishes that $\mathscr{R}_1$ and $\mathscr{R}_2$ have the same set of planes of support at $c_0$. This, in turn, establishes the assertion.

The second point of the proof is the

*Assertion. The limit sphere is the common tangent cone of the spheres* $\mathscr{R}(c(t), c(0))$.

We first show that $\mathscr{P}$ is, in fact, a cone with vertex $c(0)$. That is to say, given $p \in \mathscr{P}$, the line segment from $p$ to $c(0)$ is in $\mathscr{P}$. Since $\mathscr{P}$ is the limit of the boundary of an increasing, nested sequence of convex sets, it follows that $\mathscr{P}$ is, itself, the boundary of a convex set. Thus the line segment from $p$ to $c(0)$ is in this convex set. Assume that $p$, on this segment, is actually interior to this set. This means that $p_1$ is in the interior of $\mathscr{R}(c(t_1), c(0))$ for some $t_1$. We may then repeat the calculation of the preceding assertion to show that $p$ is interior to the sphere $\mathscr{R}(c(t_2), c(0))$ where

$$t_2 = (\|p - c(0)\|/\|p_1 - c(0)\|)t_1,$$

which is impossible, and hence $\mathscr{P}$ is a cone.

If $\mathscr{P}$ and the tangent cone are distinct, then it is clear that $\mathscr{P}$ lies between the tangent cone and the line $c(t)$. Assume that there is a point $b$ between these two cones. Then there is a hyperplane through $b$ and $c(0)$ which intersects $\mathscr{P}$ only at $c(0)$ (this is because $\mathscr{P}$ is a convex cone). This hyperplane is a plane of support of every sphere $\mathscr{R}(c(t), c(0))$ and hence in the set bounded by the tangent cone. This contradicts the assumption that $b$ lies between the tangent cone and the line $c(t)$ and establishes the assertion.

The proof of the theorem is now immediate. If $B^m$ is smooth then every tangent cone (and limit sphere) is a hyperplane. If $B^m$ is not smooth, there is a point $c(0)$ on $\partial\mathscr{S}$ where the tangent cone is not a hyperplane. Then the limit sphere associated with $c(0)$ and the line from $c(0)$ through the origin is not a hyperplane.

We now turn to a simple but important fact concerning projections.

**Lemma 11–1.** *Let $\mathscr{F}$ be a subset of $B^m$, $b$ a point not in $\mathscr{F}$ and $p$ a projection of $b$ onto $\mathscr{F}$. Then*

(a) *$p$ is a projection onto $\mathscr{F}$ of every point on the segment from $b$ to $p$,*

(b) *if $B^m$ is a Minkowski space, $p$ is the unique projection onto $\mathscr{F}$ of every interior point of this segment.*

*Proof.* Let $c$ be a point in the interior of the line segment from $b$ to $p$. Let $f \in \mathscr{F}$, then we have

$$\|c - p\| = \|b - p\| - \|b - c\|$$

since $b$, $p$ and $c$ are collinear and

$$\|c - f\| \geq \|b - f\| - \|c - b\|$$
$$\geq \|b - p\| - \|c - b\| = \|c - p\|. \quad (11\text{–}4.1)$$

This establishes part $(a)$.

The uniqueness part (b) depends on the

*Assertion. The unit sphere is strictly convex if and only if* $\|b_1 + b_2\| = \|b_1\| + \|b_2\|$ *implies* $b_1 = tb_2$ *for some number* $t$. This is to be established in Problem 11–2. If $B^m$ is strictly convex, equality is possible for the left $\geq$ sign of (11–4.1) only if $c - b = t(c - f)$ or

$$f = b + \left(1 - \frac{1}{t}\right)(c - b).$$

This implies that $f$ is on the line through $b$ and $c$. For points on this line, equality is possible for the right $\geq$ sign of (11–4.1) only if $f = p$ and hence the only point $f$ for which (11–4.1) becomes an equality is the trivial case of $f = p$.

It is very useful to have a measure of the "angle" between two lines. However, it appears difficult to define a concept of angle in Minkowski geometry which has the many properties of angle in Euclidean space. We introduce a much weaker measure of the distance between two lines as follows: Let $l_1$ and $l_2$ intersect at $b_0$ and let $b_i$ be points in $\partial \mathscr{S}(b_0, 1) \cap l_i$ for $i = 1, 2$. If $l_1$ and $l_2$ do not intersect let $d$ be the minimum distance between them and let $l_2'$ be a line parallel to $l_2$ which intersects $l_1$ at a point where the minimum distance $d$ is assumed.

**Definition 11–5.** *The angle between two lines* $l_1$ *and* $l_2$ *which intersect is*

$$\theta(l_1, l_2) = \min\left(\|b_1 - b_2\|\right)$$

*where the minimum is taken over the four ways to choose* $b_1$ *and* $b_2$. *The distance between two lines* $l_1$ *and* $l_2$ *which do not intersect is*

$$\|l_1 - l_2\| = \theta(l_1, l_2) + d.$$

The next lemma establishes some basic properties of angles and triangles. We consider a triangle formed by the three points $b_1$, $b_2$ and $b_3$. The lines defined by the sides of the triangle are denoted by

$$l_{12} = l(b_1, b_2), \quad l_{13} = l(b_1, b_3), \quad l_{23} = l(b_2, b_3).$$

**Lemma 11–2.**

(a) *The angle of Definition* 11–5 *is a metric.*

(b) *Let* $l_{23}$ *be perpendicular to* $l_{12}$, *then*

$$\|b_2 - b_3\| \le \|b_1 - b_3\|\,\theta(l_{12}, l_{13})$$

(c) *Let* $l_{23}$ *be perpendicular to* $l_{12}$, *then there is a constant* $\infty > K > 0$ *so that for* $\theta(l_{12}, l_{13}) \le \frac{1}{2}$

$$\|b_2 - b_3\| \le K\|b_1 - b_2\|\,\theta(l_{12}, l_{13}).$$

(d) *Let* $\mathscr{C}$ *be a closed cone in* $B^m$ *with vertex* $b_1$, *assume* $b_3 \notin \mathscr{C}$ *and* $b_2 \in \mathbf{P}_{\mathscr{C}}(b_3)$. *Then there is an* $0 < \eta < 1$ *so that*

$$\theta(l_{13}, l_{12}) \le \eta\theta\big(l_{13}, l(b_1, b)\big)$$

*for any* $b \in \mathscr{C}$.

(e) *Let* $\|b_1 - b_2\| = \|b_1 - b_3\| = 1$. *Then there is a constant* $\eta > 0$ *so that*

$$\|b_3 - l_{12}\| \ge \eta\theta(l_{12}, l_{13}).$$

*Proof.* (a) It is clear that $\theta(l_1, l_2) = 0$ if and only if $l_1 = l_2$. To verify the triangle inequality let $b_i$ denote generically a point associated with $l_i$ by Definition 11–5. Then we need to verify

$$\min \|b_1 - b_3\| \le \min \|b_1 - b_2\| + \min \|b_2 - b_3\|.$$

Since the unit sphere in $B^m$ is centrally symmetric, we may assume that the points $b_2$ in $\min \|b_1 - b_2\|$ and $\min \|b_2 - b_3\|$ are the same. Let $b_i^*$ denote those points for which this minimum is assumed, $i = 1, 3$. Then

$$\min \|b_1 - b_3\| \le \|b_1^* - b_3^*\| \le \|b_1^* - b_2\| + \|b_2 - b_3^*\|$$

and the triangle inequality is established.

(b) Let

$$b_3' = b_1 + \frac{(b_3 - b_1)}{\|b_3 - b_1\|},$$

$$b_2' = b_1 + \frac{(b_2 - b_1)}{\|b_3 - b_1\|}.$$

Then $b_3' \in \partial\mathscr{S}(b_1, 1)$ and $b_2'$ is the closest point on $l_{12}$ to $b_3'$. Hence

$$\theta(l_{13}, l_{12}) \ge \|b_3' - b_2'\| = \frac{\|b_3 - b_2\|}{\|b_3 - b_1\|}$$

which establishes the inequality.

(c) Write the inequality as

$$\frac{\|b_2 - b_3\|}{\|b_1 - b_2\|} \le K\theta(l_{12}, l_{13})$$

and then normalize the triangle so that $\|b_1 - b_2\| = 1$. The line $l_{13}$ intersects $\partial \mathscr{S}(b_1, 1)$ at a point $b_3'$ and

$$\theta(l_{12}, l_{13}) = \|b_2 - b_3'\|.$$

We now show that there is an $\eta$ so that for $\|b_2 - b_3'\| \leq \frac{1}{2}$

$$\frac{\|b_2 - b_3'\|}{\|b_2 - b_3\|} \geq \eta > 0.$$

Set $b_2' = b_1 + \dfrac{b_2 - b_1}{\|b_1 - b_3\|}$ and then $\|b_2 - b_3\| \leq \|b_2' - b_3\|$ or

$$\frac{\|b_2 - b_3'\|}{\|b_2 - b_3\|} \geq \frac{1}{\|b_1 - b_3\|}.$$

If $\|b_1 - b_3\| < 1$, then $\eta = 1$ suffices. If $\|b_1 - b_3\| \geq 1$, then

$$\frac{1}{\|b_1 - b_3\|} \geq \frac{1}{1 + \|b_2 - b_3'\| + \|b_2 - b_3\|}.$$

For $b_2 \neq b_3$, the number $\|b_2 - b_3'\|/\|b_2 - b_3\|$ is a continuous positive function of $b_2$ and $b_3$. Further

$$\lim_{\|b_2 - b_3\| \to 0} \frac{\|b_2 - b_3'\|}{\|b_2 - b_3\|} = 1$$

and hence $\|b_2 - b_3'\|/\|b_2 - b_3\|$ is a continuous positive function for all $b_2, b_3$ with $\theta(l_{12}, l_{13}) \leq \frac{1}{2}$ in the compact set $\partial \mathscr{S}(b_1, 1)$. Thus it has a positive minimum value which we take for $\eta$. Set $K = 1/\eta$ and the desired inequality is established.

(d) We assume that the triangle is normalized so that $\|b_1 - b_3\| = 1$. Then for $b \in \partial \mathscr{S}(b_1, 1) \cap \mathscr{C}$ we have

$$\theta(l_{13}, l(b_1, b)) = \|b - b_3\| \geq \|b_2 - b_3\|.$$

Since

$$\theta(l_{12}, l_{13}) = \frac{\|(b_1 - b_3)\|b_2 - b_1\| + b_2 - b_1\|}{\|b_2 - b_1\|}$$

we may take

$$\eta = \frac{\|b_2 - b_1\| \|b_2 - b_3\|}{\|(b_1 - b_3)\|b_2 - b_1\| + b_2 - b_1\|} > 0.$$

Simple examples show that one cannot always take $\eta = 1$.

(e) Consider $b_1$ fixed and the function

$$\phi(b_2, b_3) = \frac{\|b_3 - l_{12}\|}{\theta(l_{12}, l_{13})} = \frac{\|b_3 - b_2'\|}{\|b_3 - b_2\|}$$

where $b_2'$ is the closest point in $l_{12}$ to $b_3$. Clearly $\phi \leq 1$ and $\phi > 0$ for $b_2 \neq b_3$. Set

$$b_1' = b_2 + \frac{b_3 - b_2}{\|b_2 - b_2'\|}$$

and note that

$$\|b_1' - b_1\| = \frac{\|b_2' - b_3\|}{\|b_2' - b_2\|}.$$

If $\phi$ tends to zero with $\|b_2 - b_3\|$ then since

$$\|b_2 - b_3\| - \|b_2' - b_3\| \leq \|b_2' - b_2\| \leq \|b_2 - b_3\| + \|b_2' - b_3\|$$

we have that $\|b_1' - b_1\|$ tends to zero. Now $b_1' \in l_{23}$ and hence $b_1'$ tends to the tangent plane of $\partial \mathscr{S}(b_1, 1)$ at $b_3$. This implies that the center of this sphere is in a tangent plane of the sphere, which is contradictory. Hence $\phi(b_2, b_3)$ is bounded from zero as $\|b_2 - b_3\|$ tends to zero and $\phi(b_2, b_3)$ is then a positive continuous function for $b_2, b_3$ in the compact set $\partial \mathscr{S}(b_1, 1)$. We take $\eta$ to be the minimum value of $\phi$ and the proof is complete.

We now turn to the consideration of geometrical properties of submanifolds of $B^m$. The main objectives are (a) to define smoothness properties of a manifold in terms of tangent planes and (b) to define some useful concept of the curvature of submanifolds. The second objective is considered in a later section.

While the idea of the tangent space of a manifold at a point is standard in differential geometry, it is remarkable that a metric is normally considered in tangent space only when $B^m$ happens to be a Hilbert space. It is intuitively clear that the restriction of $B^m$ to be a Hilbert space is unnecessary and we show one way in which the metric of $B^m$ naturally induces a metric in the tangent space, and thus the tangent space can be identified as a hyperplane (the tangent hyperplane) in $B^m$. This procedure further induces a natural set of local coordinate neighborhoods in a manifold.

Let $l(b_1, b_2)$ be the line through the points $b_1$ and $b_2$. We have

**Definition 11-6.** *The line $l_0$ is a line of support of the set $\mathscr{F}$ at the point $f_0 \in \mathscr{F}$ if there exist sequences $\{a_i\}, \{b_i\} \in \mathscr{F}$ which converge to $f_0$ and such that*

$$l_0 = \lim_{\substack{a_i \to f_0 \\ b_i \to f_0}} l(a_i, b_i). \tag{11-4.2}$$

*The support cone $\mathscr{C}(f_0)$ of $\mathscr{F}$ at $f_0$ is*

$$\mathscr{C}(f_0) = \{l \mid l \text{ is a line of support of } \mathscr{F} \text{ at } f_0\}. \tag{11-4.3}$$

One may verify that a support cone of the unit sphere $\partial \mathscr{S}$ is a tangent cone.

Note that this double limiting process is stronger than usual definitions of this type and immediately implies that the *support cone depends continuously on f* in the following sense: Denote the support cone at $f$ by $\mathscr{C}(f)$. Then given $f \in \mathscr{F}$ and $\epsilon > 0$ there is a $\delta > 0$ so that $\|f - g\| < \delta$ implies that

$$\max_{l \in \mathscr{C}(g)} \quad \min_{k \in \mathscr{C}(f)} \quad \theta(l, k) < \epsilon.$$

**Lemma 11–3.** *The support cone $\mathscr{C}(f_0)$ of $\mathscr{F}$ is a closed, connected set and the dimension of $\mathscr{C}(f_0)$ is greater than or equal to the dimension of $\mathscr{F}$ at $f_0$.*

*Proof.* It is clear that the cone is connected. To show that it is closed let $l$ be a line which is the limit of support rays $\{l_\alpha\}$ in $\mathscr{C}(f_0)$. Then there are sequences $\{a_{\alpha i}\}$, $\{b_{\alpha i}\}$ in $\mathscr{F}$ such that

$$l_\alpha = \lim_{\substack{a_{\alpha i} \to f_0 \\ b_{\alpha i} \to f_0}} l(a_{\alpha i}, b_{\alpha i}).$$

Let $\|l_1 - l_2\|$ be the distance between the lines $l_1$ and $l_2$. Then

$$\|\bar{l} - l(a_{\alpha i}, b_{\alpha i})\| = \theta(\bar{l}, l'(a_{\alpha i}, b_{\alpha i})) + d_{\alpha i}$$
$$\leq \theta(\bar{l}, l_\alpha) + \theta(l_\alpha, l(a_{\alpha i}, b_{\alpha i})) + d_{\alpha i}$$

where $l'(a_{\alpha i}, b_{\alpha i})$ is parallel to $l(a_{\alpha i}, b_{\alpha i})$ and passes through $f_0$ and $d_{\alpha i}$ is the distance of $f_0$ from $l(a_{\alpha i}, b_{\alpha i})$. Thus given $\epsilon > 0$ we can choose $\alpha$ so large that $\theta(\bar{l}, l_\alpha)$ is less than $\epsilon/2$ and, given $\epsilon > 0$ and $\alpha$, we can choose $i$ so large that $d_{\alpha i} < \epsilon/2$ and hence $\bar{l}$ is a support line and in the support cone.

We define dimension by saying that a set $\mathscr{F}$ is of dimension $k$ at a point $f$ if $f$ is in a neighborhood of $\mathscr{F}$ which is homeomorphic to the open unit ball in Euclidean $k$-dimensional space $E^k$. Let $\mathscr{N}$ be a $k$-dimensional neighborhood of $\mathscr{F}$ at $f_0$. The rays $\{e \mid e = \alpha e_0, \alpha = \text{real number}\}$ in $E^k$ are mapped into $\mathscr{N}$. Call the image a curve $\gamma$. Then for each $\gamma$ there is a support ray

$$l_\gamma = \lim_{\substack{f \in \gamma \\ f \to f_0}} l(f, f_0).$$

This set of support rays has dimension $k$ and hence $\mathscr{C}(f_0)$ has dimension at least $k$.

We recall the notation $\mathscr{S}(b, \rho)$ for the sphere with center $b$ and radius $\rho$.

**Theorem 11–3.** *Let $f_0 \in \mathscr{F} \subset B^m$. Assume that $\mathscr{S}(f_0, \epsilon) \cap \mathscr{F}$ is part of the boundary of a convex set $\mathscr{K}$. Then the support cone of $\mathscr{F}$ at $f_0$ is contained in the tangent cone of $\mathscr{K}$ at $f_0$. If $\partial \mathscr{K}$ and $\mathscr{F}$ have the same dimension, $m - 1$, then the support cone of $\mathscr{F}$ at $f_0$ and the tangent cone of $\mathscr{K}$ at $f_0$ are identical.*

*Proof.* We note that the support cone of $\mathscr{F}$ is contained in the support cone of $\partial \mathscr{K}$.

*Assertion.* The tangent cone of $\mathscr{K}$ at $f_0$ and the support cone of $\partial\mathscr{K}$ at $f_0$ are identical.

It is clear that the tangent cone is contained in the support cone. We say the line $l$ is a line of support of $\mathscr{K}$ at $f_0$ if $f_0 \in l$ and $l$ contains no interior points of $\mathscr{K}$. The tangent cone is the union of the line of support of $\mathscr{K}$ at $f_0$. We now show that a support ray $l$ is a line of support. Clearly $l$ contains $f_0$. Assume that it contains a point $b$ in the interior of $\mathscr{K}$. Then there are lines $l(a_i, b_i)$ with $a_i, b_i \in \partial\mathscr{K}$ which pass as close to $b$ as we please and $b$ is not between $a_i$ and $b_i$. However, a line which intersects the boundary of a convex set at two distinct points cannot intersect the interior of the convex set except possibly between the two points. Thus $l$ is a line of support and the assertion is established and the first part of the theorem follows immediately.

If $\mathscr{F}$ has dimension $m - 1$ at $f_0$, then $\mathscr{F}$ has a neighborhood $\mathscr{N}$ of dimension $m - 1$ containing $f_0$ which lies in $\mathscr{S}(f_0, \epsilon)$. Now $\mathscr{N} \in \partial\mathscr{K}$ and since $\partial\mathscr{K}$ is of dimension $m - 1$, it follows that $\mathscr{N}$ is a neighborhood of $f_0$ in $\partial\mathscr{K}$. Thus $\mathscr{F}$ and $\partial\mathscr{K}$ are identical in some open sphere $\mathscr{S}(f_0, \epsilon_1)$ containing $f_0$ and hence their support cones are identical since they are defined locally. The second part of the theorem now follows from the assertion established above.

This theorem shows that the support cone and the more familiar tangent cone are identical for many sets. However, they are not always identical and the support cone is a more "sensitive" measure of the nature of a set at a given point than the tangent cone. This is illustrated by the following examples.

EXAMPLE 1. The function $y = x^2 \sin (1/x^2)$ has a derivative at $x = 0$ and one would be tempted to say that this means the curve in the plane defined by this function has a unique tangent "plane" at the point $(0, 0)$. The situation is clearer if we consider the curve defined by $y = 2x^2 + x^2 \sin (1/x^2)$. This curve has a unique line (the $x$-axis) of support at $(0, 0)$ which is the tangent cone at $(0, 0)$. One may directly verify that the support cone of this curve at $(0, 0)$ is the entire plane. See Fig. 11–2.

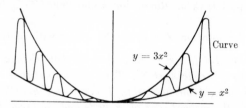

$y = 3x^2$

Curve

$y = x^2$

FIG. 11–2.   The curve defined by $y = x^2(2 + \sin (1/x^2))$.

EXAMPLE 2. We construct a curve in $E^3$ whose support cone is not convex. See Fig. 11–3.

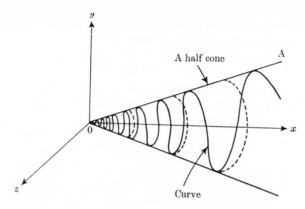

FIG. 11–3. The construction for Example 2.

The curve is the union of the positive $z$-axis and a curve in a half cone with axis along the $x$-axis. The curve in the half cone is the projection of the curve defined by $y = x \sin (1/x)$ in the $xy$-plane. One may verify that the support cone of this curve at $(0, 0, 0)$ contains (a) the $z$-axis, (b) the half cone containing part of the curve, (c) the section of the $xy$-plane from the half cone to the positive and negative $y$-axis and (d) the support cone is three dimensional (i.e. it has some interior points).

Although these pathological examples point up the differences between support cones and tangent cones, it should be kept in mind that we are usually concerned with sets of a much more regular nature. Indeed, we introduce these concepts so that we can precisely state what we mean by the adjective "smooth".

We want to be able to approximate a smooth set $\mathscr{F}$ locally by its support cone and, further, have $\mathscr{F}$'s support cone be of the same nature as $\mathscr{F}$.

**Definition 11–7.** *If $\mathscr{F}$ is $n$-dimensional at $f_0$ then $\mathscr{F}$ is said to be smooth if the support cone of $\mathscr{F}$ at $f_0$ is an $n$-dimensional flat $T$. The flat $T$ is called the tangent plane of $\mathscr{F}$ at $f_0$.*

It seems plausible that the word "flat" is unnecessary in this definition. The dependence of the tangent plane on $f$ is indicated by $T(f)$.

The remark following Definition 11–6 implies that if $\mathscr{F}$ is smooth then *the tangent plane $T(f)$ depends continuously on $f$.*

The next result shows that $\mathscr{F}$ is close to the support cone of $\mathscr{F}$ at a point whether $\mathscr{F}$ is smooth or not.

**Theorem 11–4.** *Let $\mathscr{C}$ be the support cone of $\mathscr{F}$ at $f_0$. Then*

$$\|f - \mathscr{C}\| = o(\|f - f_0\|) \quad \text{as} \quad f \to f_0. \tag{11–4.4}$$

*Proof.* Suppose that the lemma is false. Then there exists a sequence $\{f_i \mid f_i \to f_0\}$ with projections $c_i$ onto $\mathscr{C}$ such that

$$\|f_i - c_i\| \geq \eta \|f_i - f_0\|$$

where $\eta > 0$. Consider the triangle formed by $f_0$, $c_i$ and $f_i$. We have that $l(f_i, c_i) = l_{1i}$ is perpendicular to $l(f_0, c_i) = l_{0i}$ and hence from Lemma 11–2 (b) we have, with $l_{2i} = l(f_i, f_0)$,

$$\|f_i - c_i\| \leq \|f_0 - c_i\| \cdot \theta(l_{2i}, l_{0i})$$

$$\eta \|f_i - f_0\| \leq \|f_i - c_i\| \leq \frac{\|f_0 - f_i\| \cdot \theta(l_{2i}, l_{0i})}{1 - \theta(l_{2i}, l_{0i})} .$$

This implies that

$$0 < \frac{\eta}{1 + \eta} \leq \theta(l_{2i}, l_{0i})$$

and the lines $l_{2i}$ are bounded away from $l_{0i}$.

Since $l_{1i}$ is perpendicular to $l_{0i}$ we may apply Lemma 11–2 (d) which states that there is a $\mu > 0$ so that

$$\theta(l_{2i}, l_{0i}) \leq \mu \theta(l_{2i}, l(f_0, c))$$

for any $c \in \mathscr{C}$. This implies that

$$\theta(l_{2i}, l(f_0, c)) \geq \frac{\eta}{\mu(1 + \eta)} > 0$$

for all $c \in \mathscr{C}$. Thus the limit of any convergent subsequence of $\{l(f_i, f_0)\}$ is not contained in $\mathscr{C}(f_0)$. This contradicts the definition of $\mathscr{C}(f_0)$ and completes the proof.

If $\mathscr{F}$ is smooth at a point $f_0$, then $\mathscr{F}$ is a manifold in a neighborhood of $f_0$. The machinery of classical differential geometry provides us with a *tangent space* of $\mathscr{F}$ at $f_0$. However, this vector space has no metric and it is usual to introduce the Euclidean (or a Riemannian) metric into this space. This is an obviously unsatisfactory metric when considering submanifolds of a general Banach space. We show that this tangent space may be identified with the tangent plane and, since a norm is naturally defined in the tangent plane, this naturally induces a norm into the tangent space. In fact, one motivation of this analysis is to establish this intrinsic norm on the tangent space.

**Theorem 11–5.** *If $\mathscr{F}$ is smooth in a neighborhood of $f_0$, then the tangent space and tangent planes of $\mathscr{F}$ at $f_0$ may be identified.*

There is a variety of ways to define the tangent space of a manifold. We will use the one based on equivalence classes of curves in $\mathscr{F}$ through $f_0$. See, for example, Auslander and MacKensie, 1960.

*Proof.* In a neighborhood of $f_0$, $\mathscr{F}$ is then a differentiable manifold of class $C^1$ (at least).

Let $\Gamma$ be a parametrized curve of class $C^1$ in $F$ through $f_0$, say $\Gamma = \{\gamma(t) | -1 \leq t \leq +1, \gamma(0) = f_0\}$. Now if the sequence of pairs $(a_i, b_i)$ approach $f_0$ along $\Gamma$, then $a_i = \gamma(t_{i1})$, $b_i = \gamma(t_{i2})$ and $t_{i1}, t_{i2}$ tend to zero as $i$ increases. Consider then the vector

$$v_i = \gamma(t_{i1}) - \gamma(t_{i2}).$$

This vector is parallel to the line $l(a_i, b_i)$ and converges to a vector parallel to the support ray defined by the sequence $\{(a_i, b_i)\}$. Since $\Gamma$ is of class $C^1$, the limit direction of $v_i$ is independent of the particular choice of $t_{i1}$ and $t_{i2}$ (except for sign, which may be normalized by taking $t_{i1} < t_{i2}$). Thus there is only one support ray associated with any curve $\Gamma$.

If $\Gamma_1$ and $\Gamma_2$ are in the same equivalence class, then

$$v_{i1} = \gamma_1(t_{i1}) - \gamma_1(t_{i2})$$

and

$$v_{i2} = \gamma_2(t_{i1}) - \gamma_2(t_{i2})$$

converge to the same vector and hence are associated with the same support ray. Indeed, if $\Gamma_1$ is in an equivalence class which is a multiple (in the obvious sense) of the equivalence class of $\Gamma_2$, then these two sequences of vectors become, in the limit, parallel to the same support ray.

Thus, we may choose $f_0$ as the origin of a vector space in the tangent plane and the resulting vector space is identified with the equivalence classes of curves in $\mathscr{F}$ through $f_0$. This concludes the proof.

From this point on we cease to differentiate between the tangent space and the tangent plane.

The primary use of the tangent plane of $\mathscr{F}$ is as a "local approximation" to $\mathscr{F}$ if $\mathscr{F}$ is smooth. The next lemma establishes a fundamental property of the tangent plane in this respect.

**Lemma 11-4.** *In the Minkowski space $B^m$ let $\mathscr{F}$ be smooth at $f$ and $l$ be a line through $f$ in the tangent plane $T(f)$ of $\mathscr{F}$ at $f$. Then, for $b \in l$, we have*

$$\|b - \mathscr{F}\| = o(\|b - f\|) \tag{11-4.5}$$

*as $b$ tends to $f$.*

*Proof.* Suppose that the result is false. Then there is a sequence $\{b_i \mid b_i \in l, b_i \to f\}$ and an $\eta > 0$ so that

$$\|b_i - \mathscr{F}\| \geq \eta \|b_i - f\|.$$

Consider a point $g \in \partial \mathscr{S}(f, \|b_i - f\|) \cap \mathscr{F}$. We have that

$$\|b_i - g\| \geq \eta \|b_i - f\|, \quad \theta(l, l(f, g)) = \frac{\|b_i - g\|}{\|b_i - f\|} \geq \eta > 0.$$

Now since $\mathscr{F}$ is smooth, the tangent plane $T(f)$ is the union of all lines

$$\lim_{\|b_i - f\| \to 0} l(f, g)$$

for all such $g$. This implies that $l \notin T(f)$ which is contradictory and establishes the result.

Examples show that this result is not always valid if $\mathscr{F}$ is not smooth at $f$.

**Corollary.** *Let $\mathscr{F}$ be a smooth subset of the Minkowski space $B^m$ and let $G$ be a compact subset of $\mathscr{F}$. Then, with the notation of Theorems 11–4 and Lemma 11–4,*

$$\|b - \mathscr{F}\| = o(\|b - f\|),$$
$$\|g - T(f)\| = o(\|g - f\|)$$

*uniformly in $G$.*

*Proof.* We consider the second relation only, the first follows in a similar manner. Let $\phi(f, \delta)$ denote the maximum angle $\theta\big(l(f, b), l(f, g)\big)$ for $b \in T(f)$ and $g \in \mathscr{F}$ and $\|f - g\| \leq \delta$. We extend the definition to $\delta = 0$ by continuity, i.e. $\phi(f, 0) = 0$. Since $\mathscr{F}$ is smooth the tangent plane $T(f)$ depends continuously on $f$ and thus $\phi(f, \delta)$ is a continuous function of the variables $f$ and $\delta$ defined on the compact product space of $G$ and $[0, 1]$. Hence $\phi(f, \delta)$ is uniformly continuous and given $\epsilon > 0$ there is an $\eta > 0$ so that $\delta < \eta$ implies that $|\phi(f, \delta) - \phi(f, 0)| = \phi(f, \delta) < \epsilon$. Since

$$\|g - T(f)\| \leq \|g - f\| \phi(f, \delta)$$

the result is established.

The following technical result is required later. Let $\mathscr{S} = \mathscr{S}(b, 1)$ and let $H$ be a hyperplane of support of $\bar{\mathscr{S}}$ at $f \in \partial \mathscr{S}$. For any flat $T$ which contains $f$ set

$$\theta(T) = \max_{t \in T} \min_{h \in H} \theta\big(l(f, t), l(f, h)\big).$$

This might be interpreted as the "angle" from $T$ to $H$.

**Lemma 11–5.** *Let $B^m$ be a smooth Minkowski space. If $\theta(T) > 0$ then there is a $t^* \in T$ with $\|f - t^*\| = 1$ and a $\lambda_0 > 0$ (independent of $f$) so that for $0 < \lambda < \lambda_0$,*

$$f + \lambda(t^* - f) \in \mathscr{S}(b, 1).$$

*Proof.* Choose $t^* \in T$ and $h^* \in H$ of norm one so that

$$\theta(T) = \theta\big(l(f, t^*), l(f, h^*)\big).$$

The choice of $t^*$ is not unique and we choose $t^*$ so that $t^*$ is on the same side of $H$ as $b$. There is a $\lambda_1 > 0$ so that for $\lambda \leq \lambda_1$ the line through $f + \lambda(t^* - f)$ perpendicular to $H$ intersects $\partial \mathscr{S}$ in two points. Let $g(\lambda)$ denote the one closest to $H$, i.e. $l(f + \lambda(t^* - f), g(\lambda)) \perp H$.

From Lemma 11–2 we have an $\eta > 0$ so that

$$\| f + \lambda(t^* - f) - H \| \geq \eta \lambda \theta(T)$$

and from Theorem 11–4 we have

$$\| g(\lambda) - H \| = o(\| g(\lambda) - f \|).$$

Given $\epsilon > 0$ there is a $\delta(\epsilon) > 0$ so that for $\| g(\lambda) - f \| < \delta(\epsilon)$ we have

$$o(\| g(\lambda) - f \|) \leq \epsilon \| g(\lambda) - f \|.$$

Thus for $\| g(\lambda) - f \| < \delta(\epsilon)$ we have

$$\| g(\lambda) - H \| \leq \epsilon [\| h(\lambda) - f \| + \| g(\lambda) - H \|]$$

where $h(\lambda) = l(f + \lambda(t^* - f), g(\lambda)) \cap H$. It is seen that

$$\| h(\lambda) - f \| \leq \lambda(1 + \eta \theta(T))$$

and if we take

$$\epsilon_0 = \frac{\eta \theta(T)}{2 + (\eta + 2)\theta(T)}$$

then for $\| g(\lambda) - f \| \leq \delta(\epsilon_0)$ we have

$$\| g(\lambda) - H \| \leq \frac{\eta \lambda \theta(T)}{2}.$$

It is clear that $\| g(\lambda) - f \|$ tends to zero as $\lambda$ tends to zero. Thus given $\delta > 0$ there is a $\lambda(\delta) > 0$ so that $\lambda \leq \lambda(\delta)$ implies that $\| g(\lambda) - f \| \leq \delta$. Take $\lambda_0 = \lambda(\delta(\epsilon_0))$ and then for $0 < \lambda < \lambda_0$

$$\| g(\lambda) - H \| \leq \frac{\lambda \eta \theta(T)}{2} < \| f + \lambda(t^* - f) - H \|$$

and hence $f + \lambda(t^* - f) \in \mathscr{S}$. This concludes the proof.

The next theorem establishes the intuitively desirable result that projections on a smooth manifold are also projections onto the tangent plane of the manifold.

**Theorem 11–6.** *Let $\mathscr{F}$ be smooth at $f$ and let $f$ be the projection of a point $b$ onto $\mathscr{F}$. Then the line $l(b, f)$ through $f$ and $b$ is perpendicular on the tangent plane $T$ of $\mathscr{F}$ at $f$.*

*Proof.* Assume that $f$ is not a projection of $b$ onto $T$. Let $t$ be such a projection and consider the situation (shown in Fig. 11–4) in the 2-dimensional

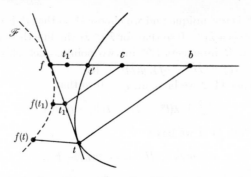

FIG. 11–4.  The construction for Theorem 11–6.

plane determined by the lines $l(b, f)$ and $l(t, f)$. The points $f(t)$ and $f(t_1)$ are the projections onto $\mathscr{F}$ of the points $t$ and $t_1$. It is possible that $f(t)$ and $f(t_1)$ do not lie in this plane. The point $c$ is between $b$ and $f$ and $t_1$ is the projection of $c$ onto $T$ corresponding to the projection $t$ of $b$ onto $T$. Note that if $B^m$ is not strictly convex, then $t$ and $t_1$ might not be uniquely determined. However, once $t$ is chosen, we may choose $t_1$ so that

$$\frac{\|t_1 - f\|}{\|c - f\|} = \frac{\|t - f\|}{\|b - f\|}.$$

The points $t'$ and $t_1'$ are determined on the line $l(f, b)$ by

$$\|b - t'\| = \|b - t\|, \quad \|c - t_1'\| = \|c - t_1\|$$

and they are between $b$ and $f$. From the triangle inequality and Lemma 11–4 we have

$$\frac{\|c - f(t_1)\|}{\|c - t_1\|} \leq 1 + \frac{o(\|f - t_1\|)}{\|c - t_1\|} .$$

We have from our assumption and Lemma 11–1 that

$$\frac{\|c - f(t_1)\|}{\|c - t_1\|} \geq \frac{\|c - f\|}{\|c - t_1\|} = 1 + \frac{\|f - t_1'\|}{\|c - t_1\|} .$$

We also note that, since we assume that $\|f - t'\| > 0$,

$$\|f - t_1\| = \|f - t_1'\| \, \|f - t\| / \|f - t'\|.$$

These three relations may be combined to give

$$1 + \frac{o(f - t_1'\|)}{\|c - t_1\|} > 1 + \frac{\|f - t_1'\|}{\|c - t_1\|}$$

as $c$ tends to $f$. This is a contradiction and concludes the proof.

The following result is to be established in Problem 11–3.

**Lemma 11–6.** *Let $\mathscr{P}$ be a k-dimensional flat in the Minkowski space $B^m$. Then every point $b \in B^m$ has a unique representation*

$$b = p + p^{\perp} \qquad (11\text{–}4.6)$$

*where $p \in \mathscr{P}$ and the line containing $p^{\perp}$ is perpendicular to $\mathscr{P}$.*

We are now able to define the *normal* of $\mathscr{F}$ at a point $f_0$.

**Definition 11–8.** *Let $T$ be the tangent plane of $\mathscr{F}$ at $f_0$. If the line $l$ described by $f_0 + \alpha b$, $-\infty < \alpha < \infty$ is perpendicular to $T$, then $b$ is said to be a normal to $\mathscr{F}$ at $f_0$ and $l$ is a normal line. The set of normals to $\mathscr{F}$ at $f_0$ is called the normal set of $\mathscr{F}$ at $f_0$. A normal ray is a semi-infinite segment of a normal line bounded by $f_0$.*

Note that if $\mathscr{F}$ is smooth then the tangent plane and normal set of $\mathscr{F}$ at $f$ depend continuously on $f$. Simple examples of $B^3$ show that the normal set need not be a flat. We have the following simple properties of normals.

**Lemma 11–7.** *Let $T$ be a subspace of a strictly convex $B^m$ and $N(t)$ be the normal set of $T$ at $t$. Then $N(t) = N(0) + t$. If $T$ is a line, then $N(0)$ separates $B^m$ into arcwise connected sets.*

*Proof.* The first conclusion that $N(t) = N(0) + t$ follows directly from the fact that the geometry is invariant under translation.

If $T$ is a line, it is separated into two parts by the origin. Call one the positive part and the other negative. Then $N(0)$ separates $B^m$ into two parts, one whose projections on $T$ are positive and one whose projections are negative. Since the projection onto a straight line is continuous in a strictly convex space, it follows that any arc joining points from the different parts of $B^m$ must contain a point whose projection on $T$ is the origin.

If $b_1$ and $b_2$ have positive projections $t_1$ and $t_2$, then the arc composed of the line segments from $b_1$ to $t_1$, $t_1$ to $t_2$ and $t_2$ to $b_2$ connects $b_1$ and $b_2$ and does not intersect $\mathscr{N}(0)$.

Let $T_i$ and $U$ be subspaces of $B^m$.

**Lemma 11–8.** *Assume that*

$$\lim_{i \to \infty} T_i = U$$

*and $\{l_i\}$ is a sequence of lines with $l_i \perp T_i$. If $l$ is any limiting line of $\{l_i\}$ then $l \perp U$.*

*Proof.* We may assume that the $l_i$ pass through the origin $O$ of $B^m$ since perpendicularity is unaffected by translation. Given $l$, take $\{l_i\}$ to be a convergent subsequence with limit $l$ and choose points $b \in l$, $b_i \in l_i$ with $\|b\| = \|b_i\| = 1$ and $b_i \to b$. Suppose that for

$$u \in \mathbf{P}_U(b)$$

we have $\|u - b\| < 1$. Denote by $t_i$ points in $T_i$ closest to $u$ with $\|t_i\| = \|u\|$. Then

$$\|b_i - t_i\| \le \|b_i - b\| + \|b - u\| + \|u - t_i\|.$$

Now $\|t_i - u\|$ tends to zero since $T_i$ tends to $U$ and

$$\|b_i - t_i\| \le \|b - u\| + o(1).$$

For $i$ sufficiently large this contradicts $l_i \perp T_i$ and establishes the lemma.


### 11-5  CURVATURE IN MINKOWSKI GEOMETRY

We are concerned with determining conditions under which a point $b \in B^m$ has a unique projection on a manifold $\mathscr{F}$. The following simple examples show that smoothness of $\mathscr{F}$ is not sufficient for this even if $b$ is arbitrarily close to $\mathscr{F}$.

EXAMPLE 1.  Take for $\mathscr{F}$ the curve in $E^2$ defined by $y = |x|^{3/2}$. Then the points $b = (0, \alpha)$ have two projections onto $\mathscr{F}$ for all positive $\alpha$.

EXAMPLE 2.  Take for $\mathscr{F}$ the curve in two-dimensional $L_p$-space, $p > 2$, defined by $x^2 + y^2 = 1$, i.e. a Euclidean circle. Then the points $b = (0, \alpha)$ and $(\beta, 0)$ have two projections onto $\mathscr{F}$ for all $\alpha$, $\beta$ satisfying $0 < \alpha, \beta < 1$.

These two examples show two important facts. First, smoothness, as defined so far, is not sufficient to imply that projections are unique, even locally. Secondly, the conditions for unique projection depend essentially on the nature of the space $B^m$. That is to say, the uniqueness of projections depends on curvature and the measure of curvature depends intrinsically on the nature of the unit sphere in $B^m$.

Attempts to define an adequate concept of curvature in non-Riemannian (i.e. non-Hilbert) spaces have not been particularly successful. As pointed out by Buseman, 1955, the reason for this is simple: curvature plays many roles in Riemannian spaces and it is unreasonable to expect that there is a single concept or measure which plays all of these roles in a more general context. Thus, the object should be to isolate the essentially distinct roles played by curvature and study them separately. This is done by Buseman to a certain extent, but, since he was not studying problems of projection so extensively, his results do not appear to be applicable in the present context. The definition of curvature in this section is due to Rice, 1967.

We are interested in measuring how "fast" $\mathscr{F}$ is bending *relative to the unit sphere*. Consider, for the moment, a one-dimensional submanifold $\mathscr{F}$ of a strictly convex $B^2$. Given three distinct points which are not collinear, then there is a unique circle (a circle is the boundary of a ball in $B^2$) which passes through them. Thus we can imitate the classical intrinsic definition of curvature in this situation. Let $f \in \mathscr{F}$ and $g_1, g_2, g_3 \in \mathscr{F}$ and denote by

$\mathscr{C}(g_1, g_2, g_3)$ the circle which passes through $g_1, g_2, g_3$ and let $\rho(\mathscr{C})$ be its radius. Then we have

**Definition 11–9.** *Let $B^2$ be a Minkowski space. The curve $\mathscr{F} \subset B^2$ is said to have radius of curvature $\rho^*$ at $f \in \mathscr{F}$ if*

$$\rho^* = \lim_{g_1, g_2, g_3 \to f} \rho[\mathscr{C}(g_1, g_2, g_3)]. \qquad (11\text{–}5.1)$$

*The curvature of $\mathscr{F}$ at $f$ is $1/\rho^*$.*

Note that according to this definition the curves in Examples 1 and 2 have infinite curvature at certain points.

We remark that this definition involves the intrinsic nature of $B^2$ much more deeply than does that of the tangent plane. Indeed, $\mathscr{F}$ has its tangent plane induced almost independently of the norm of $B^m$. It is of great interest to relate the behavior of the tangent plane along $\Gamma$ with the curvature of $\Gamma$. Both of the preceding examples show situations where the tangent plane varies smoothly (continuously) at points of $\mathscr{F}$ with infinite curvature.

Since we have a reasonable measure of curvature for curves in a plane, it is natural to attempt to use this measure in a more general situation by means of cross sections. One might try cross sections determined by a plane spanned by a tangent line and a normal line. However, such planes may well fail to intersect $\mathscr{F}$ in a curve and hence make the construction inapplicable.

We can obtain a measure of the bending of $\mathscr{F}$ in a general smooth strictly convex $B^m$ as follows. Let $\mathscr{F}$ be smooth at $f_0$ and denote by $T$ the tangent plane of $\mathscr{F}$ at $f_0$. Let $n$ be in the normal set of $\mathscr{F}$ at $f_0$ and consider a sphere $\partial \mathscr{S}(b, r)$ with center $b$ on the line defined by $n$. We assume that $f_0 \in \partial \mathscr{S}$ and hence $r = \|b - f_0\|$ and we denote by $\mathscr{H}$ the plane of support of $\partial \mathscr{S}$ at $f_0$.

Given a point $f \in \mathscr{F}$ near to $f_0$, we wish to associate a radius $r$ for the sphere $\partial \mathscr{S}$. We may do this by associating with $f$ a point $s$ and require that $\partial \mathscr{S}$ contain $s$, which then determines $r$. There are at least three ways to do this.

(a) choose $s \in \partial \mathscr{S}$ on the line through $f$ parallel to $n$;
(b) choose $s \in \partial \mathscr{S}$ so as to have the same projection on $\mathscr{H}$ as $f$ has on $T$;
(c) choose $s = f$.

A little reflection shows that, for well behaved cases, these choices lead to the same results. Thus a choice may be made either on the basis of aesthetic appeal or on the basis of technical simplicity. We choose the third possibility.

In general, different choices of $f$ lead to different values of $r$, even if one only considers the limiting case as $f$ approaches $f_0$. Since we are primarily concerned with bounding the "bending" of $\mathscr{F}$, we single out those $f$ which give the smaller limiting values for $r$.

**Definition 11–10.**  *The radius of curvature of $\mathscr{F}$ at $f$ in the direction $r(f, b)$ is $\rho(f, r)$ if (a) for every sequence $\{f_i\}$ such that $f_i \to f$ we have*

$$\liminf_{f_i \to f} \rho_i \geq \rho(f, r) \tag{11–5.2}$$

*and (b) for some sequence $\{f_i\}$ such that $f_i \to f$ we have*

$$\lim_{f_i \to f} \rho_i = \rho(f, r). \tag{11–5.3}$$

*If no interpolating sequence $\{f_i\}$ exists then $\rho(f, r) = \infty$. The curvature $\sigma(f, r)$ of $\mathscr{F}$ at $f$ in the normal direction $r(f, b)$ is $1/\rho(f, r)$. The curvature of $\mathscr{F}$ at $f$ is*

$$\sigma(f) = \max_r \rho(f, r)$$

*for all rays $r$ in the normal set of $\mathscr{F}$ at $f$.*

The example of Riemannian geometry leads us to expect that if $\mathscr{F}$ has bounded curvature at $f_0$, then $\mathscr{F}$ makes second order contact with its tangent plane $T$ at $f_0$. It is seen from Lemma 11–4 and Theorem 11–4 that if $\mathscr{F}$ is smooth, then $\mathscr{F}$ makes first order contact with $T$. The property of second order contact does not hold in a general $B^m$ as can be seen by setting $\mathscr{F} = \partial \mathscr{S}((0, 2), 1)$ in two-dimensional $L_p$-space. Then $\mathscr{F}$ has curvature equal to one at every point and the order of contact of $\mathscr{F}$ with the horizontal $t$-axis is $t^p$ for $1 < p < \infty$.

In order to investigate the order of contact of $\mathscr{F}$ with its tangent plane we relate it to the order of contact of a unit sphere $\partial \mathscr{S}_1$ with one of its planes of support, $\mathscr{H}$, at $f_0$. Specifically, let $l$ be a line in $\mathscr{H}$ through $f_0$ and let $s \in \mathscr{S}_1$ have projection $t$ onto $\mathscr{H}$ with $t \in l$. Then the function

$$h_1(t) = \|s(t) - \mathscr{H}\|$$

measures the height of $\partial \mathscr{S}_1$ above $\mathscr{H}$ and we may consider $t$ to be a single real variable. Consider another sphere $\partial \mathscr{S}_\rho$ of radius $\rho$, and with $\mathscr{H}$ as a plane of support at $f_0$. Let $h_\rho(t)$ denote the corresponding height function for a point in $\partial \mathscr{S}_\rho$. We see that

$$h_\rho(t) = \rho h_1(t/\rho). \tag{11–5.4}$$

Let $\mathscr{F}$ have curvature $\sigma(f, r) < \infty$ at $f_0$ in the normal direction $r(f, b)$.

Then, by definition, for a sequence $f_i$

$$\lim_{f_i \to f_0} 1/\rho_i \leq \sigma(f, r)$$

and, for some sequence $\{f_i\}$,

$$\rho_i = (1 + o(1))\rho(f, r) \tag{11–5.5}$$

as $f_i$ tends to $f_0$.

**Theorem 11–7.**   *Let $\{f_i\}$ be a sequence such that (11–5.5) holds. If*

$$\lim_{t \to 0} \frac{h_1[t(1 + o(1))]}{h_1(t)} = 1, \tag{11–5.6}$$

*then*

$$\|f_i - \mathscr{H}\| = \|s_i - \mathscr{H}\| + o(\|s_i - \mathscr{H}\|) \tag{11–5.7}$$

*where $s_i$ is the point in $\partial \mathscr{S}\big(b, \rho(f, r)\big)$ on the line parallel to $l(f, b)$ passing through $f_i$.*

The situation is illustrated in Fig. 11–5.

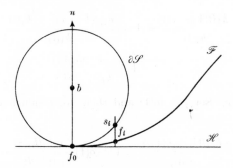

Fig. 11–5.   The situation in Theorem 11–7.

*Proof.*   Since (11–5.5) holds the distance of $f_i$ from $\mathscr{H}$ is, with $\rho = \rho(f, r)$,

$$h_{\rho_i}(t) = \frac{\rho}{1 + o(1)} h_1\left[\frac{t}{\rho}(1 + o(1))\right] = \|f_i - \mathscr{H}\|$$

$$= \rho h_1\left[\frac{t}{\rho}(1 + o(1))\right] - o(1)\rho h_1\left[\frac{t}{\rho}(1 + o(1))\right]$$

$$= h_\rho(t) \frac{h_1\left[\frac{t}{\rho}(1 + o(1))\right]}{h_1(t/\rho)} + h_\rho(t)\left(o(1) \frac{h_1\left[\frac{t}{\rho}(1 + o(1))\right]}{h_1(t/\rho)}\right).$$

It follows from the hypothesis (11–5.6) that

$$h_{\rho_i}(t) = h_\rho(t)[1 + o(1)]$$

or, equivalently,

$$\|f_i - \mathscr{H}\| = \|s_i - \mathscr{H}\| + o(\|s_i - \mathscr{H}\|).$$

**Corollary 1.**   *If (11–5.6) holds and $\{f_i\}$ is any sequence which tends to $f$, then*

$$\|f_i - \mathscr{H}\| \le \|s_i - \mathscr{H}\| + o(\|s_i - \mathscr{H}\|)$$

*with the terminology of Theorem 11–7.*

**Corollary 2.** *If $h_1(t)$ is continuously differentiable and there is a constant $M < \infty$ so that*

$$\frac{1}{h_1(t)} \frac{dh_1(t)}{dt} \leq \frac{M}{t} \tag{11–5.8}$$

*holds for all $t > 0$, then*

$$\|f_i - \mathscr{H}\| \leq \|s_i - \mathscr{H}\| + o(\|s_i - \mathscr{H}\|)$$

*and equality holds for a sequence $\{f_i\}$ for which (11–5.5) is valid.*

*Proof.* We note that

$$\frac{h_1\big(t(1 + \epsilon)\big)}{h_1(t)} = 1 + \frac{h_1[t(1 + \epsilon)] - h_1(t)}{h_1(t)}$$

$$= 1 + \frac{\epsilon}{h_1(t)} \frac{dh_1(\xi)}{dt}$$

where $|\xi - t| < \epsilon$. Set $\epsilon = to(1)$ and then, for $t$ sufficiently small, $\xi > 0$ and we have

$$\frac{h_1\big(t(1 + o(1))\big)}{h_1(t)} = 1 + o(1) \frac{t}{h_1(t)} \frac{dh_1(\xi)}{dt}$$

which, if (11–5.8) holds, tends to 1 as $t$ tends to zero. Thus (11–5.8) implies (11–5.6) and the corollary is established.

**Corollary 3.** *In every finite dimensional $L_p$-space, $1 < p < \infty$,*

$$\|f_i - \mathscr{H}\| \leq \|s_i - \mathscr{H}\| + o(\|s_i - \mathscr{H}\|)$$

*and equality holds for a sequence $\{f_i\}$ for which (11–5.5) is valid.*

The following example shows that there are situations where $\mathscr{F}$ has curvature $\rho < \infty$ at a point $f_0$ and yet the order of contact of $\mathscr{F}$ with its tangent plane $T$ is different from that which the sphere of curvature makes with its plane of support. It appears that this can only occur in spaces where the unit sphere has extremely high order contact with some of its hyperplane of support. This seems to be implied by Corollary 2 of the preceding theorem.

**EXAMPLE 3.** Consider two-dimensional space $B^2$ where the circle $\partial \mathscr{S}[(0, 1), 1]$ is explicitly given by

$$h(t) = e^{-1/|t|^p}$$

for $t \leq t_0$. It is clear that such spaces exist which are strictly convex. The set $\mathscr{F}$ is the curve defined by

$$f(t) = \big(1 + \epsilon(t)\big)e^{-\frac{[1 + \epsilon(t)]^p}{|t|^p}}$$

where

$$\lim_{t \to 0} \epsilon(t) = 0.$$

The curvature of $\mathscr{F}$ is 1 at the point $(0, 0)$ since the circle

$$\partial \mathscr{S}[(0, 1 + \epsilon(t)), 1 + \epsilon(t)]$$

interpolates $\mathscr{F}$ at $f(t)$. We compute that

$$\frac{\|f(t) - \mathscr{H}\|}{\|s(t) - \mathscr{H}\|} = [1 + \epsilon(t)]e^{-\frac{[1+\epsilon(t)]^p - 1}{|t|^p}}$$

$$= [1 + \epsilon(t)]e^{-\frac{p\epsilon(t) + o(\epsilon^2(t))}{|t|^p}}.$$

Hence, if $\epsilon(t) = |t|^q$, $q < p$, then

$$\lim_{t \to 0} \frac{\|f(t) - \mathscr{H}\|}{\|s(t) - \mathscr{H}\|} = 0.$$

If $q > p$, then

$$\lim_{t \to 0} \frac{\|f(t) - \mathscr{H}\|}{\|s(t) - \mathscr{H}\|} = 1$$

and if $\epsilon(t) = -|t|^q$, $q < p$ then

$$\lim_{t \to 0} \frac{\|f(t) - \mathscr{H}\|}{\|s(t) - \mathscr{H}\|} = \infty.$$

The relations between the orders of contact expressed in Theorem 11–7 and its corollaries may be expressed in terms of derivatives if $\mathscr{F}$ and $\partial \mathscr{S}$ are sufficiently differentiable near $f_0$. Consider that the origin of a coordinate system in $B^m$ is taken to be $f_0$ and that the normal direction $n$ is one coordinate axis and the remaining ones are contained in $\mathscr{H}$. Thus the function $h_\rho(t)$ which describes $\partial \mathscr{S}$ is of the form

$$h_\rho(t) = b_m(b_1, b_2, \ldots, b_{m-1}), \qquad t = (b_1, b_2, \ldots, b_{m-1}),$$

and may be expanded as follows

$$h_\rho(t) = h_\rho(0) + \sum_{i=1}^{m-1} b_i \left( \frac{\partial h\rho(0)}{\partial b_i} + \sum_{j=1}^{m-1} b_j \left( \frac{\partial^2 h_\rho(0)}{\partial b_i \partial b_j} + \sum_{k=1}^{m-1} \cdots \right) \right) \qquad (11\text{–}5.9)$$

It is clear that $h_\rho(0) = 0$ and, if $B^m$ is smooth, then

$$\frac{\partial h_\rho(0)}{\partial b_i} = 0, \qquad i = 1, 2, \ldots, m - 1.$$

It is not so clear that one is justified, in general, to make assumptions about the higher derivatives. The examples of $L_p$-space, $1 < p < \infty$, show that there are situations where (a) the second derivatives are infinite and (b) all derivatives up to order $p - 1$ are zero.

Note that the point $s$ in (11–5.7) varies only on an $n$-dimensional subset of $\partial \mathscr{S}$. Thus in order to actually equate coefficients in a Taylor's expansion, one must express $s(t)$ as a function of the same $n$ variables which are used to express $f(t)$ in functional form. Once this is done, then the usual relationship exists between the derivatives of $s(t)$ and $f(t)$ with respect to $t = (t_1, t_2, \ldots, t_n)$.

It is not clear that the approach that we take is the correct one. We intend to say something about the uniqueness of projections in terms of curvature as defined above. However, there are intuitive reasons to believe that we are discussing something (projections and their uniqueness) which is very intrinsic and natural in terms of something (curvature) which is somewhat less intrinsic. Thus a more correct approach may well be to define curvature in terms of the uniqueness of projections. We consider two related concepts, the $\alpha$-*hull* (Efimov and Steckin, 1959) and the *reach* (Federer, 1959, for Euclidean space) of a set, which one might use to carry out this alternative approach. We have

**Definition 11–11.** *The $\alpha$-hull of the set $\mathscr{F}$ is the complement of the set*

$$\cup \{\mathscr{S} \mid \mathscr{S} = \text{ball of radius } \alpha \text{ and } \mathscr{S} \cap \mathscr{F} \text{ is empty}\}. \qquad (11\text{–}5.10)$$

*The set $\mathscr{F}$ is said to be $\alpha$-convex if $\mathscr{F}$ is the $\alpha$-hull of itself.*

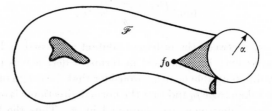

Fig. 11–6.  A set $\mathscr{F}$ in $E_2$ and its $\alpha$-hull. This set is not $\alpha$-convex for any $\alpha$ due to its nature at $f_0$.

The $\alpha$-hull of a set $\mathscr{F}$ may alternatively be defined in terms of spheres of support of radius $\alpha$. A sphere $\partial \mathscr{S}(b, \alpha)$ is said to be a *sphere of support* of $\mathscr{F}$ if $\mathscr{F}$ contains no interior point of $\mathscr{S}(b, \alpha)$ and if $\mathscr{F} \cap \partial \mathscr{S}(b, \alpha)$ is not empty. Then the boundary of the $\alpha$-hull of $\mathscr{F}$ is defined by the spheres of support of $\mathscr{F}$ of radius $\alpha$. The $\alpha$-hull concept seems to be most useful for the study of $m$- or $(m - 1)$-dimensional sets in $B^m$. Simple examples show that a lower dimensional set in $B^m$ may be $\alpha$-convex for all $\alpha < \infty$ and yet not be smooth or regular in any intuitive sense. Thus the two-dimensional set shown in Fig. 11–6 is $\alpha$-convex for all $\alpha < \infty$ in $E^3$.

Some properties of the $\alpha$-hull of a set which follow directly from the definition are given in Problem 11–4.

The curvature of $\mathscr{F}$ and the radii of the spheres of support of $\mathscr{F}$ can be related in the following manner.

**Theorem 11–8.** *Let $B^m$ be a Minkowski space and let $\mathscr{F} \subset B^m$ have bounded curvature. The sphere $\partial \mathscr{S}(b, \|b - f\|)$ is a sphere of support of $\mathscr{F}$ at $f$ only if $r(f, b)$ is a normal ray and $\|b - f\| \leq \rho(f, r)$. If $r(f, b)$ is a normal ray and $\|b - f\| < \rho(f, r)$ then there is an $\epsilon > 0$ such that $\partial \mathscr{S}(b, \|b - f\|)$ is a sphere of support of $\mathscr{F} \cap \mathscr{S}(f, \epsilon)$ at $f$.*

*Proof.* It is clear that $r(f, b)$ is a normal ray if $\partial \mathscr{S}(b, \|b - f\|)$ is a sphere of support at $f$. Every sphere $\partial \mathscr{S}(b', \|b' - f\|)$ with $b' \in r(f, b)$ and $\|b' - f\| < \|b - f\|$ is in $\mathscr{S}(b, \|b - f\|)$ except for the point $f$. From Definition 11–10 we have a sequence $\{f_i\} \subset (F)$ and associated $b_i \in r(f, b)$, $\rho_i = \|b_i - f\|$ so that $f_i \in \partial \mathscr{S}(b_i, \rho_i)$ and

$$\lim_{f_i \to f} \rho_i = \rho(f, r).$$

Hence if $\|b - f\| < \rho(f, r)$ then for $i$ sufficiently large $\mathscr{S}(b, \|b - f\|)$ contains every point $f_i$ and $\partial \mathscr{S}(b, \|b - f\|)$ is not a sphere of support of $\mathscr{F}$ at $f$. This is contradictory and establishes the first statement of the theorem.

Assume that $\|b - f\| < \rho(f, r)$ and $r(f, b)$ is a normal ray of $\mathscr{F}$ at $f$. Suppose $\partial \mathscr{S}(b, \|b - f\|)$ is not a sphere of support of $\mathscr{F} \cap \mathscr{S}(f, 1/i)$ for infinitely many $i$. Then for each of these $i$, $\mathscr{S}(b, \|b - f\|)$ contains a point $f_i \in \mathscr{F}$ with $\|f_i - f\| < 1/i$. Consider the spheres $\partial \mathscr{S}(b_i, \rho_i)$, $b_i \in r(f, b)$, $\rho_i = \|b_i - f\|$ which contain $f_i$. Clearly $\rho_i < \|b - f\|$. The sequence $\{f_i\}$ satisfies the requirements of Definition 11–10 and hence

$$\rho(f, r) \leq \liminf_{f_i \to f} \rho_i \leq \|b - f\|.$$

This contradicts $\|b - f\| < \rho(f, r)$ and establishes the second statement.

The study of uniqueness of projections leads to the following:

**Definition 11–12.** *A point $b \in B$ is said to be a nup point (nonunique projection) of $\mathscr{F}$ if $b$ has two or more projections onto $\mathscr{F}$. We set*

$$\text{nup } \mathscr{F} = \overline{\{b \mid b \text{ is a nup point of } \mathscr{F}\}} \tag{11–5.11}$$

*where the bar indicates that the closure has been taken.*

The idea of the *reach* of a set $\mathscr{F}$ is directly related to the nup points of $\mathscr{F}$. We have

**Definition 11–13.** *The reach of $\mathscr{F}$ at $f_0$ is*

$$\omega(f_0) = \lim_{\varepsilon \to 0} \min_b \{\|f_0 - b\| \mid b \in \text{nup } [\mathscr{F} \cap \mathscr{S}(f_0, \epsilon)]\}. \tag{11–5.12}$$

*The reach of $\mathscr{F}$ is*

$$\omega(\mathscr{F}) = \inf_{\in \mathscr{F}} \omega(f).$$

The definition of reach at a point given originally by Federer, 1959, did not involve the dependence on $\epsilon$ and implied that the reach was not a local property of $\mathscr{F}$. The above definition makes the reach a local property of $\mathscr{F}$.

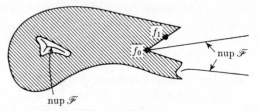

FIG. 11–7.   A set $\mathscr{F}$ in $E_2$ with portions of nup $\mathscr{F}$ shown. The reach $\omega(\mathscr{F})$ is zero as $\omega(f_0) = 0$. The reach of $\mathscr{F}$ at $f_1$ is $+\infty$.

A few properties of the reach are to be established in Problem 11–5.

The concept of the $\alpha$-hull is a direct extension of ordinary convexity and, in smooth spaces $B^m$, the convex bodies are the $\infty$-convex bodies (a body is a set of dimension $m$). On the other hand, the concept of the reach of a set is oriented toward extending the concept of curvature. Both concepts are closely related to each other and to the study of projections (especially uniqueness questions) onto sets in $B^m$.

## 11–6  MOTZKIN SETS AND UNIQUE PROJECTIONS

In problems arising from approximation theory we are very much interested in establishing uniqueness theorems. In the context of projections, we are then led to consider sets which have a unique projection property. We have

**Definition 11–14.** *A set $\mathscr{M}$ in the Banach space $B$ is a Motzkin set if every point of $B$ has a unique projection onto $\mathscr{M}$.*

Such sets are often called Tchebycheff sets in the literature, but there is no historical reason for this. Since there is a surplus of things named Tchebycheff and since Motzkin established the first important result in this area, we adopt the above terminology.

This definition immediately implies that $\mathscr{M}$ is closed (Problem 11–7). There is a connection between Motzkin sets and Tchebycheff sets as defined in Definition 3–2. See Problem 11–6.

The first result establishes some conditions under which we may state that the Motzkin sets are the convex sets.

**Theorem 11–9.**   *Let $B^m$ be a Minkowski space. Then $B^m$ is smooth if and only if every Motzkin set is convex.*

*Proof.* We can apply Theorem 11–2 to reduce the proof to establishing the statement: *All limit spheres of $B^m$ are hyperplanes if and only if every Motzkin set is convex.* Consider the limit sphere

$$\mathscr{P} = \lim_{t \to \infty} \mathscr{R}[c(t), c(0)]$$

and let $\mathscr{K}_+$ and $\mathscr{K}_-$ be the sets with boundary $\mathscr{P}$ which do and do not, respectively, contain $c(1)$. We may assume that $c(0) = 0$.

*Assertion.* If $B^m$ is strictly convex then $\mathscr{K}_-$ is a Motzkin set.

We note that $\mathscr{P}$ is the tangent cone of $\mathscr{R}[c(t), 0]$ for any $t$ and, by simple translation, $\mathscr{P} + b$ is the tangent cone of $\mathscr{R}\big(c(t) + b, b\big)$ for any element $b \in B^m$. Let $d \in B^m$ be a point not in $\mathscr{K}_-$ and let the line $d + c(t)$ intersect $\mathscr{P}$ at $d^*$. With $c_0 = c(t_0) = d - d^*$, the sphere $\mathscr{R}(c_0, 0) + d^*$ is the sphere $\mathscr{R}(d, d^*)$ with center $d$ through $d^*$. Then $\mathscr{P} + d^*$ is the tangent cone of $\mathscr{R}(d, d^*)$ at $d^*$. Assume that a second point $d^1 \neq d^*$ lies in $\mathscr{P} \cap \mathscr{R}(d, d^*)$ $\big($i.e. in $\mathscr{K}_- \cap \mathscr{R}(d, d^*)\big)$, e.g. $d^*$ is not the unique projection of $d$ onto $\mathscr{K}_-$. It is clear that $[\mathscr{K}_+ - \mathscr{P}] + d^* \subset [\mathscr{K}_+ - \mathscr{P}]$ if $d^* \in \mathscr{K}_+$, since $\mathscr{K}_+$ is a convex cone. Since $d^1 \in \mathscr{K}(d, d^*)$ we have $d^1 - d^* \in \mathscr{R}(c_0, 0)$ and since $B^m$ is strictly convex $d^1 - d^* \in [\mathscr{K}_+ - \mathscr{P}]$. Hence $d^1 \in [\mathscr{K}_+ - \mathscr{P}] + d^*$ and $\{[\mathscr{K}_+ - \mathscr{P}] + d^*\} \cap \mathscr{K}_- \subset [\mathscr{K}_+ - \mathscr{P}] \cap \mathscr{K}_-$ is empty. This contradicts the definition of $d^1$ and establishes the assertion.

We note that $\mathscr{K}_-$ is convex if and only if $\mathscr{P}$ is a hyperplane and we have proved that if some limit sphere is not a hyperplane, then some Motzkin set is not convex, i.e. the "if" portion of the proof is established.

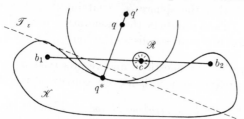

FIG. 11–8.  The construction of Theorem 11–9.

If $\mathscr{K}$ is a closed set in $B^m$ which is not convex, we proceed to show that there is a point $q \in B^m$ which has at least two projections onto $\mathscr{K}$. Let $b_1, b_2$ and $c$ be on a line (see Fig. 11–8) with $b_1, b_2 \in \mathscr{K}$, $c \notin \mathscr{K}$ and $c$ is a convex combination of $b_1$ and $b_2$. Let $\mathscr{R}$ be a closed ball with center $c$ so that $\mathscr{R} \cap \mathscr{K}$ is empty. For $b \notin \mathscr{K}$, define $\mathscr{S}_b$ as the ball, with center $b$ and radius $\|b - b^*\|$ where $b^*$ is the projection of $b$ onto $K$. Consider the class of balls

$$\mathscr{P} = \{\mathscr{S}_b \mid \mathscr{S}_b \supset \mathscr{R}\}.$$

*Assertion. The class $\mathscr{P}$ is bounded.*

We first note that any half space which contains $\mathscr{R}$ contains either $b_1$ or $b_2$ in its interior. Suppose the contrary, e.g. there is a sequence $\mathscr{S}^i \in \mathscr{P}$ which becomes unbounded. Now $\partial\mathscr{S}^i$ intersects either the segment $b_1 c$ or $b_2 c$ (or both) and we may choose a subsequence, also denoted by $\mathscr{S}^i$, so that $\partial\mathscr{S}^i$ intersects $b_1 c$ or $b_2 c$ (say $b_1 c$ for concreteness) at $d_i$ and the points $d_i$ of intersection converge to $d_0$. Consider the hyperplanes $\mathscr{T}_i$ of support of the $\mathscr{S}^i$ at $d_i$. A further subsequence, again denoted by $\mathscr{S}^i$, may be chosen so that the $\mathscr{T}_i$ converge to a hyperplane $\mathscr{T}_0$. Since $B^m$ is smooth, the tangent cones of the $\mathscr{S}^i$ are the hyperplanes $\mathscr{T}_i$. Since the radius of $\mathscr{S}^i$ becomes unbounded, $\partial\mathscr{S}^i$ converges to $\mathscr{T}_i$, which in turn converges to $\mathscr{T}_0$, in any fixed bounded region of $B^m$. Now $b_2$ is in the interior of the half spaces defined by $\mathscr{T}_i$ and $\mathscr{T}_0$ which contains $\mathscr{R}$. Hence, for $i$ sufficiently large, $b_2$ is in the interior of $\mathscr{S}^i$. This contradicts the definitions of the elements of the class $\mathscr{P}$ and establishes the assertion.

It is clear that $\mathscr{P}$ is closed and thus there is a sphere $\mathscr{S}_q$ in $\mathscr{P}$ of largest radius. The following construction shows that if $q$ has a unique projection $q^*$ on $\mathscr{K}$, then another contradiction is reached. Let $\mathscr{T}$ be the hyperplane of support of $\mathscr{S}_q$ at $q^*$. Consider the parallel hyperplane $\mathscr{T} + \epsilon(q - q^*) = \mathscr{T}_\epsilon$. We may choose $\epsilon$ sufficiently small so that (a) $\mathscr{R}$ is in the half space $\mathscr{H}_\epsilon$ bounded by $\mathscr{T}_\epsilon$ which contains $q$ and (b) the projections of the points in $\mathscr{S}_q \cap \mathscr{T}_\epsilon$ onto the line through $q$ and $q^*$ lie between $q$ and $q^*$. Let $q' = q^* + \sigma(q - q^*)$. There exists a $\sigma > 1$ and a sphere $\mathscr{S}'$ with center $q'$ so that (i) $\mathscr{S}' \supset \mathscr{H}_\epsilon \cap \mathscr{S}_q$ and (ii) $\mathscr{S}' \cap \mathscr{K}$ is empty. It follows from the second requirement (b) on the choice of $\epsilon$ that the radius of $\mathscr{S}'$ is larger than that of $\mathscr{S}_q$. Note that the sphere $\mathscr{S}'$ contains $\mathscr{R}$ and hence $\mathscr{S}_{q'}$ contains $\mathscr{R}$ and $\mathscr{S}_{q'} \in \mathscr{P}$. This contradicts the assumption that $\mathscr{S}_q$ has the largest radius of the spheres in $\mathscr{P}$ and establishes the "only if" portion of the theorem.

There is a variety of questions and results related to this one. For example, if $B^m$ is strictly convex then every convex set is a Motzkin set, e.g.

**Corollary 1.** *Let $B^m$ be a Minkowski space. Then the class of convex sets coincides with the class of Motzkin sets if and only if $B^m$ is smooth.*

The assumption that $B^m$ is strictly convex is vital here. There are spaces $B^m$ where every Motzkin set is convex, but $B^m$ is not smooth. Such an example is to be constructed in Problem 11–8. On the other hand, it is to be shown in Problem 11–9 that if $m = 2$, then the fact that all Motzkin sets are convex implies that $B^2$ is smooth. The example $B^m$ constructed in Problem 11–8 is not smooth, but the "corner" of the unit sphere is not as "sharp" as it could be. This can be stated precisely in terms of the dimension $d(b)$ of the set of hyperplanes of support of the unit sphere at $b$. Clearly $0 \leq d(b) \leq m - 1$. It appears that the construction of the first part of the proof of Theorem 11–9 may be modified to establish the

*Conjecture. If $d(b) = m - 1$ for some $b \in \partial\mathscr{S}$, then there is a Motzkin set in $B^m$ which is not convex.*

That is to say, if every Motzkin set is convex then $d(b) < m - 1$ for all $b \in \partial\mathscr{S}$. Even if this conjecture is established, we have not yet characterized those spaces in which every Motzkin set is convex. For example, we have in the proof of Theorem 11–9 established the stronger statement:

**Corollary 2.** *If $B^m$ is smooth then every Motzkin set is convex.*

The hypothesis of strict convexity does not enter into the proof of the "only if" portion of Theorem 11–9.

## 11–7  PROJECTIONS ON SUBMANIFOLDS

In this section we begin a general study of projections on submanifolds of $B^m$. We will consider, in varying degrees of depth, the three basic questions: (a) the existence of projections, (b) the characterization of projections and (c) the uniqueness of projections. The first of these questions is easily resolved. We have

**Theorem 11–10.** *Every point of $B^m$ has a projection on $\mathscr{F}$ if and only if $\mathscr{F}$ is closed.*

Note that $\mathscr{F}$ is not required to be a manifold here.

*Proof.* If $\mathscr{F}$ has a limit point $b_0$ which is not in $\mathscr{F}$, then clearly $b_0$ does not have a projection on $\mathscr{F}$. On the other hand, if $\mathscr{F}$ is closed then $\mathscr{F} \cap \mathscr{S}(b, 2\|b - \mathscr{F}\|)$ is compact and hence any sequence $\{f_i\}$ in $\mathscr{F}$ such that

$$\lim_{i \to \infty} \|b - f_i\| = \|b - \mathscr{F}\|$$

has a convergent subsequence with limit point in $\mathscr{F}$.

The first characterization result is very basic, but not very powerful. It is stated in terms of spheres of support.

**Theorem 11–11.** *The point $f^* \in \mathscr{F}$ is a projection of $b$ onto $\mathscr{F}$ if and only if the sphere $\partial\mathscr{S}(b, r^*)$ is a sphere of support of $\mathscr{F}$ and $f^* \in \partial\mathscr{S}(b, r^*)$. Furthermore $r^* = \|b - \mathscr{F}\|$.*

*Proof.* Suppose that $\partial\mathscr{S}(b, r^*)$ is a sphere of support of $\mathscr{F}$ at $f$. Then $\|b - f\| = r^* \geq \|b - \mathscr{F}\|$. On the other hand $r < r^*$ implies that $\partial\mathscr{S}(b, r) \cap \mathscr{F}$ is empty and hence $\|b - \mathscr{F}\| \geq r^*$. This implies that $f$ is a projection of $b$ onto $\mathscr{F}$ and $r^* = \|b - \mathscr{F}\|$.

Suppose $f$ is a projection of $b$ onto $\mathscr{F}$ and $r^* = \|b - f\|$. Then $\|b - \mathscr{F}\| = r^*$ and, clearly, $f \in \partial\mathscr{S}(b, r^*)$. Furthermore $f_1 \in \mathscr{F}$ implies $\|b - f_1\| \geq \|b - f\|$ and no point of $\mathscr{F}$ is in the interior of $\mathscr{S}(b, r^*)$.

This theorem is little more than a restatement of the definition of projection. However, if either $\mathscr{F}$ or $\mathscr{S}(b, r^*)$ have additional properties then sharper results may follow. An obvious example is

**Corollary 1.**   *Let $\mathscr{F}$ be convex, then $f \in \mathscr{F}$ is a projection of $b$ onto $\mathscr{F}$ if and only if $\mathscr{F}$ and $\mathscr{S}(b, \|b - \mathscr{F}\|)$ have a common hyperplane of support at $f$.*

Another rather direct consequence of this theorem is

**Corollary 2.**   *Let $\mathscr{F}$ be smooth, then $f \in \mathscr{F}$ is a projection of $b$ onto $\mathscr{F}$ only if the tangent plane of $\mathscr{F}$ at $f$ is in a hyperplane of support of $\mathscr{S}(b, \|b - \mathscr{F}\|)$ at $f$. Furthermore $b$ is contained in the normal set of $\mathscr{F}$ at $f$.*

This follows directly from Theorems 11–11, 11–6 and the definitions. The line of thought of Corollary 2 is extended further by

**Corollary 3.**   *Let $\mathscr{F}$ be smooth at $f_0$ and $B^m$ be a smooth Minkowski space. If $f_0$ is a projection of $b$ onto $\mathscr{F}$ then $f_0$ is a critical point of $\|b - f\|$.*

We define a *critical point* of a function $\alpha(x_1, x_2, \ldots, x_k)$ to be a point where

$$\frac{\partial \alpha(x_1, x_2, \ldots, x_k)}{\partial x_i} = 0, \qquad i = 1, 2, \ldots, k.$$

Since $\mathscr{F}$ is smooth at $f_0$, $f_0$ has a neighborhood $\mathscr{N}$ with coordinates introduced by a system of coordinates in the tangent plane $T$ of $\mathscr{F}$ at $f_0$. Thus we have coordinates $(x_1, x_2, \ldots, x_n)$ in $\mathscr{N}$ and the points of $\mathscr{N}$ may be written as $f(x_1, \ldots, x_n)$. This, of course, makes $\|b - f\|$ a function of $n$ real variables. We need to establish two facts: (a) that $f(x_1, x_2, \ldots, x_n)$ is a differentiable function of $x_1, x_2, \ldots, x_n$ and (b) that $\|g\|$ is a differentiable function of $g$. Let $v$ be one of the coordinate vectors in $T$ of length one and, for simplicity of notation, assume it is labeled as the first one. Then the real number $x_1$ is the coefficient of $v$ in this coordinate system. It is clear that we may assume that $b = 0$, again for simplicity of notation. The coordinates of $f_0$ are $(0, 0, \ldots, 0)$. We are thus concerned with the partial derivative

$$\frac{\partial \| f(x_1, 0, \ldots, 0)\|}{\partial x_1} = \lim_{x_1 \to 0} \frac{\| f(x_1, 0, \ldots, 0)\| - \|f_0\|}{x_1}.$$

We note that

$$\|f(x_1, 0, \ldots, 0)\| - \|f_0\|$$
$$= \|f(x_1, 0, \ldots, 0)\| - \|f_0 + x_1 v\| + \|f_0 + x_1 v\| - \|f_0\|$$

and, by Theorem 11–4

$$\lim_{x_1 \to 0} \frac{\|f(x_1, 0, \ldots, 0)\| - \|f_0 + x_1 v\|}{x_1} = 0.$$

Let $b_0$ denote the projection of $f_0 + x_1 v$ onto $\mathscr{S}(0, \|0 - \mathscr{F}\|)$. Then

$$\|f + x_1 v\| - \|f_0\|$$
$$= \|f_0 + x_1 v\| - \|b_0\| + \|b_0\| - \|f_0\| = \|f_0 + x_1 v\| - \|b_0\|.$$

Now $T$ is in the hyperplane of support of $\mathscr{S}$ at $f_0$ and it follows from Lemma 11–4 (applied to $\partial \mathscr{S}$) that

$$\lim_{x_1 \to 0} \frac{\|f_0 + x_1 v\| - \|b_0\|}{x_1} = 0.$$

This establishes Corollary 3.

The preceding results on the existence and characterization questions are what one intuitively expects. They are more or less direct extensions of familiar facts. The uniqueness question is not of this nature, there is no direct extension of the familiar results such as presented in the linear theory. The first result in this area states that no global uniqueness theorem is possible for nonlinear approximation if $B^m$ is smooth. This result (Rice, 1965) is based on Corollary 2 of Theorem 11–9.

**Theorem 11–12.** *Let $\mathscr{F}$ be a closed submanifold of a smooth space $B^m$. Then $\mathscr{F}$ is a Motzkin set only if $\mathscr{F}$ is a linear manifold.*

*Proof.* It follows from Corollary 2 of Theorem 11–9 that $\mathscr{F}$ is a Motzkin set only if $\mathscr{F}$ is convex. The proof is completed by showing that a closed convex manifold is a linear manifold.

Consider a point $f_0 \in \mathscr{F}$ and a coordinate neighborhood $\mathscr{N}$ in $\mathscr{F}$ of $f_0$. Let $n$ be the dimension of $\mathscr{F}$ and $(x_1, x_2, \ldots, x_n)$ be the coordinates. Choose $n$ points in $\mathscr{N}, f_i = (0, \ldots, 0, x_i, 0, \ldots, 0)$ with $x_i \neq 0$. Set $\epsilon = \min \|f_0 - f_i\|$ and denote by $\mathscr{H}$ the convex hull of the $n$ points $f_i$. Now $\mathscr{H}$ is a subset of the $n$-dimensional linear manifold $\mathscr{L}$ determined by $f_0$ and the $f_i$.

Assume that $\mathscr{N}_0 = \mathscr{S}(f_0, \epsilon) \cap \mathscr{N}$ contains a point $f_{n+1}$ not in $\mathscr{L}$. The convex hull of $\mathscr{H}$ and $f_{n+1}$ is in $\mathscr{N}_0 \subset \mathscr{N}$ and it follows that the dimension of $\mathscr{N}$ is at least $n + 1$. This is a contradiction and we have established that every point of $\mathscr{F}$ has a neighborhood which is the intersection of a ball and an $n$-dimensional linear manifold.

Consider two distinct points $f_1$ and $f_2$ and the line $l(f_1, f_2) = l$ determined by them. Then $l \cap \mathscr{F}$ is closed. Assume, if possible, that $l \cap \mathscr{F}$ has a boundary point $f_0$ in the relative topology of $l$. Then $f_0$ has a neighborhood $\mathscr{N}$ which is contained in an $n$-dimensional linear manifold $\mathscr{L}$. If $\mathscr{N} \cap l = f_0$, then the convex hull of $\mathscr{N}$ and the $f_i$ is $(n + 1)$-dimensional and contained in $\mathscr{F}$. This is impossible. Hence $\mathscr{N} \cap l$ contains a segment of $l$ and $l \subset \mathscr{L}$. This contradicts the assumption that $f_0$ is a boundary point of $l \cap \mathscr{F}$. It immediately follows that $\mathscr{F} \supset \mathscr{L}$ where $\mathscr{L}$ is the linear manifold defined at $f_1$. If $\mathscr{F}$ contains a point not in $\mathscr{L}$, then the dimension of $\mathscr{F}$ is at least $n + 1$, which is not possible. Hence $\mathscr{L} = \mathscr{F}$ and the theorem is established.

**Corollary 1.** *Let $\mathscr{F}$ be a closed submanifold of a smooth Minkowski space $B^m$. Then $\mathscr{F}$ is a Motzkin set if and only if $\mathscr{F}$ is a linear manifold.*

**Corollary 2.** *Let $\mathscr{F}$ be nonlinear and unisolvent, $X$ finite and $\| \|_p$ denote an $L_p$-norm $1 < p < \infty$. Then there exists a function $f(x)$ defined on $X$ such that*

$$\|f - F(A_1)\|_p = \|f - F(A_2)\|_p = \|f - \mathscr{F}\|_p \qquad (11\text{–}7.1)$$

*and $A_1 \neq A_2$.*

**Corollary 3.** *Let $\mathscr{F}$ be nonlinear, locally unisolvent and closed, $X$ finite and $\| \|_p$ and $L_p$-norm, $1 < p < \infty$. Then there exists a function $f(x)$ defined on $X$ such that (11–7.1) holds and $A_1 \neq A_2$.*

The second corollary states that no global uniqueness theorem is possible for $L_p$-approximation, $1 < p < \infty$, by a nonlinear unisolvent approximating function. This fact may be compared with this result that best approximations are unique in the $L_\infty$-norm for such an approximating function.

We have the curious situation that there is a complete change in "polarity" for the uniqueness question when we go from the linear to the nonlinear problem. This is illustrated by the following diagram

|                        | $L_1$-norm                              | $L_p$-norm, $1 < p < \infty$              | $L_\infty$-norm                          |
|------------------------|-----------------------------------------|-------------------------------------------|------------------------------------------|
| linear problems        | global unique-ness for some problems    | global uniqueness trivially established    | global uniqueness for some problems      |
| nonlinear problems     | unknown                                 | no possibility for global uniqueness       | global uniqueness for some problems      |

One might say that $L_1$- and $L_\infty$-norms are somehow "neutral" for the global uniqueness question and the change from linear to nonlinear does not affect them. In either case the uniqueness question is delicate and is not resolved *a priori* in either direction. On the other hand, then $L_p$-norms for $1 < p < \infty$ are directly affected by the change from linear to nonlinear and the global uniqueness question is resolved *a priori* one way or the other. It should be noted from Theorem 11–12 that the relevant distinguishing feature of the $L_1$- and $L_\infty$-norms is that they have corners and not that they are not strictly convex.

The uniqueness of projections is closely connected with the continuity of the projection operator

$$\mathbf{P}_{\mathscr{F}} : b \to \{f \mid \|f - b\| = \|\mathscr{F} - b\|\}.$$

**Theorem 11–13.** *Let $\mathscr{F}$ be closed. The projection operator $\mathbf{P}_{\mathscr{F}}$ is continuous at $b$ if and only if $b$ is not a nup point.*

*Proof.* Assume $b_0$ is a nup point and has distinct projections $f_1$ and $f_2$ onto $\mathscr{F}$. Then $\mathbf{P}_{\mathscr{F}}$ is multivalued at $b_0$ and hence discontinuous.

Assume that $b_0$ is not a nup point and has projection $f^*$ onto $\mathscr{F}$. We establish that given $\epsilon > 0$ there is a $\delta$ such that $\mathscr{S}(b_0, \|b_0 - f^*\| + \delta) \cap \mathscr{F}$ lies in the ball $\mathscr{S}(f^*, \epsilon)$. For assume the contrary, then there is a point $f_k \in \mathscr{F}$ so that $f_k \in \mathscr{S}(b_0, \|b_0 - f^*\| + 1/k)$ and $\|f^* - f_k\| \geq \eta > 0$ for each $k$. Let $f_0$ be a limit of the sequence $\{f_k\}$. A limit $f_0$ exists because $\mathscr{F}$ is closed and hence boundedly compact. Then

$$\|f_0 - b_0\| \leq \lim_{k \to \infty} \|f^* - b_0\| + \frac{1}{k} = \|f^* - b_0\|$$

which implies that $f_0$ is a projection of $b_0$ onto $\mathscr{F}$. This is a contradiction and establishes the result.

**Corollary.** *Let $B^m$ be a smooth Minkowski space. Then $\mathbf{P}_{\mathscr{F}}$ is continuous for all $b \in B^m$ if and only if $\mathscr{F}$ is convex.*

This follows from the above theorem and the corollaries of Theorem 11–9.

The above results may be rephrased to say that if $B^m$ is smooth and $\mathscr{F}$ is a nonlinear manifold then

$$\text{nup } (\mathscr{F}) \neq \text{empty.}$$

The obvious question at this point is then: just how big is nup $(\mathscr{F})$? In problems arising from approximation, we are, hopefully, not so interested in approximating functions far from $\mathscr{F}$, but rather functions "relatively" close to $\mathscr{F}$. Thus, we would like to know if every point close to $\mathscr{F}$ lies outside nup $(\mathscr{F})$. Example 4 of Section 11–5 shows that smoothness is not sufficient for nup $(\mathscr{F})$ to be bounded away from $\mathscr{F}$. However, with the assumption of bounded curvature it is sufficient to establish a "local" uniqueness theorem.

Recall that we use the differential topology definition of a submanifold (i.e., the topology on the submanifold is induced by the topology of the containing space $B^m$). This implies in particular that every neighborhood $N$ of $f$ in $\mathscr{F}$ contains $\mathscr{F} \cap \mathscr{S}(f, \epsilon)$ for some $\epsilon > 0$.

**Lemma 11–9.** *Let $(F)$ be a closed smooth submanifold of $B^m$ and $f \in \mathscr{F}$. Then there is an $\epsilon(f) > 0$ such that $g \in \mathscr{F}$, $\|f - g\| \leq \epsilon(f)$ implies that $\mathscr{S}(g, \lambda) \cap \mathscr{F}$ is connected for all $\lambda \leq \epsilon(f)$.*

*Proof.* Suppose to the contrary that there is a sequence $\{g_i \mid g_i \to f\}$ such that $\mathscr{S}(g_i, \lambda_i) \cap \mathscr{F}$ is disconnected for some $\lambda_i \leq \|g_i - f\|$. Let $E_i$ be a connected component of $\mathscr{S}(g_i, \lambda_i) \cap \mathscr{F}$ which does not contain $g_i$.

Since $\mathscr{F}$ is a closed manifold we have $\partial E_i \subset \partial \mathscr{S}(g_i, \lambda_i)$ and hence there is a point $e_i \in E_i$ so that $\|g_i - E_i\| = \|g_i - e_i\|$. By Corollary 2 of Theorem 11–11 we have that $l_i = l(g_i, e_i)$ is perpendicular to the tangent plane $T(e_i)$ of $\mathscr{F}$ at $e_i$. Since $\mathscr{F}$ is smooth we have $T(e_i) \to T(f)$ and we have from Lemma 11–8 that any limit $l$ of $\{l_i\}$ has $l \perp T(f)$. Clearly such a limit exists and since $l_i$ interpolates $\mathscr{F}$ at $g_i$ and $e_i$, $l \subset T(f)$ by definition. This is a contradiction and establishes the result.

**Corollary.** *Let $G$ be a compact subset of a closed, smooth submanifold $\mathscr{F}$. Then there is an $\epsilon > 0$, independent of $f$, so that for $f \in G$, $\lambda \leq \epsilon$, $\mathscr{S}(f, \lambda) \cap \mathscr{F}$ is connected.*

*Proof.* Let $\epsilon(f)$ be as in Lemma 11–9. The set

$$\bigcup_{f \in G} \mathscr{S}(f, \epsilon(f))$$

covers $G$ and hence there is a finite set $f_i$, $i = 1, 2, \ldots, q$ so that $\mathscr{S}(f_i, \epsilon(f_i))$ covers $G$. Take $\epsilon = \min[\epsilon(f_i)]$, $i = 1, 2, \ldots, q$.

We consider a closed submanifold $\mathscr{F}$ of $B^m$, and compact connected subsets of $\mathscr{F}$ are denoted generically by $\Gamma$. We define the maximal distance $|\ |^*$ from a point $b$ to a set $G$ as

$$|b - G|^* = \sup\{\|b - g\| \mid g \in G\}$$

**Lemma 11–10.** *Suppose $G$ is compact and $G \subset \Gamma_1$. Then for any $b \in B^m$ there exists a $\Gamma_0$ so that*

$$|b - \Gamma_0|^* = \inf|b - \Gamma|^* < \infty$$

*where the infimum is over all $\Gamma$ which contain $G$.*

*Proof.* Denote $\inf|b - \Gamma|^*$ by $d$ and let $\Gamma_i$ be the connected component of $\mathscr{F} \cap \bar{\mathscr{S}}(b, d + 1/i)$ which contains $G$. It is clear that $d \leq |b - \Gamma_1|^* < \infty$. Further $\Gamma_{i+1} \subset \Gamma_i$ and hence $\{\Gamma_i\}$ is a nested sequence of compact connected sets. Thus

$$\Gamma_0 = \bigcap_{i=2}^{\infty} \Gamma_i$$

is a compact connected set and it clearly contains $G$. Since

$$|b - \Gamma_0|^* = \lim_{i \to \infty}|b - \Gamma_i|^* = d,$$

the proof is complete.

We denote by $\Gamma^*$ the subset of $\Gamma$

$$\Gamma^* = \{f \mid f \in \Gamma, \ \|b - f\| = |b - \Gamma|^*\}.$$

**Lemma 11–11.**  *Let $B^m$ be a smooth Minkowski space and $\mathscr{F}$ be a smooth submanifold and $G$ be a compact subset of $\mathscr{F}$. If*

$$|b - G|^* < |b - \Gamma_0|^* = \inf |b - \Gamma|^* = d < \infty$$

*where the infimum is taken over all $\Gamma$ containing $G$, then there is a point $f^* \in \Gamma_0^*$ so that $l(b, f^*) \perp T(f^*)$ where $T(f^*)$ is the tangent plane of $\mathscr{F}$ at $f^*$.*

*Proof.*  The proof is by contradiction. Let $H(f)$ denote the tangent plane of $\partial\mathscr{S}(b, \|b - f\|)$ at $f$. Consider a point $f + t(f) \in T(f)$ such that $\|t(f)\| = 1$ and $\|f + t(f) - H(f)\|$ is maximized. We choose $t(f)$ so that $f + t(f)$ is on the same side of $H(f)$ as $b$. By Lemma 11–6 each $t(f)$ may be written as $h(f) + n(f)$ where $f + h(f) \in H(f)$ and $n(f) \perp H(f)$. If $\|n(f)\| = 0$ then $l(b, f) \perp T(f)$. Assume that $\|n(f)\| > 0$ for each $f \in \Gamma_0^*$. Since $\|n(f)\|$ is continuous and $\Gamma_0^*$ is compact there is an $\eta$ so that $\|n(f)\| \geq \eta > 0$ for $f \in \Gamma_0^*$.

It follows from Lemma 11–5 that there is a $\lambda(\|b - f\|)$ so that for $0 < \lambda < \lambda(\|b - f\|)$ we have

$$f + \lambda t(f) \in \mathscr{S}(b, \|b - f\|).$$

It is clear from the homothetic nature of the geometry that $\lambda(\|b - f\|)$ is proportional to $\|b - f\|$. Since $G$ and $\Gamma_0^*$ are compact and $|b - G|^* < |b - \Gamma_0^*|^*$ there is an $\epsilon_1 > 0$ so that $\|f - \Gamma_0^*\| \leq \epsilon \leq \epsilon_1$ implies that $\|f - G\| > 0$. We take $\epsilon_1 < 1$ and set

$$E = \{f \,|\, \|f - \Gamma_0^*\| < \epsilon_1\}.$$

Take $\lambda_0 = \min[\lambda(\|b - f\|)]$ for $\|b - E\| \leq \|b - f\| \leq d$. Further take $\lambda_1 = d - \max\|b - f\| > 0$ with the maximum taken for $f \in \Gamma_0, f \notin E$.

For $f \in E$ we have the following consequences of Theorems 11–4 and and Lemma 11–4. First

$$\|c - H(f)\| \leq o_1(\epsilon), \quad c \in \overline{\mathscr{S}}(f, \epsilon) \cap \partial\mathscr{S}(b, \|b - f\|).$$

Since the closure of $E$ is compact it follows that $o_1(\epsilon)$ is independent of $f$. Likewise

$$\|u - \mathscr{F}\| \leq o_2(\epsilon), \quad u \in \overline{\mathscr{S}}(f, \epsilon) \cap T(f)$$

and $o_2(\epsilon)$ is independent of $f$ for $f \in E$. The Corollary of Theorem 11–8 implies that there is an $\epsilon_0 > 0$ so that for each $f \in \mathscr{F}$ if $\lambda \leq \epsilon_0$ then $\mathscr{S}(f, \lambda) \cap \mathscr{F}$ is connected. Choose $\lambda_2$ so that $0 < \lambda < \lambda_2$ implies that

$$o_1(\lambda), \quad o_2(\lambda) \leq \min[\epsilon_0, \eta\lambda/8].$$

Take

$$\lambda^* = \tfrac{1}{2}\min[\lambda_0, \lambda_1, \lambda_2]$$

9

and for $f \in \Gamma_0, f \notin E$ set

$$U(f) = \mathscr{S}(f, \eta\lambda^*/2) \cap \mathscr{F}.$$

We note for $f \in E$ that if $f_1, f_2$ are projections of $f + \lambda^*t(f)$ onto $\mathscr{F}$, then $\|f_1 - f_2\| \le \eta\lambda^*/4$ since

$$\|f + \lambda^*t(f) - \mathscr{F}\| \le \eta\lambda^*/8.$$

Thus if we choose one such $f_1$ and for $f \in E$ set

$$U(f) = \mathscr{S}(f_1, \eta\lambda^*/2) \cap \mathscr{F}$$

then we have

$$U(f) \supset \mathbf{P}_{\mathscr{F}}(f + \lambda^*t(f))$$

and $U(f)$ is a connected open set.

Consider $f \in E$ and choose

$$f_1 \in \mathbf{P}_{\mathscr{F}}(f + \lambda^*t(f)), \quad g_1 \in \mathbf{P}_{\mathscr{F}}(g + \lambda^*t(g)).$$

We have

$$\|f_1 - g_1\| \le \|f_1 - f - \lambda^*t(f)\| + \|g_1 - g - \lambda^*t(f)\| + \|f + \lambda^*t(f) - g - \lambda^*t(g)\|.$$

Since $t(f)$ is a continuous function on the closure of $E$, there is a $\delta_1 > 0$ so that $\|f - g\| < \delta_1$ implies that the third term is less than $\eta\lambda^*/8$. Hence, for $\|f - g\| < \delta_1$ we have

$$\|f_1 - g_1\| \le \tfrac{3}{8}\eta\lambda^*.$$

This implies if $\delta = \min[\delta_1, \lambda^*\eta/8]$ then for all $f \in \Gamma_0$ and any $g$ with $\|f - g\| < \delta$, the set $U(f) \cap U(g)$ is not empty.

We now establish for each $f \in \Gamma_0$ that the closure $\overline{U}(f)$ of $U(f)$ is in the open ball $\mathscr{S}(b, d)$. If $f \notin E$ this is obvious. Suppose $f \in E$ and let $u \in \overline{U}(f), p \in \partial\mathscr{S}(b, \|b - f\|)$ be such that

$$\|u - p\| = \min \|c - \overline{U}(f)\|$$

with the minimum taken for $c \in \partial\mathscr{S}(b, \|b - f\|)$. Then

$$\|u - p\| \ge \|f + \lambda^*t(f) - H(f)\| - \|u - f - \lambda^*t(f)\| - \|c - H(f)\|$$
$$\ge \eta\lambda^*[\tfrac{1}{2} - \tfrac{1}{8} - \tfrac{1}{8}] > 0.$$

Since $f + \lambda^*t(f) \in \mathscr{S}(b, \|b - f\|)$ it follows that $u \in \mathscr{S}(b, \|b - f\|)$. Hence we have

$$\overline{U}(f) \subset \mathscr{S}(b, d).$$

Set

$$\Gamma_1 = \bigcup_{f \in \Gamma_0} \overline{U}(f).$$

It is clear that $\Gamma_1$ is compact, $\Gamma_1$ contains $G$ and $\Gamma_1 \subset \mathscr{S}(b, d)$.

We show that it is also connected. Suppose, to the contrary, that there are nonempty sets $V_1$, $V_2$ open in $\Gamma_1$ so that

$$\Gamma_1 = V_1 \cup V_2$$

and $V_1 \cap V_2$ is empty. Consider the mapping $M$ defined on $\Gamma_0$ by

$$M : f = \begin{cases} 0, & \overline{U}(f) \subset V_1, \\ 1, & \overline{U}(f) \subset V_2. \end{cases}$$

The mapping $M$ is well defined since $\overline{U}(f)$ is connected, i.e. $g \in \overline{U}(f)$, $g \in V_i$ implies $\overline{U}(f) \subset V_i$. Further if $\overline{U}(f) \subset V_i$ and $\overline{U}(f) \cap \overline{U}(g)$ is not empty then $\overline{U}(g) \subset V_i$. If $\|f - g\| < \delta$ then $\overline{U}(f) \cap \overline{U}(g)$ is not empty and hence $M$ is continuous. Since $V_1$ and $V_2$ are not empty, the mapping $M$ is onto. Thus $M$ is a continuous mapping of $\Gamma_0$ onto $\{0, 1\}$ which contradicts the connectedness of $\Gamma_0$. Thus $\Gamma_1$ is connected.

We have established that $\Gamma_1$ is a compact connected subset of $\mathscr{F}$ which contains $G$ and that

$$|b - \Gamma_1|^* < |b - \Gamma_0|^*.$$

This contradicts the definition of $\Gamma_0$ and establishes the lemma.

**Lemma 11–12.** *Let $\mathscr{F}$ be a smooth subset of $B^m$ and consider $f \in \mathscr{F}$, $b \in B^m$ such that $l(b, f) \perp T(f)$. If $f$ is an accumulation point of points in $\mathscr{F} \cap \overline{\mathscr{S}}(b, \|b - f\|)$, then the radius of curvature $\rho(f, r(f, b))$ of $\mathscr{F}$ at $f$ in the direction $r(f, b)$ satisfies*

$$\rho(f, r(f, b)) \leq \|b - f\|.$$

*Proof.* Consider a sequence $\{f_i\} \subset \mathscr{F} \cap \overline{\mathscr{S}}(b, \|b - f\|)$ so that $f_i \to f$. Associate with each $f_i$ a point $b_i \in l$ so that $\|b_i - f\| = \|b_i - f_i\|$. Then

$$f_i \in \partial \mathscr{S}(b_i, \|b_i - f_i\|) \subset \overline{\mathscr{S}}(b, \|b - d\|).$$

Definition 11–10 implies immediately that

$$\rho(f, r(f, b)) \leq \lim_{i \to \infty} \|b_i - f_i\| \leq \|b - d\|.$$

With these lemmas, we may establish the following result (Rice, 1967).

**Theorem 11–14.** *Let $\mathscr{F}$ be a closed submanifold of a smooth Minkowski space $B^m$ and assume for each compact subset $G$ of $\mathscr{F}$ there is a $K$ so that $\sigma(f) \leq K < \infty$ for $f \in G$. Then there is an open neighborhood $\mathscr{F}_u$ of $\mathscr{F}$ so that every point $b \in \mathscr{F}_u$ has a unique projection onto $\mathscr{F}$, i.e. $\mathbf{P}_{\mathscr{F}}(b)$ is a single point.*

Note that this does not imply that $\partial \mathscr{F}_u$ is bounded away from $\mathscr{F}$.

*Proof.* For $f \in \mathscr{F}$ we have from Lemma 11–9 that there is an $\epsilon_1 > 0$

so that $\mathscr{S}(f, \epsilon_1) \cap \mathscr{F}$ is connected. Let $K$ be the bound on the curvature $\sigma(f)$ in $\overline{\mathscr{S}}(f, \epsilon_1) \cap \mathscr{F}$. Set

$$\epsilon = \min\left[\frac{1}{3K}, \frac{\epsilon_1}{2}\right].$$

We show that if $b \in \mathscr{S}(f, \epsilon)$ and $b$ has two projections, $f_1$ and $f_2$, onto $\mathscr{F}$, then a contradiction is reached. It is clear that $f_1, f_2 \in \mathscr{S}(f, \epsilon_1) \cap \mathscr{F}$. We have $\mathscr{S}(b, 3\epsilon) \supset \mathscr{S}(f_1, \epsilon)$ and hence $\mathscr{S}(b, 3\epsilon) \cap \mathscr{F}$ has a compact connected component $\Gamma_1$ which contains the compact set $f_1 \cup f_2$. From Lemma 11–10 we have a compact connected subset $\Gamma_0$ of $\mathscr{F}$ so that

$$|b - \Gamma_0|^* = \inf_{\Gamma} |b - \Gamma|^* = d$$

where the infimum is taken over all $\Gamma$ which contain $f_1$ and $f_2$.

If $|b - \Gamma_0|^* = \|b - \mathscr{F}\|$ then clearly $\Gamma_0 \subset \partial \mathscr{S}(b, \|b - \mathscr{F}\|)$, i.e. $\Gamma_0 = \Gamma_0^*$ in the notation of Lemma 11–11. It follows from Theorem 11–6 that $l(b, f_1) \perp T(f_1)$ and we set $f^* = f_1$.

If $\|b - \mathscr{F}\| < |b - \Gamma_0|^*$ then Lemma 11–11 implies that there is a point $f^* \in \Gamma_0^*$ so that $l(b, f^*) \perp T(f^*)$. In either case $f^*$ is an accumulation point of points $f_i \in \overline{\mathscr{S}}(b, |b - \Gamma_0|^*) \cap \mathscr{F}$. Lemma 11–12 implies that

$$\rho(f^*, r(f^*, b)) \leq |b - \Gamma_0|^*.$$

We have then that

$$\frac{1}{K} \leq |b - \Gamma_0|^* \leq |b - \Gamma_1|^* < 3\epsilon \leq \frac{1}{K}.$$

This is a contradiction and establishes that each $b \in \mathscr{S}(f, \epsilon)$ has a unique projection onto $\mathscr{F}$. Set

$$\mathscr{F}_u = \bigcup \mathscr{S}(f, \epsilon)$$

for $f \in \mathscr{F}$ and the theorem is established.

**Definition 11–15.** *The folding $\eta(f)$ of $\mathscr{F}$ at $f$ is $\eta(f) = \sup \{\rho \mid \mathscr{S}(f, \lambda) \cap \mathscr{F}$ is connected for all $\lambda \leq \rho\}$.*

Lemma 11–9 states that a smooth submanifold of $B^m$ has positive folding at each point. The following is a quantitative restatement of Theorem 11–14.

**Corollary 1.** *With $\mathscr{F}$ and $B^m$ as in Theorem 11–14, let $b \in B^m$ and $f \in \mathbf{P}_{\mathscr{F}}(b)$ be given. Set*

$$\sigma = \max_{g} \{\sigma(g) \mid \|f - g\| \leq \eta(f)\},$$

$$\epsilon = \min\left[\frac{1}{3\sigma}, \frac{\eta(f)}{2}\right].$$

*If $\|b - \mathscr{F}\| < \epsilon$ then $f$ is the unique projection of $b$ onto $\mathscr{F}$.*

It appears that $1/(3\sigma)$ might be replaced by $1/\sigma$, in which case this Corollary is obviously sharp. However, the method of proof of Theorem 11–14 does not allow this. A related result with a stronger hypothesis is given in the next section.

Another consequence of the proof of Theorem 11–14 is

**Corollary 2.** *With $\mathscr{F}$ and $B^m$ as in Theorem 11–14, suppose that a connected component of $\mathscr{S}(b, d) \cap \mathscr{F}$ contains $f_1, f_2 \in \mathbf{P}_{\mathscr{F}}(b)$. Then $\mathscr{F}$ has curvature of at least $\frac{1}{3}d$ in $\overline{\mathscr{S}}(b, d) \cap \mathscr{F}$.*

Let us recall

**Definition 11–12.** *A point $b \in B^m$ is a nup (nonunique projection) point of $\mathscr{F}$ if $\mathbf{P}_{\mathscr{F}}(b)$ consists of more than one point. Further*

$$\mathrm{nup}(\mathscr{F}) = \overline{\{b \mid b \text{ is a nup point of } \mathscr{F}\}}$$

*where the bar indicates that the closure is taken.*

In a study of the uniqueness of projections onto $\mathscr{F}$ we are naturally interested in the nature of nup $(\mathscr{F})$.

The closure operation may add a certain number of points to nup $(\mathscr{F})$ which are not nup points. These are rather special points which one would intuitively expect to be "centers of curvature". Conditions under which this is true are given in the next theorem.

**Theorem 11–15.** *Let $\mathscr{F}$ be a submanifold with continuous curvature of a Minkowski space $B^m$. Suppose that $b \in nup\,(\mathscr{F})$ and $b$ is not a nup point and $f \in \mathbf{P}_{\mathscr{F}}(b)$. Then*

$$\|b - \mathscr{F}\| = \rho[f, r(f, b)].$$

*Proof.* For compactness of notation set

$$r^* = r(f, b), \qquad \rho^* = \rho(f, r^*).$$

It follows from Theorem 11–8 that $\|b - \mathscr{F}\| \leq \rho^*$. The assumption that $\|b - \mathscr{F}\| = \rho^* - \eta$, $\eta > 0$, leads to a contradiction as follows. Since the curvature is continuous at $f$, there is a $\epsilon > 0$ so that

$$\|f - g\| \leq \epsilon, \quad \|r^* - r(g, c)\| < \epsilon$$

implies that $\rho(g, r(g, c)) \geq \rho^* - \eta/2$. It is known, Theorem 11–13, that $\mathbf{P}$ is continuous at $b$ in the sense that given $\epsilon > 0$ there is a $\delta > 0$ so that $\|b - c\| < \delta$ implies $\|f - \mathbf{P}(c)\| < \epsilon$. Thus there is a $\delta > 0$ so that $\|b - c\| < \delta$ implies that $\|f - \mathbf{P}(c)\| < \epsilon$ and $\|r^* - r(\mathbf{P}(c), c)\| < \epsilon$. Hence every point $c$ in $\mathscr{S}(b, \delta)$ has $\mathbf{P}_{\mathscr{F}}(g) \subset \mathscr{S}(f, \epsilon) \cap \mathscr{F}$ and $\rho[g, r(g, c)] \geq \rho^* - \eta/2$. Since $B^m$ is Minkowskian, every point $h$ on $r(g, c)$ with $\|h - \mathscr{F}\| \leq \rho^* - 3\eta/4$

has a unique projection onto $\mathscr{F}$. Set $\mu = \min[\delta, \eta/4]$ and this implies that

$$\mathscr{S}(b, \mu) \cap \operatorname{nup}(\mathscr{F})$$

is empty. This is a contradiction and completes the proof.

## 11–8  NON-MANIFOLD PROBLEMS

The study of projections on submanifolds is a natural and essential first step toward a geometric theory of nonlinear approximation. However, such a theory does not apply to many of the most interesting nonlinear approximation problems. This section explores this point in some detail and the next section considers what results one can obtain (or hope for) concerning projections on objects more general than manifolds.

The requirement for a connected set $\mathscr{F} \subset B^m$ to be a manifold is, intuitively speaking, that $\mathscr{F}$ be connected together in such a way that every little piece looks the same topologically (and, in fact, looks like a little piece of Euclidean space). This implies that $\mathscr{F}$ has constant dimension and rules out such sets as illustrated in Fig. 12–1. We have already seen in Section 11–3 that unisolvent and locally unisolvent functions lead to projection problems involving manifolds. It has been remarked several times that such functions (nonlinear ones) are uncommon. We now consider two common nonlinear approximating functions and examine in some detail the mechanisms by which they fail to be manifolds.

EXAMPLE 1.

$$X = \{0 \leq x_1 < x_2 < x_3 < x_4 \leq 1\},$$

$$F(A, x) = \frac{a + bx}{c + dx}, \qquad A \in P,$$

$$P = \{(a, b, c, d) \mid c^2 + d^2 = 1; \quad c + dx > 0, \quad x \in [x_1, x_4]\}.$$

Then

$$\mathscr{F} = \{(F(A, x_1), \quad F(A, x_2), \quad F(A, x_3), \quad F(A, x_4)) \mid A \in P\}$$

is the set in $B^4$ (the set of functions defined on $X$) upon which we wish to project. It is readily verified that $\mathscr{F}$ is homeomorphic to the interior of a double wedge plus the line of intersection of the planes defining the wedge. A two-dimensional cross section of such a set is shown in Fig. 11–9. This set is not closed, and as observed in Chapter 9, best approximations do not exist for all functions defined on $X$. The set $\mathscr{F}$ may be closed by adjoining the pseudo-rational functions which are constant on $[x_1, x_4]$ except for a jump discontinuity at $x_1$ or $x_4$. The appropriate functions are shown in Fig. 11–9. These pseudo-rationals are the functions connected with the concept of stabilized best approximations of Section 9–3, although they were not

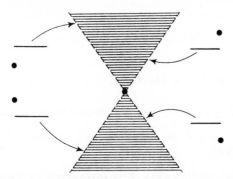

FIG. 11–9. A cross section of the set $\mathscr{F}$ for the approximating function $(a + bx)/(c + dx)$. The pseudo-rational functions required to close the set are shown also.

specifically introduced there. A concrete case of such pseudo-functions is seen in the final section of Chapter 8.

The exceptional points of this set $\mathscr{F}$ is the line where the two wedges meet (which is in $\mathscr{F}$). This line is the set of constants and there the varisolvent degree of $F(A, x)$ is two rather than three. In this case the varisolvent degree can be related to the dimension of $\mathscr{F}$ as follows: If $F(A, x)$ has varisolvent degree $m(A)$ at $A$, then neighborhoods of $A$ in $\mathscr{F}$ contain subsets homeomorphic to Euclidean neighborhoods of maximum dimension $m(A)$.

If we choose to consider the closure $\overline{\mathscr{F}}$ of $\mathscr{F}$ in $B^4$, one still does not have a manifold.

EXAMPLE 2. $X$ as above and

$$F(A, x) = ae^{tx} + b.$$

The definition of $F(A, x)$ is extended as in Chapter 8. It is readily verified that the set $\mathscr{F}$ obtained from this approximating function is homeomorphic to that of Example 1.

The properties exhibited by these two examples are shared to some extent by all varisolvent approximating functions. Thus a geometric theory of projections which is relevant to the most interesting nonlinear approximation problems must consider more general geometric objects than manifolds. We examine some of the geometric properties of sets defined by varisolvent approximating functions.

Let $F(A, x)$ be a varisolvent function and let

$$m_0 = \max_{A \in P} m(A)$$

be the maximum degree of $F(A, x)$. Define

$$\mathscr{F}_k = \{F(A, x) \mid m(A) \geq k.\}$$

We have

**Lemma 11–13.** (a) *The set $\mathscr{F}_k$ is open in $\mathscr{F}$,* (b) *$\mathscr{F}_{m_0}$ is a manifold of dimension $m_0$.*

*Proof.* Statement (a) is Theorem 7–1 and (b) follows by the reasoning of Theorem 11–1.

The first result concerning sets $\mathscr{F}$ obtained from varisolvent functions is

**Theorem 11–16.** *Let $\mathscr{F}$ be varisolvent and connected, $X$ finite. Then $\mathscr{F}$ is not a manifold.*

Here, and later, when we say $\mathscr{F}$ is varisolvent we imply that $\mathscr{F}$ is not, in fact, unisolvent or locally unisolvent, i.e. that the degree $m(A)$ of $F(A, x)$ is *not constant*.

*Proof.* Assume that $\mathscr{F}$ is a manifold. From Lemma 11–13 and connectedness, it follows that $\mathscr{F}$ is a manifold of dimension $m_0$. Let $f \in \mathscr{F}$ be a point where $m(A) = p < m_0$. Such a point must exist since $m(A)$ is not constant. Since $\mathscr{F}$ has Property Z of degree $p$ at $f$, it follows that no point of the set $\mathscr{F} - f$ contains any of the $(m - p)$-dimensional coordinate subspaces defined by

$$b_{i_k} = 0, \qquad k = 1, 2, \ldots, p$$

where $b \in B^m$ has coordinates $(b_1, b_2, \ldots, b_m)$.

Now every $m_0$-dimensional neighborhood of the origin intersects every $(m - m_0 + 1)$-dimensional (and hence every $(m - p)$-dimensional) neighborhood of the origin. This contradicts Property Z of degree $p < m_0$ and establishes the theorem.

**Theorem 11–17.** *Let $\mathscr{F}$ be varisolvent, $X$ finite. Then $\mathscr{F}$ is not convex.*

We ignore the trivial case where $\mathscr{F}$ consists of a single point $F(A_0, x)$ and $m(A_0) = 0$.

*Proof.* Let $m_0 = \max \{m(A) \mid A \in P\}$. Assume $\mathscr{F}$ is convex. Then the closure $\overline{\mathscr{F}}_{m_0}$ contains $\mathscr{F}$ and is convex. The reasoning of Theorem 11–12 may be applied directly to show that $\mathscr{F}$ lies in some $m_0$-dimensional linear manifold $\mathscr{L}$ in $B^m$. In the remainder of the proof we restrict our attention to $\mathscr{F}$ as a subset of $\mathscr{L}$.

Consider a point $f \in \mathscr{F}$ of degree $p < m_0$. Such a point must exist and it lies on the boundary of $\mathscr{F}$. There is a hyperplane $H$ (in $\mathscr{L}$) of support to $\mathscr{F}$ at $f$. Consider the coordinate system of $B^m$ translated to $f$ (or, equivalently, the set $\mathscr{F} - f$). There is at least one coordinate semi-axis which is separated from $\mathscr{F}$ by $H$. For concreteness assume that it is the $k$th negative semi-axis. Then it is not possible to solve the equation (with $F(A_0, x) = f$)

$$F(A, x_k) = F(A_0, x_k) - \epsilon$$

for any $\epsilon > 0$. Thus $\mathscr{F}$ is not locally solvent of any degree at $F(A_0, x)$. This is a contradiction and concludes the proof.

**Theorem 11–18.** *Let $\mathscr{F}$ be varisolvent, $X$ finite. Then $\mathscr{F}$ is not closed.*

Note that this theorem is not true if $X$ is an interval, e.g. the rationals $(a + bx)/(c + dx)$ with the Tchebycheff norm.

*Proof.* We show that $\mathscr{F}$ does not contain $\overline{\mathscr{F}_{m_0}}$. Choose $m_0$ points $x_i \subset X$ and consider $\mathscr{F}$ in $B^{m_0}$ (the space of functions defined on $x_i$). Now $\mathscr{F} \neq B^{m_0}$ because $\mathscr{F}$ is not a manifold. If $f = F(A, x)$ is any boundary point of $\overline{\mathscr{F}_{m_0}}$, then $m(A) < m_0$ since $\mathscr{F}_{m_0}$ is open. Consider the origin of $B^{m_0}$ translated to a boundary point $f$. Then, since $f = F(A, x)$ has Property $Z$ of degree $m(A) < m_0$ at $f$, the set $\mathscr{F}$ does not intersect any $(m_0 - 1)$-dimensional coordinate hyperplane.

*Assertion. Let $\mathscr{G}$ be an open set in $B^m$ with the property: given $g \in \partial\mathscr{G}$, then $\mathscr{G} - g$ does not intersect any $(m - 1)$-dimensional coordinate hyperplane of $B^m$. Then $\mathscr{G}$ is either empty or the whole space $B^m$.*

This assertion is similar to Lemma 3–12 in spirit and purpose.

Assume that $\mathscr{G}$ is not the whole space $B^m$ and choose a point $g_1 \in \mathscr{G}$. Let $\mathscr{S}$ be the largest open Euclidean ball with center $g_1$ which is entirely in $G$. There is a point $g_2$ which is a boundary point of both $\mathscr{S}$ and $\mathscr{G}$ (otherwise $\mathscr{S}$ would not be the largest such ball). The ball $\mathscr{S} - g_2$ has the origin of $B^m$ as a boundary point and is contained in $\mathscr{G} - g_2$. The hypothesis states that this ball $\mathscr{S} - g_2$ does not intersect any $(m - 1)$-dimensional coordinate plane of $B^m$. This is clearly a contradictory statement and hence $\mathscr{G}$ must be empty.

If $\mathscr{F} \subset \overline{\mathscr{F}_{m_0}}$, then this assertion may be applied immediately to $\mathscr{F}_{m_0}$ in the present context and one concludes that $\mathscr{F}_{m_0}$ is either empty or the whole space $B^{m_0}$. It is noted above that $\mathscr{F}_{m_0} \neq B^{m_0}$ and, by definition, $\mathscr{F}_{m_0}$ is not empty so that the possibility that $\mathscr{F} \subset \overline{\mathscr{F}_{m_0}}$ is not tenable. This concludes the proof.

These three theorems show that if $\mathscr{F}$ is varisolvent then it is neither a manifold nor convex nor closed. Thus a geometrical theory of projections which is relevant to nonlinear approximation on finite point sets must consider objects which are neither manifolds nor convex nor closed.

It is rather remarkable that approximation by $(a + bx)/(c + dx)$ and $ae^{tx} + c$ should lead to such similar problems when interpreted as projection problems. Of course the mechanics of the projections are distinct, but the intrinsic nature of the problems must be similar. This raises the interesting (and probably difficult) question of what features of the projection (approximation) are invariant under a homeomorphism of $\mathscr{F}$. That there are some such features is implied by the result in the next section which relates topological invariants of the set $\mathscr{F}$ with those of the set nup $(\mathscr{F})$ of points with nonunique projections onto $\mathscr{F}$.

The following example shows that one cannot conclude that every pair of varisolvent functions with similar behavior in the degree $m(A)$ lead to sets $\mathscr{F}$ which are homeomorphic.

EXAMPLE 3. $X$ finite in $[0, 1]$.

$$F(A, x) = a + bx + cx^2$$

$$P = \{(a, b, c) \mid |a| < \infty, \quad |b| < \infty \quad \text{if} \quad c = 0, b > 0 \quad \text{and}$$

$$b + 2c > 0 \quad \text{if} \quad c \neq 0\}.$$

This is the constrained linear approximating function consisting of all straight lines plus all parabolas strictly increasing on $[0, 1]$. This function is varisolvent with degree

$$m(A) = \begin{cases} 3 & \text{if} \quad b > 0 \quad \text{and} \quad b + 2c > 0, \\ 2 & \text{if} \quad b \leq 0. \end{cases}$$

A cross section of the set $\mathscr{F}$ is shown in Fig. 11–10.

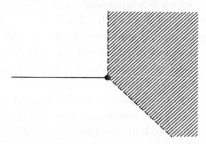

FIG. 11–10.   A cross section (for $a = 0$) of $\mathscr{F}$ for Example 3.

One can also consider the set of all parabolas strictly monotonic on $[0, 1]$ (i.e. whose derivatives have no zeros in $[0, 1]$) plus all constants. This is also a varisolvent approximating function and this set $\mathscr{F}_p$ is homeomorphic to those of Examples 1 and 2. As in those examples, the constant functions have degree 2 while the others have degree 3.

Even though the set $\mathscr{F}_p$ defined here is homeomorphic to the set $\mathscr{F}_R$ of Example 1, there is a certain incompatibility present. To show this, we define the homeomorphism explicitly as follows:

$$\frac{a + bx}{c + dx} \iff \alpha + \beta x + \gamma x^2$$

if

(a) $\dfrac{a+b}{c+d} = \alpha + \beta + \gamma = v_2,$

(b) $\dfrac{a+b/2}{c+d/2} = \alpha + \dfrac{\beta}{2} + \dfrac{\gamma}{4} = v_1,$

(c) $\dfrac{a}{c} = v_0 + \dfrac{(\alpha - v_0)}{v_0 + 2(v_1 - v_2) - \alpha}$

where $v_0 = 2v_1 - v_2$. In particular the limiting case of $\left|\dfrac{a}{c}\right| = \infty$ is associated with the limiting case $\alpha + 2\gamma = 0$. One of these limiting functions is bounded (the parabola) and hence lies in $B^m$. The other one is not bounded and hence does not lie in $B^m$.

We may draw the analogy with the following fact: the interior of the unit square in $E^2$ is homeomorphic to the interior of the first quadrant of $E^2$. However, there is no homeomorphism of $E^2$ into itself which carries these two sets into one another. Likewise, *there is no homeomorphism of $B^m$ into itself which carries $\mathscr{F}_p$ into $\mathscr{F}_R$*. Thus, even though $\mathscr{F}_p$ and $\mathscr{F}_R$ are homeomorphic, we should expect the approximation (or projection) problems to differ in some essential way.

## 11–9  PROJECTIONS ON OBJECTS

The discussion in the preceding section indicates that we should consider projections onto geometrical objects more general than manifolds. The word "object" is used to denote any set in $B^m$ and is intended to connote the geometrical nature of the development given here. It is clear that we cannot obtain many general results without some further hypothesis on these objects, but there are a few results presented in this section. These results, which are in some cases rather weak, give starting points for a more detailed analysis involving a more specific class of geometrical objects. We have immediately the following restatements of Theorem 11–10 and 11–11.

**Theorem 11–10A.** *Let $\mathscr{F}$ be an object in $B^m$. Then every point of $B^m$ has a projection on $\mathscr{F}$ if and only if $\mathscr{F}$ is closed.*

**Theorem 11–11A.** *Let $\mathscr{F}$ be an object in $B^m$. The point $f^* \in \mathscr{F}$ is a projection of $b$ onto $\mathscr{F}$ if and only if the sphere $\partial \mathscr{S}(b, r^*)$ is a sphere of support of $\mathscr{F}$ and $f^* \in \partial \mathscr{S}(b, r^*)$ where $r^* = \|b - \mathscr{F}\|$.*

Note also that Corollary 2 of Theorem 11–9 applies to any closed object $\mathscr{F}$. That result shows that in smooth spaces the question of a global uniqueness theorem for projections is the question of convexity of $\mathscr{F}$. Simple examples show that if $B^m$ is not smooth, then there may be Motzkin sets which are not convex. Precise conditions under which this may occur are not known and deserve further study.

Since varisolvent (and many other) nonlinear approximation problems lead to objects which are not convex, there is considerable interest in a neighborhood of unique projection similar to that obtained for manifolds. The analysis there is difficult because of the desire to give conditions for the existence of such neighborhoods in terms of the geometrical concept of curvature. It was pointed out previously that there is room to question whether the curvature is the more intrinsic of the properties. In the present situation there is no classical concept of the curvature of objects and hence we feel free to omit such a concept. It seems that the concept of *reach* is a natural one to use in the discussion of the uniqueness of projections onto objects and, indeed, it is for this purpose that Federer originally introduced the concept in Euclidean spaces. We have

**Theorem 11–19.** *Let $\mathscr{F}$ be a closed object with positive reach at each point. Then $\mathscr{F}$ has a neighborhood $\mathscr{F}_u$ in $B^m$ such that $b \in \mathscr{F}_u$ implies that $b$ has a unique projection onto $\mathscr{F}$. If $r_0 > 0$ is the infimum of the reach in $\mathscr{F}$, then $\mathscr{F}_u$ may be taken as*

$$\{b \mid \|b - \mathscr{F}\| < r_0\}.$$

*Proof.* This theorem follows directly from Definition 11–11.

Theorem 11–19 immediately raises the question of determining the reach of a set $\mathscr{F}$ at any or all of its points. Lower bounds on the reach are also of interest. The points of a set $\mathscr{F}$ that can be "seen" from a point $b$ outside $\mathscr{F}$ form a manifold—or piecewise manifold for most well behaved sets. This implies that machinery developed for projections onto manifolds can frequently be applied to projection problems involving more general objects.

Simple examples of one-dimensional objects in the plane show that the topological nature of $\mathscr{F}$ may imply that $\mathscr{F}$ does not have positive reach at certain points. See Fig. 11–11.

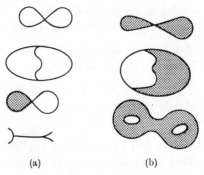

(a)                    (b)

FIG. 11–11.  Sets in the plane which (a) are not homeomorphic to any set with positive reach, and (b) have positive reach.

The situation is more complicated in higher dimensions and it is not known, in general, how to distinguish on a topological basis sets which might have positive reach.

There is a definite topological relationship between $\mathscr{F}$ and the set nup $(\mathscr{F})$. In order to establish this we perform the one point compactification of $B^m$ to obtain the $m$-sphere $S^m$ (which is to be distinguished from a sphere in $B^m$). See Dugundji, 1966, XI, 8. We assume that the one "ideal" point added is in nup $(\mathscr{F})$. We require

**Definition 11–16.** *Let $B_1 \subseteq B_2$ be subsets of $B^m$ and let $I = [0, 1]$. The set $B_1$ is a deformation retract of $B_2$ if there exists a continuous function $\phi(t, b)$ defined on $I \otimes B_2$ such that $\phi(0, B_2) = B_2$ and $\phi(1, B_2) = B_1$.*

**Theorem 11–20.** *Let $\mathscr{F}$ be a closed submanifold with continuous curvature of a Minkowski space $B^m$. Then nup $(\mathscr{F})$ is a deformation retract of $S^m - \mathscr{F}$.*

*Proof.* For $b \notin \mathscr{F}$, $b \notin$ nup $(\mathscr{F})$ set $f = \mathbf{P}(b)$, $r^* = r(f, b)$,

$$\alpha'(b) = \min \{\|f - c\| \mid c \in r^* \cap \text{nup } (\mathscr{F})\}, \qquad (11\text{-}9.1)$$

$$\alpha(b) = \alpha'(b)/\|f - b\|.$$

We take the minimum of the empty set to be $+\infty$ and note that $\alpha(b) > 1$. Define $\phi(t, b) = b$ for $b \in$ nup $(\mathscr{F})$ and

$$\phi(t, b) = \mathbf{P}(b) + \frac{b - \mathbf{P}(b)}{1 - t\left[1 - \dfrac{1}{\alpha(b)}\right]}, \qquad b \notin \text{nup } (\mathscr{F}). \quad (11\text{-}9.2)$$

It is clear that $\phi(0, b) = b$ and $\phi(1, b) \in$ nup $(\mathscr{F})$. For $b \notin$ nup $(\mathscr{F})$, $\mathbf{P}(b)$ is a continuous function of $b$. Further $\phi(t, b)$ is continuous in $t$ and $\alpha$ for $0 \leq t \leq 1$ and $\alpha > 1$ in the topology of $S^m$. We show that $\alpha(b)$ is a continuous function of $b$. It follows directly from Theorem 11–8 that

$$\alpha(b) \leq \rho(f, r^*).$$

The assumption that there is a sequence $\{c_i\}$ which converges to $b \notin$ nup $(\mathscr{F})$ so that $|\alpha(c_i) - \alpha(b)| \geq \eta > 0$ leads to a contradiction as follows. If $\alpha(c_i) < \alpha(b)$ for infinitely many $i$ then a subsequence of $\{\phi(1, c_i)\}$ converges to a point $c \in$ nup $(\mathscr{F}) \cap r^*$. Thus $\|f - c\| < \|f - \phi(1, b)\| = \alpha'(b)$ which contradicts the definition of $\alpha'(b)$.

Suppose that $\alpha(b) < \alpha(c_i)$ for infinitely many $i$ then $\phi(1, b)$ is contained in the interior of the segment $s(f, c)$. Since $B^m$ is Minkowskian it follows from Lemma 11–1 that $\phi(1, b)$ is not a nup point. Since $\phi(1, b) \in$ nup $(\mathscr{F})$ it follows from Theorem 11–15 that

$$\|\phi(1, b) - \mathscr{F}\| = \rho(f, r^*) = \rho^*.$$

Since the curvature is continuous given $\eta/2 > 0$ there is a $\delta > 0$ so that $\|f - g\| < \delta$ implies that $\rho(g, r(g, c)) < \rho^* + \eta/2$. Thus for $\|c_i - b\|$ sufficiently small

$$\alpha'(c_i) \leq \rho\left(\mathbf{P}(c_i), r[\mathbf{P}(c_i), c_i]\right) < \rho^* + \epsilon = \alpha'(b) + \eta/2$$

which contradicts the supposition on $\alpha(c_i)$.

If $b \in \text{nup}(\mathscr{F})$ and $b$ is not a nup point then the preceding argument shows that $\alpha(b)$ is continuous.

Suppose that $b$ is a nup point. For points $c \in \text{nup}(\mathscr{F})$ then the continuity of $\phi(t, b)$ is clear. Further if $c_i \to b$ and $\alpha(c_i) < 1 - \eta$, then a contradiction is reached as before. Likewise if $\|b - \mathscr{F}\| + \eta < \alpha'(c_i) \leq K < \infty$ a preceding argument leads to a contradiction.

Finally, we show that if $\alpha(b) < \infty$, then $|\alpha(c_i) - \alpha(b)|$ cannot be unbounded. If $\phi(1, b)$ is not a nup point, then the above argument applies. The remaining case is based on the following fact: Let $\partial \mathscr{S}_1$ and $\partial \mathscr{S}_2$ be two closed spheres in a Minkowski space $B^m$ which have a common hyperplane of support at a common point which is collinear with the centers of the spheres. Then either $\partial \mathscr{S}_1 = \partial \mathscr{S}_2$ or $\partial \mathscr{S}_1 \cap \partial \mathscr{S}_2$ consists of a single point. Let $z$ be a point on the ray $r(f, b)$ with $\|z - \mathscr{F}\| = 2\|\phi(1, b) - \mathscr{F}\|$. Then $\mathscr{S}(z, \|z - f\|)$ contains points of $\mathscr{F}$. Furthermore, as $c_i \to b$, there are points $z_i \in r(\mathbf{P}(c_i), c_i)$ which converge to $z$ and if $|\alpha(c_i)| \to +\infty$, these points have a unique projection onto $\mathscr{F}$ near $f$. However, $\mathscr{S}(z_i, \|z_i - \mathscr{F}\|)$ is arbitrarily close to $\mathscr{S}(z, \|z - f\|)$ and hence for $i$ sufficiently large $\mathscr{S}(z_i, \|z_i - \mathscr{F}\|)$ contains points of $\mathscr{F}$ bounded away from $f$. This is a contradiction and concludes the proof.

That the hypothesis of continuous curvature is essential to the method of proof of Theorem 11–20 is shown by the following example. However, this example also suggests that the theorem is valid with a weaker hypothesis on $\mathscr{F}$.

EXAMPLE 1. We define a surface $\mathscr{F}$ in the unit square of Euclidean three-space. The surface is represented by the function $f = f(x, y)$ where

  (a) $f = 0$ if $|x| \geq |y|$,
  (b) $f = y^2$ on the curves $x = \pm y^2$,
  (c) if $|x| < y^2$ then $f(x, y)$ is the $z$-coordinate of the boundary of a sphere of radius $\frac{1}{4}$, with center on the line $(0, y, z)$ and whose boundary contains the points $(\pm y^2, y, y^2)$,
  (d) if $|y| > |x| > |y|^2$ then $f(x, y)$ is defined so as to be linear in $x$ for $y$ fixed and $|y| \leq x \leq y^2$.

The surface is illustrated in Fig. 11–12.

In the notation of the proof of Theorem 11–20, one may verify that

(a) $b_0 = (0, 0, \frac{1}{8})$ implies $\mathbf{P}(b_0) = (0, 0, 0)$, $z^* = (0, 0, \frac{1}{4})$,

(b) $b_k = \left(1/(4k^2), 1/k, \frac{1}{8}\right)$ implies $z_k = \left(1/k, 0, \frac{1}{4} + (1 + o(1))/k^2\right)$,

(c) $b_k = (1/k, 0, \frac{1}{8})$ implies $z_k = (1/k, 0, \beta)$, $\beta > \frac{1}{2}$.

Thus $\alpha'(b)$ is not continuous at $b = (0, 0, \frac{1}{8})$ and the mapping $\phi(t, b)$ defined by (11–9.2) is not continuous for this $\mathscr{F}$.

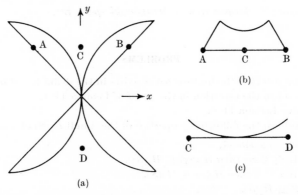

FIG. 11–12.    (a) the regions in the definition of $f(x, y)$, (b) a cross section of $\mathscr{F}$ with $y$ fixed, (c) a cross section of $\mathscr{F}$ in the $yz$-plane.

The component of nup $(\mathscr{F})$ above $\mathscr{F}$ is contained in the $xz$-plane and the $yz$-plane. A sketch is shown in Fig. 11–13.

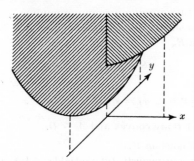

FIG. 11–13.    A component of nup $(\mathscr{F})$ for Example 1. We see from this figure that this component of nup $(\mathscr{F})$ is a deformation retract of the component of $S^m - \mathscr{F}$ above $\mathscr{F}$.

It is likely that the assumption that $B^m$ is strictly convex can also be weakened but, again, examples show that the mapping (11–9.2) is not always continuous for this case.

One may combine Theorem 11–20 and the Alexander duality theorem to establish a precise relationship between the topological nature of $\mathscr{F}$ and nup ($\mathscr{F}$). Let $R_\pi^p(x)$ denote the $p$th Betti number of $x$ for chains mod $\pi$ (see Lefschetz, 1949). We have

**Corollary.** *Assume $\mathscr{F}$ has continuous curvature and is such that the Alexander duality theorem is applicable. Then the following relation exists between Betti numbers of $\mathscr{F}$ and nup ($\mathscr{F}$).*

$$R_\pi^p(\mathscr{F}) = R_\pi^p \left(\text{nup} (\mathscr{F})\right) + \delta_{p,m-1} - \delta_{p,0}$$

*in the space $S^m$ formed from a Minkowski space $B^m$.*

## PROBLEMS

11–1.  Establish that the limiting set $\mathscr{P}$ exists in the definition of limit sphere.

11–2.  Establish the assertion in the proof of Lemma 11–1.

11–3.  Prove Lemma 11–6.

11–4.  Establish the following properties of the α-hull $H_\alpha(S)$ of a set $S$.

   (a)  $H_\alpha(S)$ is closed.

   (b)  If $S_1 \subseteq S_2$ then $H_\alpha(S_1) \subseteq H_\alpha(S_2)$.

   (c)  If $\alpha < \beta$ then $H_\alpha(S) \subseteq H_\beta(S)$.

   (d)  $S \subseteq H_\alpha(S)$.

   (e)  Let $L$ be a linear submanifold of $B$ and $S \subset L$. Then $H_\alpha(S) \cap L$ is contained in the α-hull of $S$ as a subset of the space $L$.

   (f)  Suppose $S \subseteq B^m$, where $B^m$ is smooth Minkowski space with $m < \infty$. If $H_\alpha(S) = S$ for some $\alpha > 0$ then $S$ is convex or $S$ lies in a linear submanifold of $B^m$.

(Efimov and Steckin, 1958.)

11–5.  We consider a subset $S$ of Euclidean space $E_m$. Let $U = E_n - \text{nup}(S)$ and $x, y, z$ be points in $E_n$

   (a)  $\left| \|x - S\| - \|y - S\| \right| \le \|x - y\|$

   (b)  If $s \in S$ and
$$A = \{x \mid \mathbf{P}_s(s + x) = s\}, \quad B = \{x \mid \|s + x - S\| = \|x\|\}$$
then $A$ and $B$ are convex and $A \subset B$.

   (c)  $\mathbf{P}_s$ is continuous on $U$.

   (d)  $\|x - S\|$ is continuously differentiable on Int $(U - S)$ and $\|x - S\|^2$ is continuously differentiable on Int $U$ with
$$\text{grad} \|x - S\|^2 = 2[x - \mathbf{P}_s(x)].$$

   (e)  If $s \in S$ and
$$0 < \tau == \sup \{t \mid \mathbf{P}_s(s + tx) = S\} < \infty$$
then $s + \tau x \notin \text{Int } U$.

   (f)  If $0 < r < q < \infty$, $x, y \in U$ and
$$\|x - S\| \le r, \|y - S\| \le r, \omega(\mathbf{P}_s(x)) \ge q, \omega(\mathbf{P}_s(y)) \ge q$$

then

$$\|\mathbf{P}_S(x) - \mathbf{P}_S(y)\| \le \frac{q}{q-r} \|\ x - y\|.$$

(Federer, 1959.)

11–6. Show that the only finite dimensional and linear Motzkin sets in the space of continuous functions (with the $L_\infty$-norm) are subspaces (or translates of subspaces) spanned by a Tchebycheff set of functions.

11–7. Show that a Motzkin set must be closed.

11–8. Give an example of a 3-dimensional space $B^3$ where every Motzkin set is convex, but $B^3$ is not smooth.

11–9. Prove that an example such as in Problem 11–8 cannot be constructed for $m = 2$.

# 12

# Multivariate Approximation

## 12–1 INTRODUCTION

In the other chapters of this book, it is almost always assumed that we are considering the approximation to functions defined on a one-dimensional set. In this chapter, we consider an extension of the results of the linear theory for $L_2$- and Tchebycheff approximation. It is seen that there is, in the theory, no obstacle to the extension of the linear $L_2$-theory to the abstract setting of Hilbert space. This is carried out in the next section and the following section indicates simplifications possible when tensor products are involved.

There is, however, an essential difficulty in the extension of the Tchebycheff theory to functions of more than one variable. The basic problem as discussed in Section 12–4, is that there are no Tchebycheff sets of functions of more than one variable. The properties of Tchebycheff sets are used frequently and essentially in the linear theory of Chapter 3 and the multivariate extension of the linear Tchebycheff theory is considerably changed by the absence of these properties. The bulk of the Chapter (Sections 12–4 through 12–8) presents this extension. The difficulty of the extension occurs in going from one to two dimensions and once the two-variable theory is developed, there is little difficulty in extensions to abstract spaces. We develop the theory for functions defined on a metric space $X$, but most of the results may be readily generalized to spaces with less topological structure.

The final section discusses three topics concerning computation. They are (1) orthogonalization, (2) exchange algorithms for Tchebycheff and strict approximations and (3) the structure of critical point sets of Tchebycheff approximations. Another promising computational method (Lawson, 1961) for multivariate Tchebycheff approximation is presented at the end of Chapter 13. See also Rice and Usow, 1968.

It is appropriate to point out that one must expect an essential increase in the size of the computational problem with an increase in dimension. This is due to the fact that a function $f(x, y)$ of two variables presents essentially more information than a function $g(x)$ of one variable and of comparable "smoothness". Thus if we think of $g(x)$ as "smooth and well behaved" if it is adequately approximated by a cubic polynomial with 4 coefficients, then we must consider $f(x, y)$ as smooth and well behaved if it is adequately approximated by a bi-cubic polynomial with 16 coefficients. It is apparent that anything more than the simplest problems in three or more dimensions will require a sizeable computation (at least by present standards).

## 12–2  LEAST SQUARES AND GENERAL ORTHONORMAL SYSTEMS

In many ways there is really nothing new encountered in least squares approximation to functions of several variables. The theoretical developments of Chapter 2 may be extended in a satisfying and straightforward way. We shall outline this procedure briefly in the first part of this section and then present a few concrete realizations of the abstract theory.

There are, however, difficulties encountered when one attempts actually to compute approximations. This problem is discussed in more detail in the last section of this chapter, but we indicate here the source of the new difficulties. The two major sources of difficulty are (a) the lack of readily available and well-known orthogonal functions and (b) the increased size of the problem. The next section shows how (a) may be avoided by the use of tensor products for a special, but unfortunately common, class of problems. One can, of course (theoretically) generate an orthogonal set of functions from any given set. However, the difficulty (b) enters directly and often dramatically into such a procedure.

The difficulty of increased size is something of a subjective nature. One can have one-dimensional problems of arbitrarily large "size". Nevertheless, a "smooth well-behaved" surface represents an order of magnitude more informative than a "smooth well-behaved" curve and this is reflected in the fact that problems in several variables tend to be considerably larger than one-dimensional problems.

Let us consider the set $H$ of real continuous functions $f(x)$ defined on a set $X$. We assume for concreteness that $X$ is contained in finite dimensional Euclidean space. We assume that we have defined an *inner product* (dot product) $(f, g)$ on $H$. The inner product has the usual properties of

Linearity:    $(f + g, h) = (f, h) + (g, h)$,
Symmetry:    $(f, g) = (g, h)$,
Homogeneity:  $(\alpha f, g) = \alpha(f, g)$,
Positivity:    $(f, f) \geq 0$  and  $(f, f) = 0$ if and only if $f(x) \equiv 0$.

The inner product defines the *norm* on $H$ by

$$\|f\| = \sqrt{(f, f)}$$

and this is the $L_2$-norm. Two functions $f$ and $g$ are *orthogonal* if $(f, g) = 0$. The function $f$ is *normalized* if $(f, f) = 1$.

Let us consider approximation by the linear approximating function

$$L(A, x) = \sum_{i=1}^{n} a_i \phi_i(x) \tag{12–2.1}$$

where $\phi_i \in H$. We may immediately establish a theorem which simultaneously answers the existence, characterization and uniqueness questions. This is the direct analog of Theorem 2–1.

**Theorem 12–1.** *Let $f \in H$ and let $\{\phi_i\}$ be an orthogonal system of functions in $H$. Then $f$ possesses a unique $L_2$-approximation of the form $L(A^*, x)$ and the coefficients $a_i^*$ are given by*

$$a_i^* = (f, \phi_i). \tag{12–2.2}$$

In view of this theorem, the least squares approximation problem is easily solved provided that the inner product may be evaluated without too much difficulty and provided that one has an orthonormal set $\{\phi_i\}$.

One should logically follow the pattern of Chapter 2 and discuss in some detail various systems of orthogonal functions and their properties. However, the elegant results for the interval [0, 1] simply do not exist when $X$ is a higher dimensional space.

We will thus turn to some concrete examples of least squares approximation problems for functions of two variables. The analogs for more than two variables are clear.

EXAMPLE 1. (Simple Line Integral.) Let $X$ be a curve (one we can integrate over) in the plane. We define the inner product by

$$(f, g) = \int_X f(x) g(x) \, ds, \tag{12–2.3}$$

where $s$ is arc length along the curve. It is clear that we can introduce a positive weight function into the integral (12–2.3). We remark that this problem is really not a two-dimensional one. We can parameterize the curve $X$ in such a way to reduce the problem to approximation on an interval (possibly with a periodicity condition if $X$ is a closed curve).

EXAMPLE 2. (Complicated Line Integral.) Let $X$ be the union of a number of curves such as illustrated in Fig. 12–1. One can define the inner product by (12–2.3) for this example, but one cannot easily reduce the approximation problem to a one-dimensional one.

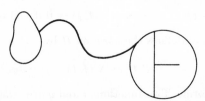

FIG. 12–1.   A set $X$ which is the union of a number of simple curves.

EXAMPLE 3. (Area Integral.) Let $X$ be the set composed of a smooth closed curve and its interior. Then an inner product may be defined in terms of a double integral by

$$(f, g) = \int\int_X f(x, y)g(x, y)dx\,dy. \tag{12–2.4}$$

This is the inner product that one would normally use for the least squares approximation of functions of two variables, e.g. for surfaces. One can introduce a positive weight function into (12–2.4).

EXAMPLE 4. (Sums.) Let $X$ be a finite point set in Euclidean space, i.e. $X = \{x_i | i = 1, 2, \ldots, m\}$. We may then define the inner product by

$$(f, g) = \sum_{i=1}^{m} f(x_i)g(x_i). \tag{12–2.5}$$

In this case $X$ is zero-dimensional. However such situations are usually encountered when one replaces a truly higher dimensional set with a finite point set in order to make computations possible. Thus the main features of Example 3 are present here if $X$ is obtained by choosing a certain number of points in the region above.

## 12–3  TENSOR PRODUCTS

If $X$ is a product space, formed as the product of a number of intervals, then one may apply certain one-dimensional results to least squares approximation on $X$. If $X$ is the product of intervals, then it is a "rectangular box" and clearly we may assume that it is the unit cube in $k$-dimensional Euclidean space:

$$X = \{(x_1, x_2, \ldots, x_k) \mid -1 \leq x_i \leq 1\}.$$

An inner product in $H$ is

$$(f, g) = \int_X \cdots \int f(x_1, x_2, \ldots, x_k)g(x_1, x_2, \ldots, x_k)\,dx_1\,dx_2\cdots dx_k. \tag{12–3.1}$$

The *tensor product* of two sets of functions $\{\phi_i \mid i = 1, 2, \ldots, p\}$ and $\{\psi_i \mid i = 1, 2, \ldots, q\}$ is the set $\{\phi_i\psi_j \mid 1 \leq i \leq p, 1 \leq j \leq q\}$. We denote this product by $\{\phi_i\} \otimes \{\psi_j\}$.

We consider approximation with a linear approximating function which is a *tensor product*, i.e.

$$L(A, x) = \sum_{i_1, \ldots, i_k=1}^{n_1, \ldots, n_k} a_{i_1 \ldots i_k}\phi_{i_1}^{(1)} \cdots \phi_{i_k}^{(k)}. \tag{12–3.2}$$

where $\phi_i^{(j)}$ is a function of $x_j$ alone. Note that this framework *does not include*, for example, approximation by

$$a + bx_1 + cx_2 + dx_1^2 + ex_1x_2 + fx_2^2$$

but *does include* approximation by

$$a + bx_1 + cx_2 + dx_1x_2.$$

We have the following

> **Lemma 12–1.** *Let each set $\{\phi_i^{(j)} \mid i = 1, \ldots, n_j\}$ be an orthonormal set of functions on $[-1, 1]$. Then $\{\phi_i^{(1)}\} \otimes \{\phi_i^{(2)}\} \otimes \cdots \otimes \{\phi_i^{(k)}\}$ is an orthornormal set of functions on $X$.*

*Proof.* We have

$$\int_X \cdots \int \phi_{i_1}^{(1)} \lambda_{i_2}^{(2)} \cdots \phi_{i_k}^{(k)} \cdot \phi_{j_1}^{(1)} \phi_{j_2}^{(2)} \cdots \phi_{j_k}^{(k)} \, dx_1 \, dx_2 \cdots dx_k$$

$$= \int_{-1}^{1} \phi_{i_1}^{(1)} \phi_{j_1}^{(2)} \, dx_1 \cdot \int_{-1}^{1} \phi_{i_2}^{(2)} \phi_{j_2}^{(2)} \, dx_2 \cdots \int_{-1}^{1} \phi_{i_k}^{(k)} \phi_{j_k}^{(k)} \, dx_k.$$

The product on the right is zero unless $i_1 = j_1$, $i_2 = j_2$, ..., $i_k = j_k$, in which case it is 1. This concludes the proof.

It is clear that we can establish the result of Lemma 12–1 if $\{\phi_i^{(j)}\}$ is orthonormal with respect to a weight function $w_j(x_j)$ merely by including the weight function $w(x) = w_1(x_1)w_2(x_2) \cdots w_k(x_k)$ in the definition of the inner product.

We may now apply Theorem 12–1 and compute the coefficients $A^*$ of the best $L_2$-approximation of the form (12–3.2),

$$a_{i_1 i_2 \cdots i_k}^* = (f, \phi_{i_1}^{(1)} \phi_{i_2}^{(2)} \cdots \phi_{i_k}^{(k)}). \tag{12–3.3}$$

Since $\phi_i^{(l)}$ depends only on $x_l$, the formula (12–3.3) may be evaluated by performing $k$ single integrations of functions of one variable. This is often substantially less work than performing a single integration of a function of $k$ variables.

We may also consider the approximation problem when the $\{\phi_i^{(l)}\}$ are not orthonormal sets of functions. One can, of course, orthonormalize them and this would not be an unwise procedure. However, one can also take advantage of the tensor product structure of the problem without orthonormalizing. To solve the least squares problem, we have to solve the *normal* equations

$$\sum_{i_1, i_2, \ldots, i_k}^{n_1, n_2, \ldots, n_k} a_{i_1 i_2 \cdots i_k}^* (\phi_{i_1}^{(1)} \phi_{i_2}^{(2)} \cdots \phi_{i_k}^{(k)}, \phi_{j_1}^{(1)} \phi_{j_2}^{(2)} \cdots \phi_{j_k}^{(k)})$$

$$= (f, \phi_{j_1}^{(1)} \cdots \phi_{j_k}^{(k)}), \quad j_i = 1, 2, \ldots, n_i; \quad i = 1, 2, \ldots, k. \tag{12–3.4}$$

Let us denote the coefficient matrix of (12–3.4) by $M$. This matrix is of a particularly simple form and can be inverted by inverting $k$ matrices of order $n_i$, $i = 1, 2, \ldots, k$ rather than inverting the matrix $M$ of order $n_1 n_2 \cdots n_k$.

In order to accomplish this we define the *tensor product* $P \otimes Q$ of the $n \times n$ matrix $P$ and $m \times m$ matrix $Q$ to be the $nm \times nm$ matrix

$$P \otimes Q = \begin{pmatrix} p_{11}Q & p_{12}Q & \cdots & p_{1n}Q \\ p_{21}Q & p_{22}Q & \cdots & p_{2n}Q \\ \cdot & \cdot & & \cdot \\ \cdot & \cdot & & \cdot \\ \cdot & \cdot & & \cdot \\ p_{n1}Q & p_{n2}Q & \cdots & p_{nn}Q \end{pmatrix}. \qquad (12\text{-}3.5)$$

One may readily establish that the tensor product of matrices has the following properties:

(i) $(P + Q) \otimes R = P \otimes R + Q \otimes R$

(ii) $(P \otimes Q)(R \otimes S) = PR \otimes QS$

(iii) $(P \otimes Q)^* = P^* \otimes Q^*$

(iv) $(P \otimes Q)^{-1} = P^{-1} \otimes Q^{-1}$

(v) $\rho(P \otimes Q) = \rho(P)\rho(Q)$

(vi) $\operatorname{tr}(P \otimes Q) = \operatorname{tr}(P) \operatorname{tr}(Q)$

(vii) $\lambda(P \otimes Q) = \{\lambda_i(P)\lambda_j(Q)\}$

(viii) $\det(P \otimes Q) = [\det(P)]^m[\det(Q)]$

We have used the following matrix notation:

$* = $ conjugate transpose, $^{-1} = $ inverse, $\rho(P) = $ rank of $P$, $\operatorname{tr}(P) = $ trace of $P$, $\lambda(P) = $ set of eigenvalues $\lambda_i(P)$, $\det(P) = $ determinant of $P$.

Let us denote by $M_l$ the matrix $(\phi_i^{(l)}, \phi_j^{(l)})$. Then we have

**Lemma 12–2.** *The coefficient matrix $M$ of (12–3.4) has the form*

$$M = M_1 \otimes M_2 \otimes \cdots \otimes M_k. \qquad (12\text{-}3.6)$$

*Proof.* This result may be established by induction on $k$. First consider the case $k = 2$. We have

$$(\phi_{i_1}^{(1)}\phi_{i_2}^{(2)}, \phi_{j_1}^{(1)}\phi_{j_2}^{(2)}) = \int_{-1}^{1} \int_{-1}^{1} \phi_{i_1}^{(1)}(x_1)\phi_{i_2}^{(2)}(x_2)\phi_{j_1}^{(1)}(x_1)\phi_{j_2}^{(2)}(x_2) \, dx_1 \, dx_2$$

$$= \int_{-1}^{1} \phi_{i_1}^{(1)}(x_1)\phi_{j_1}^{(1)}(x_1) \, dx_1 \cdot \int_{-1}^{1} \phi_{i_2}^{(2)}(x_2)\phi_{j_2}^{(2)}(x_2) \, dx_2$$

$$= (\phi_{i_1}^{(1)}, \phi_{j_1}^{(1)}) \cdot (\phi_{i_2}^{(2)}, \phi_{i_2}^{(2)})$$

If we now order the equations in (12–3.4) according to the ordering of the coefficients $a_{1j}, a_{2j}, \ldots, a_{n_1j}$; $j = 1, 2, \ldots, n_2$, then it follows immediately that $M = M_1 \otimes M_2$.

Because of the cumbersome notation we will not carry out the general induction step. Its logic exactly parallels the case $k = 2$.

If we let $F$ denote the vector on the right hand side of (12–3.4), then the parameters $A^*$ of the best $L_2$-approximation to $f$ are given by

$$A^* = M_1^{-1} \otimes M_2^{-1} \otimes \cdots \otimes M_k^{-1} F. \qquad (12\text{–}3.7)$$

## 12–4 TCHEBYCHEFF APPROXIMATION—NONUNIQUENESS

We now turn our attention to Tchebycheff approximation. The results here are in considerable contrast with those obtained for $L_2$-approximation. There is no difficulty in extending the $L_2$-theory and there is no possibility of extending the $L_\infty$-theory. The reader may have noticed that the results of Chapter 3 were developed almost exclusively with the assumption that the set $\{\phi_i(x)\}$ forms a Tchebycheff set. Without that assumption the development breaks down. We will soon see that there are *no Tchebycheff sets of functions of several variables*. This is made more precise later. This section is concerned with establishing this result and exploring its consequences.

We begin by noting that Haar's theorem, Theorem 3–13, extends directly to functions of several variables. In order to formulate this extension we assume that $X$ is a metric space, $\phi_i(x)$, $i = 1, 2, \ldots, n$ and $f(x)$ are functions continuous on $X$. We have the following direct extension of Lemma 3–13:

**Lemma 12–3.** *If every continuous function $f(x)$ on $X$ has a unique best approximation of the form $L(A, x)$, then $L(A, x)$ has Property Z.*

*Proof.* The proof is a formal repetition of the proof of Lemma 3–13 and is not repeated here.

We obtain the classical result of Haar once we assume that the parameter space $P$ is all of $E_n$. The proof is essentially the same as for functions of one variable—see Theorem 3–13.

**Theorem 12–2.** *If $P = E_n$ then every continuous function on $X$ possesses a unique best Tchebycheff approximation of the form*

$$L(A, x) = \sum_{i=1}^{n} a_i \phi_i(x) \qquad (12\text{–}4.1)$$

*if and only if $\{\phi_i(x)\}$ is a Tchebycheff set.*

It follows from this theorem that the uniqueness question depends essentially on existence or nonexistence of Tchebycheff sets. It was first shown by Mairhuber (1956) that Tchebycheff sets exist only on special one-dimensional spaces.

We give a somewhat different proof based on the following two lemmas. The first is given in Buck, 1959, and follows a line of argument due essentially to Haar. We say $X$ contains a *tripod-like set* if it contains a subset homeomorphic to the set illustrated in Fig. 12–2(a).

**Lemma 12-4.** *If $X$ contains a tripod-like set, then there is no Tchebycheff set $\{\phi_i \mid i = 1, 2, \ldots, n\}$ of continuous functions defined on $X$ for $n > 1$.*

We note that the set $\{\phi_i(x) \equiv 1\}$ forms a Tchebycheff set for any $X$.

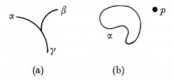

(a)                    (b)

FIG. 12–2.   (a) A tripod-like set, (b) a simple closed curve and another point.

*Proof.* The set $\{\phi_i(x)\}$ is a Tchebycheff set if and only if the determinant

$$\Delta(x_1, x_2, \ldots, x_n) = \det \begin{vmatrix} \phi_1(x_1) \cdots \phi_n(x_1) \\ \phi_1(x_2) \cdots \phi_n(x_2) \\ \cdot \qquad \cdot \\ \cdot \qquad \cdot \\ \cdot \qquad \cdot \\ \phi_1(x_n) \cdots \phi_n(x_n) \end{vmatrix} \qquad (12\text{-}4.2)$$

is zero only when two of the points $x_i$ coincide in $X$. Suppose $X$ contains a tripod-like set. Choose a set of $n$ distinct points in $X$ such that $x_1$ lies on the limb $\alpha$ and $x_2$ lies on the limb $\gamma$. If $X$ consists only of the tripod-like set, assume that $x_1$ and $x_2$ are the points closest to the common point of $\alpha$, $\beta$ and $\gamma$ on the limbs $\alpha$ and $\gamma$, respectively.

The determinant $\Delta$ is a continuous function of the points $x_i$. We now interchange $x_1$ and $x_2$ in the following continuous manner:

(a) Move $x_1$ along $\alpha$ to the common point of $\alpha$, $\beta$ and $\gamma$ and then move it up the limb $\beta$.

(b) Move $x_2$ along the limb $\gamma$ onto the limb $\alpha$ and to the point where $x_1$ was originally.

(c) Move $x_1$ down the limb $\beta$ to the common point of $\alpha$, $\beta$ and $\gamma$ and then along the limb $\gamma$ to the point where $x_2$ was originally. It is clear that in this procedure none of the $x_i$ have coincided. Furthermore, the determinant $\Delta$ has changed sign as the first two rows have been interchanged. Thus at some place the determinant $\Delta$ was zero and hence $\{\phi_i(x)\}$ is not a Tchebycheff set. This concludes the proof.

**Lemma 12-5.** *If $X$ contains a curve homeomorphic to a circle (and another point) then there is no Tchebycheff set $\{\phi_i \mid i = 1, 2, \ldots, n\}$ of continuous functions defined on $X$ for $n$ odd, $n > 1$ (for $n$ even).*

*Proof.* Consider again the determinant (12–4.2). If $n$ is odd choose $n$ distinct points on the curve $\alpha$ homeomorphic to a circle. Order these points along $\alpha$, then we may continuously move $x_i$ to where $x_{i+1}$ was originally $(i = 1, 2, \ldots, n - 1)$ and move $x_n$ to where $x_1$ was originally. This corresponds to an odd number of interchanges of rows in $\Delta$ and hence the sign of $\Delta$ has changed. Since none of the $x_i$ have coincided and $\Delta$ has changed sign, it follows that $\{\phi_i\}$ is not a Tchebycheff set.

If $n$ is even choose as $x_1$ a point $p$ not on $\alpha$ and choose $n - 1$ points ordered along $\alpha$. The above procedure is carried out for the points $x_2, x_3, \ldots, x_n$ and we again conclude that $\{\phi_i\}$ is not a Tchebycheff set.

It is intuitively plausible that a set $X$ which contains neither a tripod-like set nor a circle (unless it consists entirely of a circle) is in fact homeomorphic to a subset of a circle. We will not actually construct the homeomorphism, but rather state without proof

> **Theorem 12–3.**  *Let* $\{\phi_i(x) \mid i = 1, 2, \ldots, n\}$ *be a Tchebycheff set of continuous functions defined on $X$ with $n > 1$. Then $X$ is homeomorphic to a subset of a circle.*

We note that for the usual cases of $X$, the two lemmas are sufficient to establish the nonexistence of Tchebycheff sets on $X$.

Not only does the absence of Tchebycheff sets imply the absence of a uniqueness theorem, but it also implies that the characterization Theorem 3–1 cannot be extended to functions of several variables. The lack of a characterization theorem is even more detrimental than the lack of a uniqueness theorem. Indeed, the characterization of best approximation by the alternation $n$ times of the error curve is perhaps *the* important tool in the development of the one-variable theory.

The nonexistence of Tchebycheff sets also has implications for approximation on finite point sets. Thus if $X$ is a finite point set in, say, the plane, then there are Tchebycheff sets defined on $X$. However, it is likely that we have, in fact "approximated" a region by the finite set $X$ and thus have a set $\{\phi_i(x)\}$ which is not necessarily a Tchebycheff set on $X$. This is particularly true if $\{\phi_i(x)\}$ happens to be a set of polynomials and $X$ a rectangular mesh of points, as is often the case. Thus, not only do we have to develop a new theory for a region $X$ in a higher dimensional space, but we also have to consider approximation on finite point sets and intervals without the assumption that $\{\phi_i(x)\}$ is a Tchebycheff set.

## 12–5  TCHEBYCHEFF APPROXIMATION—CHARACTERIZATION

The first question to be considered is the existence of best Tchebycheff approximations. One may readily verify that the proofs of Lemma 1–1 and Theorem 1–3 generalize immediately and without essential change to the present case. Thus we have

**Theorem 12–4.**  *Let $f(x)$ and $\{\phi_i(x) \mid i = 1, 2, \ldots, n\}$ be continuous functions on the compact metric space $X$. Then there are parameters $A^*$ such that*

$$\max_{X} |f(x) - L(A^*, x)| = \inf_{A} \max_{X} |f(x) - L(A, x)|. \quad (12\text{--}5.1)$$

For the remainder of the discussion of Tchebycheff approximation we assume that $X$ is compact, all functions are continuous and that all maxima are taken over $X$ unless otherwise indicated.

We now turn to the consideration of the characterization of best Tchebycheff approximations. A good deal of the analysis has already been made in the consideration of general rational approximation in Chapter 9. We will reformulate those results here, insert minor required modifications of proofs and obtain some other results. In particular, we recall the definition of extremal points and formulate (Rice, 1963)

**Definition 12–1.**  *The positive and negative points of the set of extremal points of an approximation $L(A, x)$ to $f(x)$ are, respectively*

$$\mathscr{P} = \{x \mid x \in X, \quad f(x) - L(A, x) = \quad \max |f(x) - L(A, x)|\},$$

$$\mathscr{N} = \{x \mid x \in X, \quad f(x) - L(A, x) = -\max |f(x) - L(A, x)|\}.$$

*The sets $\mathscr{P}$ and $\mathscr{N}$ are said to be isolable if there is an $A$ such that*

$$\begin{aligned} L(A, x) &> 0, & x &\in \mathscr{P} \\ L(A, x) &< 0, & x &\in \mathscr{N}. \end{aligned} \quad (12\text{--}5.2)$$

The following definition is equivalent to Definition 9–3. The critical point sets play a central role in the theory developed here.

**Definition 12–2.**  *A subset $\mathscr{R}$ of the extremal points is said to be a critical point set if the positive and negative points of $\mathscr{R}$ are not isolable, but if any point is deleted from $\mathscr{R}$ then the positive and negative points of the resulting set are isolable.*

Note that a critical point set is defined relative to a particular function $f(x)$ and approximation $L(A, x)$.

The first characterization is almost a tautology, yet it is of fundamental importance in the theory. It would be a corollary of Theorem 9–3 except for the minor modification required for the more general set $X$.

**Theorem 12–5.**  *$L(A^*, x)$ is a best Tchebycheff approximation to $f(x)$ if and only if the set $\mathscr{E}$ of extremal points contains a critical point set.*

*Proof.* If $\mathscr{E}$ does not contain a critical point set, then the positive and negative points $\mathscr{P}$ and $\mathscr{N}$ of $\mathscr{E}$ may be isolated, say by $L(A_0, x)$. Set

$$d = \max |f(x) - L(A^*, x)|,$$
$$\eta = \max_x |L(A_0, x)|, \quad x \in \mathscr{P} \cup \mathscr{N},$$
$$\epsilon = \max |L(A_0, x)|,$$
$$X_1 = \{x \mid \text{sgn} [L(A_0, x)] = \text{sgn} [f(x) - L(A^*, x)],$$
$$|f(x) - L(A^*, x)| \geq \tfrac{3}{4}d, \quad |L(A_0, x)| \geq \tfrac{1}{2}\eta\}$$
$$\mu = \max_x |f(x) - L(A^*, x)|, \quad x \notin X_1.$$

Note that $\eta > 0$ and $\mu < d$. Set

$$\lambda = \min \left[ \frac{d - \mu}{\epsilon}, \frac{1}{4}, \frac{d}{4\eta} \right].$$

The approximation $L(A^* - \lambda A_0, x) = L(A_1, x)$ has the following properties:

(a) $\max\limits_x |f(x) - L(A_1, x)| < d, \quad x \notin X_1,$

(b) $|f(x) - L(A^*, x)| > |f(x) - L(A_1, x)| > \tfrac{1}{2}d, \quad x \in X_1,$

(c) $\text{sgn} [f(x) - L(A^*, x)] = \text{sgn} [f(x) - L(A_1, x)], \quad x \in X_1.$

This implies that $\max |f(x) - L(A_1, x)| < d$ and $L(A^*, x)$ is not a best approximation. This establishes the "only if" portion of the theorem.

Let $L(A_0, x)$ be a better approximation to $f(x)$ than $L(A^*, x)$. Then $L(A_0 - A^*, x)$ isolates the positive and negative points of $\mathscr{E}$. Thus $\mathscr{E}$ does not contain a critical point set and this concludes the proof.

The following corollary states the result in the same form as Theorem 9–3.

**Corollary 1.** *$L(A^*, x)$ is a best Techebycheff approximation to $f(x)$ if and only if the system (12–4.2) of linear inequalities is inconsistent.*

We also have another simple, but useful corollary

**Corollary 2.** *Let $L(A^*, x)$ be a best Tchebycheff approximation to $f(x)$ on $X$ and let $\mathscr{R}$ be a critical point set. Then $L(A^*, x)$ is a best approximation to $f(x)$ on $\mathscr{R}$.*

It was shown in Chapter 9 that, for a critical point set, the system (12–4.2) is of a particular nature, namely, it is *irreducibly inconsistent*, a concept due to Carver, 1922. Lemma 9–8 gives conditions for a system to be irreducibly inconsistent and we have the following corollary of that lemma, analogous to Corollary 2 of it.

**Corollary (of Lemma 9–8).** *A critical point set contains at most $n + 1$ points.*

With the aid of results from the theory of linear inequalities we can cast the characterization result in other forms. We have

**Corollary 3 (of Theorem 12–5).**  *A necessary and sufficient condition that $L(A^*, x)$ be a best approximation to $f(x)$ is that the zero vector be in the convex hull of the set of vectors*

$$\{\sigma(x)(\phi_1(x), \phi_2(x), \ldots, \phi_n(x))\,|$$
$$x \text{ extremal};\ \sigma(x) = 1, x \in \mathscr{P};\ \sigma(x) = -1, x \in \mathscr{N}\} \quad (12\text{–}5.3)$$

A characterization theorem of this form is given by Cheney and Goldstein, 1962.

With some reformulation, we obtain the "variational lemma" of Rivlin and Shapiro, 1961, which they use as a basic tool to develop a unified approach to problems of Tchebycheff approximation and minimization. Let $\mathscr{V}$ denote an $n$-dimensional subspace of the space of functions continuous on $X$. Let $f(x)$ be given and denote by $L^*$ the element of $\mathscr{V}$ of best approximation to $f(x)$. Then set $f^* = f - L^*$ and we have

$$\max |f^* + L| \leq \max |f^*| \quad (12\text{–}5.4)$$

for all $L \in \mathscr{V}$. It is clear that (12–5.4) holds for all $L$ if and only if $L^*$ is a best approximation to $f(x)$.

**Corollary 4.**  *A necessary and sufficient condition that (12–5.4) hold for all $L \in \mathscr{V}$ is that, for any basis $\{\phi_i \mid i = 1, 2, \ldots, n\}$ of $\mathscr{V}$, the zero vector is in the convex hull of the set of vectors*

$$\{f^*(x)(\phi_i(x), \phi_2(x), \ldots, \phi_n(x)) \mid x \text{ extremal, i.e. } |f^*(x)| = \max |f^*(x)|\}$$

We have discussed at some length the fact that best approximations may not be uniquely determined. The next theorem shows that there is, however, a particular uniquely determined subset of $X$ associated with all best approximations.

**Theorem 12–6.**  *The sets of critical point sets of two distinct best Tchebycheff approximations are identical.*

Note that it is possible for a particular best approximation to have more than one critical point set. This occurs, for instance, in a one-dimensional problem with $n$ parameters where $f(x) - L(A^*, x)$ alternates more than $n$ times.

*Proof.* Let $L(A_1, x)$ and $L(A_2, x)$ be distinct best approximations to $f(x)$ on $X$. Let $\mathscr{R}_1$ be a critical point set of $L(A_1, x)$ with positive and negative points $\mathscr{P}_1$ and $\mathscr{N}_1$, respectively.

Assume, if possible, that $\mathscr{R}_1$ is not a critical point set for $L(A_2, x)$. We have

$$L(A_2, x) - L(A_1, x) \geq 0, \quad x \in \mathscr{P}_1,$$
$$L(A_2, x) - L(A_1, x) \leq 0, \quad x \in \mathscr{N}_1.$$

Since $\mathscr{R}_1$ is not a critical point set for $L(A_2, x)$, there must be strict inequality for at least one $x \in \mathscr{R}_1$. Let $\mathscr{R}_1'$ denote the subset of $\mathscr{R}_1$ where equality holds. Set $A_3 = A_1 + \lambda(A_2 - A_1)$. For $\lambda$ suitably chosen we have

$$L(A_3, x) = L(A_1, x), \qquad x \in \mathscr{R}_1',$$
$$|L(A_3, x) - f(x)| < |L(A_1, x) - f(x)|, \qquad x \notin \mathscr{R}_1', x \in \mathscr{R}_1.$$

Since $\mathscr{R}_1$ is a critical point set, the positive and negative points of $\mathscr{R}_1'$ can be isolated, say by $L(A_4, x)$.

It follows that $L(A_3 + \mu A_4, x)$, for $\mu$ suitably chosen, isolates the positive and negative points of $\mathscr{R}_1$. This is not possible and concludes the proof.

**Corollary.** *Let* $d = \max |f(x) - L(A^*, x)|$ *for a best approximation* $L(A^*, x)$ *on* $X$. *Then all best approximations satisfy the equations*

$$f(x) - L(A, x) = d, \qquad x \in \mathscr{P},$$
$$f(x) - L(A, x) = -d, \qquad x \in \mathscr{N},$$

*where* $\mathscr{P}$ *and* $\mathscr{N}$ *are the positive and negative points of the set of critical point sets.*

The nature of the Tchebycheff norm tends to emphasize the importance of certain finite subsets of $X$. These are the extremal points and, especially, the critical point sets. The intimate relation between approximation on $X$ and approximation on particular subsets is illustrated by the following result. For one-dimensional problems this result serves as the basis for several computational schemes.

**Theorem 12–7.** *Let* $L(A^*, x)$ *be a best Tchebycheff approximation to* $f(x)$ *with a critical point set* $\mathscr{R}$ *of* $k$ *points. Then* $L(A^*, x)$ *is a best approximation to* $f(x)$ *on* $\mathscr{R}$ *and is characterized as a best approximation with largest deviation* $\rho$ *among all best approximations to* $f(x)$ *on subsets of* $k$ *points of* $X$.

*Proof.* It is noted in Corollary 2 above that $L(A^*, x)$ is a best approximation on $\mathscr{R}$. It is clear that

$$\rho \geq \max |f(x) - L(A^*, x)|$$

for $\mathscr{R}$ is one of the subsets of $k$ points of $X$. On the other hand

$$\rho \leq \max |f(x) - L(A^*, x)|$$

since the deviation of a best approximation on a subset of $X$ must be less than or equal to the deviation of a best approximation on all of $X$.

## 12–6 CONDITIONS FOR NONUNIQUENESS

In this section we investigate the conditions under which best Tchebycheff approximations may be nonuniquely determined. It is seen that a very special set of circumstances must be present in order for nonuniqueness to occur. Let us define

$$\Gamma(A) = \{x \mid x \in X, \quad L(A, x) = 0\} \tag{12–6.1}$$

and call this a "curve" though it is not, of course, a curve in the usual sense of the word. We have

**Theorem 12–8.** *If there is not a unique best Tchebycheff approximation to $f(x)$, then all the critical point sets lie on a curve* (12–6.1).

*Proof.* Let $L(A_1, x)$ and $L(A_2, x)$ be distinct best approximations to $f(x)$ and let $\mathcal{R}$ be a critical point set. Then

$$|f(x) - L(A_1, x)| = |f(x) - L(A_2, x)|, \qquad x \in \mathcal{R}.$$

Let $\mathcal{R}_0$ be the subset, if any, of $\mathcal{R}$ where $L(A_1, x)$ and $L(A_2, x)$ differ. Let $\mathcal{P}$ and $\mathcal{N}$ be the positive and negative points, respectively, of $\mathcal{R}$ with reference to $L(A_1, x)$. We have

$$L(A_1 - A_2, x) > 0, \qquad x \in \mathcal{P}, x \in \mathcal{R}_0$$
$$L(A_1 - A_2, x) < 0, \qquad x \in \mathcal{N}, x \in \mathcal{R}_0$$
$$L(A_1 - A_2, x) = 0, \qquad x \in \mathcal{R}, x \notin \mathcal{R}_0$$

The reasoning of the proof of Theorem 12–6 may be applied to show that this system of inequalities contradicts the assumption that $\mathcal{R}$ is a critical point set. This concludes the proof.

Note that Haar's theorem, Theorem 12–2, is a converse of this theorem.

If we assume that the functions involved are differentiable and $X$ is a subset of Euclidean space, then we obtain a somewhat sharper form of this theorem.

**Corollary 1.** *Let $f(x)$ and $\{\phi_i(x)\}$ be differentiable on $X \subset E_m, m > 1$. If there is not a unique best approximation to $f(x)$; then all the critical points lie on a curve $\Gamma(A_0)$ and the differential of $L(A_0, x)$ vanishes at those points of the critical point sets which are interior points of $X$.*

From this corollary we may obtain a provocative result of Collatz, 1956.

**Corollary 2.** *If $f(x, y)$ has continuous first partial derivatives at all interior points of a closed convex set $X$ of the plane, then there exists a unique linear polynomial $a_1 + a_2x + a_3y$ of best approximation to $f(x, y)$ on $X$.*

*Proof.* The differential of $a_1 + a_2x + a_3y$ vanishes only if $a_2 = a_3 = 0$ and clearly $a_1$ is uniquely determined in this case. A curve $\Gamma(A_0)$ is a straight line in the plane, and thus the only possibility is that the critical points lie on the boundary of $X$. Thus there are at most 2 critical points; however, it is readily shown that two points cannot form a critical point set for $a_1 + a_2x + a_3y$.

This corollary is provocative because it gives some hope that there may be a reasonably restricted approximation problem for which best approximations are unique. However, Rivlin and Shapiro, 1960, have shown that no such possibility exists. They established the following result

**Theorem 12-9.** *Let* $\{\phi_i(x) \mid i = 1, 2, \ldots, n\}$ *be twice continuously differentiable on an open set containing* $X \subset E_m, m < 1$. *Suppose that for some* $L(A_0, x)$ *(not identically zero) both* $L(A_0, x)$ *and its differential vanish at* $n$ *points of* $X$. *Then there exists an infinitely differentiable function defined on* $E_m$ *which has infinitely many best Tchebycheff approximations.*

*Proof.* Denote by $\mathcal{R}$ the set of $n$ points where $L(A_0, x)$ and its differential are zero. We may assume that max $|L(A_0, x)| \leq \frac{1}{2}$. There is a $\lambda$ and a $\delta$ with $0 < \delta < \frac{1}{4} \min |x_1 - x_2|$, $x_1, x_2 \in \mathcal{R}$ such that

$$|L(A_0, x_0)| < \lambda|x - x_0|^2, \qquad x_0 \in \mathcal{R}$$

where $|x - x_0|$ denotes the Euclidean distance. This follows from the differentiability assumption.

Since $L(A_0, x) = 0$ at $n$ points $\mathcal{R}$, it follows that the $n$ by $n$ matrix $= \{\phi_i(x_j) \mid x_j \in \mathcal{R}\} = \Phi$ is singular. Thus for some nonzero vector $\mathbf{v}$ the equations $\Phi A = \mathbf{v}$ do not have a solution. Divide $\mathcal{R}$ into positive and negative points according to the sign of the corresponding component of $\mathbf{v}$. Delete those points for which the corresponding component is zero. Set

$$\mu = \min \left[ \frac{\sqrt{\lambda}}{2}, \frac{\delta}{2} \right].$$

We define $f(x)$ as follows

(a) for $|x - x_0| \leq \mu, f(x) = \begin{cases} 1 - \lambda|x - x_0|^2, & x_0 \in \mathcal{P}, \\ -1 + \lambda|x - x_0|^2, & x_0 \in \mathcal{N}, \end{cases}$

(b) for $|x - x_0| \geq \delta, f(x) = 0, x_0 \in \mathcal{P} \cup \mathcal{N}$,

(c) for $\mu < |x - x_0| < \delta$, $x_0 \in \mathcal{P} \cup \mathcal{N}$, $f(x)$ is defined so that it is infinitely differentiable and $|f(x)| \leq 1 - \lambda\mu^2$.

We do not explicitly construct $f(x)$ for (c), but it is clear that such a construction is possible.

The vector $\mathbf{v}$ was chosen in such a way that $L(A_0, x)$ is a best approximation to $f(x)$ with max $|f(x) - L(A_0, x)| = 1$. Furthermore if

$$|\alpha| < \min [\lambda, 2\lambda\mu^2]$$

then we have

$$\max \left| f(x) - \alpha L(A_0, x) \right| \leq 1 - \lambda \mu^2 + \frac{|\alpha|}{2} < 1,$$

$$|x - x_0| \geq \mu, \quad x_0 \in \mathscr{P} \cup \mathscr{N},$$

$$\max \left| f(x) - \alpha L(A_0, x) \right| \leq 1 - (\lambda - |\alpha|)|x - x_0|^2 \leq 1,$$

$$|x - x_0| \leq \mu, \quad x_0 \in \mathscr{P} \cup \mathscr{N}.$$

Thus $\alpha L(A_0, x)$ is a best approximation for infinitely many values of $\alpha$. We have the following

**Corollary.** *Let $X$ be a subset of the Euclidean plane. Then there exists an $f(x, y)$ infinitely differentiable in the plane which possesses infinitely many best Tchebycheff approximations on $X$ by quadratic polynomials.*

If best approximations by quadratic polynomials in two variables are not uniquely determined even for the smoothest functions, it is extremely unlikely that there are any interesting restricted Tchebycheff approximation problems in several variables for which best approximations are unique.

## 12–7  STRICT APPROXIMATION

Since best Tchebycheff approximations are not uniquely determined, it is natural to consider additional criteria which would single out one of the best approximations as the "best of the best". Such a consideration has lead to the *strict approximation* as the "best" approximation. There are many additional criteria possible, but the one chosen here seems to be the most natural. Heuristically, the approach is as follows: when the best Tchebycheff approximation is not uniquely determined, then there is a certain degree of freedom in determining the best approximation on certain points. These points are "independent" of the set of critical point sets, for the value of *all* best Tchebycheff approximations is determined there. Thus it seems reasonable to ask that, for those points where some freedom of determination still exists, we require the maximum deviation to be as small as possible. It is possible that one may have to repeat this process several times in order to reach a uniquely defined approximation. This approximation is called the strict approximation.

It turns out that this process can be carried out only if $X$ is a finite point set. This is, of course, a severe drawback to the theory presented here. We can, hopefully, look forward to a partial removal of this drawback. However, the results in the next section indicate that there is a real difficulty in extending the analysis to approximation on regions.

The material here is basically as given by Rice, 1963. An intuitive description of such a procedure is given by Remes, 1957, but he did not develop the idea. A similar approach is used in game theory problems by Buck, 1958.

There is some machinery needed to discuss these approximations. The $n$-vector $\boldsymbol{\phi}$ for a point $x$ in $X$ is defined by

$$\boldsymbol{\phi} = \boldsymbol{\phi}(x) = (\phi_1(x), \phi_2(x), \ldots, \phi_n(x))$$

Square brackets [ ] denote the closure by linear combinations of a set of vectors, or equivalently, denote the smallest subspace of $E_n$ containing a given set of vectors. Thus

$$[\boldsymbol{\phi}_1, \boldsymbol{\phi}_2] = \{\boldsymbol{\phi} \mid \boldsymbol{\phi} = \alpha\boldsymbol{\phi}_1 + \beta\boldsymbol{\phi}_2; \ |\alpha|, |\beta| < \infty\}.$$

We shall also use the notation $\boldsymbol{\phi}(\mathscr{R})$ where $\mathscr{R}$ is a set in $X$. This denotes the collection $\boldsymbol{\phi}(\mathscr{R}) = \{\boldsymbol{\phi}(x) \mid x \in \mathscr{R}\}$. The *dimension* of a set $\mathscr{R}$ in $X$ is defined to be the dimension of the subspace $[\boldsymbol{\phi}(\mathscr{R})]$. Thus the dimension of a set $\mathscr{R}$ is the dimension of the subspace of $E_n$ spanned by the vectors $\boldsymbol{\phi}(x), x \in \mathscr{R}$. A point $x \in X$ is said to be dependent on a set $\mathscr{R}$ if $\boldsymbol{\phi}(x)$ is contained in $[\boldsymbol{\phi}(\mathscr{R})]$.

In order to avoid uninteresting special cases, one must require that $X$ contains a "sufficient" number of points. For one variable approximation one requires that $X$ contains $n + 1$ points. The general situation requires a slightly more complicated condition. A set $\mathscr{R}$ in $X$ is said to be *non-degenerate* if there is no point $x_0 \in \mathscr{R}$ such that $\boldsymbol{\phi}(x_0)$ is linearly independent of the set $\{\boldsymbol{\phi}(x) \mid x \in \mathscr{R}, x \neq x_0\}$. That is to say that every point of $\mathscr{R}$ is to be dependent on the remaining points of $\mathscr{R}$. The following is assumed throughout the discussion of strict approximation.

ASSUMPTION. *X is a nondegenerate finite set.*

**Definition 12–3.** *Let $\mathscr{L}$ denote a subcollection of the approximating functions (12–4.1). $\mathscr{R}$ is a critical point set with respect to $\mathscr{L}$ if the positive and negative parts of $\mathscr{R}$ cannot be isolated by a member of $\mathscr{L}$.*

The strict approximation is defined by the following inductive definition which formalizes the heuristic description given above.

**Definition 12–4.** *Let $\mathscr{R}_1$ be the set of critical point sets of best approximations to $f(x)$ on $X$. Set*

$$X_1 = \{x \mid \boldsymbol{\phi}(x) \in [\boldsymbol{\phi}(\mathscr{R}_1)]\}$$

*and denote by $\mathscr{L}_1$ the set of best approximations to $f(x)$ on $X$. Denote by $\mathscr{L}_2$ the set of $L(A^*, x)$ such that*

$$\max_x |L(A^*, x) - f(x)| \leq \max_x |L(A, x) - f(x)|, \quad \text{all} \quad x \in X - X_1$$

*for all* $L(A, x) \in \mathscr{L}_1$. *Let* $\mathscr{R}_2$ *be the set of critical point sets with respect to* $\mathscr{L}_1$ *of the approximations* $\mathscr{L}_2$. *Set*

$$X_2 = \{x \mid \boldsymbol{\phi}(x) \in [\boldsymbol{\phi}(\mathscr{R}_1 \cup \mathscr{R}_2)]\}$$

*and denote by* $\mathscr{L}_3$ *the set of* $L(A^*, x)$ *such that*

$$\max_x |L(A^*, x) - f(x)| \leq \max_x |L(A, x) - f(x)|, \quad \text{all } x \in X - X_2$$

*The construction is continued until* $X = X_k$ *for some* $k$. *The members of* $\mathscr{L}_k$ *are said to be strict approximations to* $f(x)$ *on* $X$.

**Definition 12–5.** *Let* $X_1, X_2, \ldots, X_k$ *be subsets of* $X$ *such that* $X_k = X$, $[\boldsymbol{\phi}(X_i)] \supset [\boldsymbol{\phi}(X_{i-1})]$ *and let* $L(A, x)$ *be an approximation to* $f(x)$ *on* $X$ *such that*

$$\max_x |L(A, x) - f(x)| = d_i, \quad x \in X - X_i$$

*with* $d_i < d_{i-1}$. *A point* $x \in X_i$ *for which the value* $d_i$ *is assumed by* $|L(A, x) - f(x)|$ *is said to be an extremal point of the approximation* $L(A, x)$.

On each of the sets $\mathscr{R}_i$, the strict approximations have a certain deviation from $f(x)$. Denote this deviation by $d_i$ and denote the dimension of $\mathscr{R}_i$ by $m_i$. The *deviation vector* $\mathbf{d}$ is the vector whose first $m_1$ components are $d_1$, whose next $m_2$ components are $d_2$ and so forth.

$$\mathbf{d} = (\overbrace{d_1, \ldots, d_1,}^{m_1} \ \overbrace{d_2, \ldots, d_2,}^{m_2} \ d_3, \ldots, d_{k_1}, \ \overbrace{d_k, \ldots, d_k}^{m_k}) \quad (12\text{--}7.1)$$

In the analysis of approximations it is necessary to compare the "size" of the deviation of various approximations to $f(x)$ on various subsets of $X$. In the usual one-variable theory, the components of the deviation vector are all equal and hence there is a simple ordering of the magnitudes of the deviations.

In the present situation, the natural ordering of the vectors (12–7.1) is the *lexicographic* ordering. Thus the vector $(2, 2, 1, 1)$ is smaller than $(2, 2, 2, 1)$ and $(3, 0, 0, 0)$ but larger than $(2, 2, 1, 0)$.

A *strict critical point set* is the union of one critical point set with respect to $\mathscr{L}_{i-1}$ from each set $\mathscr{R}_i$, $i = 2, 3, \ldots, k$. Let $\{\mathscr{S}_i\}$ be a collection that forms a strict critical point set and denote by $\mathscr{P}_i$ and $\mathscr{N}_i$ the positive and negative points, respectively, of $\mathscr{S}_i$. The following system of equations and inequalities is analogous to the system (12–4.2) for the results obtained in Section 12–5. Indeed (12–4.2) is the first of the systems enumerated below.

$$L(A_1, x) > 0, \qquad x \in \mathscr{P}_1,$$
$$L(A_1, x) < 0, \qquad x \in \mathscr{N}_1.$$
$$L(A_2, x) = 0, \qquad x \in \mathscr{S}_1,$$
$$L(A_2, x) > 0, \qquad x \in \mathscr{P}_2,$$
$$L(A_2, x) < 0, \qquad x \in \mathscr{N}_2.$$

$\cdot$

$\cdot$                                                                          (12–7.2)

$\cdot$

$$L(A_i, x) = 0, \qquad x \in \bigcup_{j=1}^{i-1} \mathscr{S}_j,$$
$$L(A_i, x) > 0, \qquad x \in \mathscr{P}_i,$$
$$L(A_i, x) < 0, \qquad x \in \mathscr{N}_i.$$

$\cdot$

$\cdot$

$\cdot$

We now establish some simple facts about the strict approximation, which include showing that it is well defined.

**Lemma 12–6.**

(a) *The sets $\mathscr{R}_i$ are not empty if $d_i > 0$.*

(b) *The sets $\mathscr{R}_i$ and $X_i$ are uniquely determined.*

(c) *There are at most n sets $\mathscr{R}_i$.*

(d) *The deviation vector of a strict approximation has exactly n components.*

(e) *If $L(A, x)$ is such that:* (i) *$|L(A, x) - f(x)| = d_i$, for $x \in \mathscr{R}_i$, $i = 1, 2, \ldots, j - 1$,* (ii) *$|L(A, x) - f(x)| \neq d_j$ for some $x \in \mathscr{R}_j$; then*

$$\max_{x \in \mathscr{R}_j} |L(A, x) - f(x)| > d_j.$$

*Proof.* (a) Since $d_i > 0$ and $X - X_{i-1}$ is compact, there is a set of extremal points in $X - X_{i-1}$. If the positive and negative points of this set could be isolated, it would contradict the fact that this is a set of extremal points of best approximations on $X - X_{i-1}$. Thus for some subset of these points, the positive and negative points cannot be isolated and hence $\mathscr{R}_i$ is not empty.

(b) By Theorem 12–6 the set $\mathscr{R}_1$ is uniquely determined and hence so are $\mathscr{L}_1$ and $X_1$. The argument of the proof of Theorem 12–6 may be applied in the same way to show necessarily that $\mathscr{R}_i$ and hence $\mathscr{L}_i$ and $X_i$ are uniquely determined.

(c) By the construction of Definition 12–4 it follows that $\phi(x)$, $x \in \mathscr{R}_i$ is independent of

$$\phi\left(\bigcup_{j=1}^{i-1} \mathscr{R}_j\right).$$

Thus $[\boldsymbol{\phi}(X_i)]$ is a subspace of $E_n$ of at least one more dimension than $[\boldsymbol{\phi}(X_{i-1})]$. Since $E_n$ has dimension $n$ there can be at most $n$ sets $X_i$ and hence $n$ sets $\mathscr{R}_i$.

(d) Since $X$ is non degenerate, $X = X_k$ only when

$$E_n = \left[ \boldsymbol{\phi} \left( \bigcup_{i=1}^{k} \mathscr{R}_i \right) \right].$$

The difference in dimension between $X_{i-1}$ and $X_i$ is the dimension $m_i$ of $\mathscr{R}_i$. Thus the dimension of $X_k$ is

$$\sum_{i=1}^{k} m_i = n.$$

(e) The condition in (i) implies that $L(A, x)$ is a member of the set $\mathscr{L}_{j-1}$. All of the members of $\mathscr{L}_j$ agree on the set $\mathscr{R}_j$ (this follows, for example, from the corollary of Theorem 12–6). Thus $L(A, x)$ is not in $\mathscr{L}_j$ and the conclusion follows.

The following result establishes that the strict approximation is uniquely determined.

**Lemma 12–7.** *The strict approximation is unique.*

*Proof.* Let $L(A^*, x)$ be a strict approximation to $f(x)$ on $X$ and let $\mathscr{S} = \bigcup_{i=1}^{k} \mathscr{R}_i$ be a strict critical point set. Let $\mathscr{P}_i$, $\mathscr{N}_i$ and $m_i$ be positive points, negative points and dimension of $\mathscr{R}_i$, respectively. It follows from the preceding lemma, part (e), that $L(A^*, x)$ satisfies

$$\begin{aligned} L(A^*, x) &= f(x) - d_i, & x \in \mathscr{P}_i, \\ L(A^*, x) &= f(x) + d_i, & x \in \mathscr{N}_i. \end{aligned} \qquad (12\text{--}7.3)$$

This is a system of linear equations in $n$ unknowns. By the construction of the $\mathscr{R}_i$, each subsystem corresponding to an index $i$ is of rank $m_i$ and the coefficient vectors $\boldsymbol{\phi}(x)$, $x \in \mathscr{R}_i$ are linearly independent of the vectors $\boldsymbol{\phi}(x)$, $x \in \bigcup_{j=1}^{i-1} \mathscr{R}_j$. Thus the rank of the entire system (12–7.3) is $\sum m_i = n$. This implies that it has a unique solution $A^*$ and establishes the lemma.

**Corollary.** *The strict approximation is the unique solution of the system* (12–7.3) *of linear equations.*

The system (12–7.3) cannot be used directly for the calculation of the strict approximation because one does not know the sets $\mathscr{P}_i$, $\mathscr{N}_i$ nor the deviation vector **d**.

The main points of the theory of strict approximation are given in the following theorem. Note its similarity with Theorem 3–10 for approximation with Tchebycheff sets.

**Theorem 12–10.** *Let* $f(x)$ *be defined on the nondegenerate finite set* $X$. *Then*
(a) $f(x)$ *possesses a strict approximation of the form* $L(A, x)$.
(b) *A necessary and sufficient condition that* $L(A^*, x)$ *is a strict approxima-tion is that the set of extremal points of* $L(A^*, x) - f(x)$ *contains a strict critical point set.*
(c) *The strict approximation to* $f(x)$ *is unique.*

*Proof.* (a) The classical argument of Chapter 1 may be applied succes-sively to show that $\mathscr{L}_1, \mathscr{L}_2, \ldots$ are not empty.

(b) The existence of a better approximation than $L(A^*, x)$ implies that one of the systems (12–7.2) of the strict critical point set has a solution. This contradicts the definition of the sets $\mathscr{R}_i$ and establishes the sufficiency part of (b).

On the other hand, if the set of extremal points does not contain a strict critical point set, then one of the systems (12–7.2) has a solution, say $A_1$. The reasoning of Theorem 12–5 may be applied to show that $L(A^* - \lambda A_1, x)$ is a better approximation than $L(A^*, x)$ for $\lambda$ suitably chosen. Indeed the reasoning is somewhat simplified due to the fact that $X$ is a finite set.

(c) This is established in Lemma 12–7.

The following examples illustrate some of the possibilities in strict approximation.

EXAMPLE 1. $X = \{(x, y) \mid x = 0, \pm 1, \pm 2; \; y = 0, \pm 1, \pm 2\}$. The approxi-mating function is $L(A, x, y) = a_1 + a_2 x + a_3 y$ and two functions $f_1(x, y)$ and $f_2(x, y)$ are tabled below. The $x$ varies in the horizontal and $y$ varies in the vertical with point (2, 2) on the upper right.

| 0 | 0 | $-\frac{1}{4}$ | 0 | 0 | | $-1$ | 0 | 0 | $-\frac{1}{2}$ | $-1$ |
|---|---|---|---|---|---|---|---|---|---|---|
| $\frac{1}{2}$ | 0 | 0 | 0 | $\frac{1}{4}$ | | $-\frac{1}{2}$ | $\frac{1}{4}$ | $\frac{1}{4}$ | 0 | $-\frac{1}{4}$ |
| 1 | 0 | $-1$ | 0 | 1 | | 0 | $\frac{1}{2}$ | 1 | $\frac{3}{4}$ | $\frac{1}{2}$ |
| $\frac{1}{2}$ | 0 | 0 | 0 | $\frac{1}{4}$ | | $-\frac{1}{2}$ | 0 | $\frac{1}{2}$ | $\frac{1}{2}$ | $\frac{3}{4}$ |
| 0 | 0 | $\frac{1}{4}$ | 0 | 0 | | $-1$ | $-\frac{1}{4}$ | 0 | $\frac{1}{2}$ | 1 |

$$f_1(x, y) \qquad\qquad\qquad f_2(x, y)$$

$L(A^*, x) = 0$ $\qquad\qquad\qquad\qquad L(A^*, x) = \frac{1}{8}x - \frac{1}{8}y$

$\mathscr{R}_1 = \{(-2, 0), (0, 0), (2, 0)\}$ $\qquad\quad \mathscr{R}_1 = \{(-2, -2), (0, 0), (2, 2)\}$

$\mathscr{R}_2 = \{(-2, -1), (-2, 1)\}$ $\qquad\qquad \mathscr{R}_2 = \{(-1, 0), (1, 0)\}$

$\mathbf{d} = (1, 1, \frac{1}{2})$ $\qquad\qquad\qquad\qquad\quad \mathbf{d} = (1, 1, \frac{5}{8})$

EXAMPLE 2. $X$ as in Example 1.
The approximating function is

$$L(A, x, y) = \sum_{i+j \le 2} a_{ij} x^i y^j.$$

The function $f_3(x, y)$ is tabled with the format of Example 1.

$$
\begin{array}{ccccc}
5\frac{3}{4} & 8 & 10\frac{1}{8} & 12\frac{1}{8} & 13\frac{7}{8} \\
1\frac{7}{8} & 3 & 4\frac{5}{8} & 6 & 7\frac{3}{8} \\
-1\frac{1}{2} & 0 & \frac{3}{2} & 2\frac{1}{4} & 2\frac{1}{2} \\
-\frac{3}{2} & -\frac{3}{8} & 0 & -\frac{1}{4} & \frac{3}{8} \\
-1 & 0 & 1 & -1 & 1
\end{array}
$$

$$f_3(x, y)$$

$$
L(A^*, x, y) = 1 + x + \frac{5y}{2} + \frac{xy}{2} + y^2 = \left(1 + \frac{y}{2}\right)(1 + x + 2y)
$$

$$
\mathcal{R}_1 = \{(-2, -2), (0, -2), (1, -2), (2, -2)\}
$$

$$
\mathcal{R}_2 = \{(-2, 0), (1, 0), (2, 0)\}
$$

$$
\mathcal{R}_3 = \{(1, -1), (-2, 2)\}
$$

$$
\mathbf{d} = (1, 1, 1, \tfrac{1}{2}, \tfrac{1}{2}, \tfrac{1}{4})
$$

The basic technique of the strict approximation is to isolate the effect of the critical points $\mathcal{R}_k$ from the determination of the set $\mathcal{L}_{k+1}$ of best approximation on $X - X_k$. If $X$ is finite, we can do this by simply deleting the set $\mathcal{R}_k$ (and all points dependent on it) from further consideration. This procedure does not work, however, if $X$ is a region, for by the continuity of $f(x)$ and the $\phi_i(x)$ there would be no decrease in the deviation due to deleting $\mathcal{R}_k$ from consideration. Indeed, it is exactly at this place that Definition 12–4 breaks down. One cannot, in such a case, establish part (a) of Lemma 12–6, i.e. there may be no critical—or indeed extremal—points for approximation on $X - X_k$, for $X - X_k$ might not be compact.

It is, of course, possible to make $X - X_k$ compact by some artificial means. Thus one would delete neighborhoods of $\mathcal{R}_k$ of some size fixed *a priori*. This, however, is an unnatural choice and is unlikely to lead to satisfying results. That this difficulty is an essential feature of the problem is shown by the example given in the next section.

We note that the fact that $f(x)$, $\{\phi_i(x)\}$ are functions defined on $X$ plays absolutely no role in the development of the results of this section. The problem may be treated abstractly as a linear algebra problem as follows. Consider the system of equations

$$
A \cdot \boldsymbol{\phi}_i = f_i, \qquad i = 1, 2, \ldots, m
$$

where $A$, $\boldsymbol{\phi}_i$ are $n$-vectors, $f_i$ is a number and $m > n$. The dot product notation is used. This system in general does not have a solution, thus we may wish to determine $A$ so as to minimize

$$
\max_i |A \cdot \boldsymbol{\phi}_i - f_i|.
$$

Again we might not have a unique solution and the procedure of Definition 12-4 may be applied to determine a "strict" solution, which is uniquely determined.

## 12–8  THE POLYA ALGORITHM

We recall from Chapter 1 that the Polya algorithm considers the best $L_p$-approximations $L(A_p, x)$ to $f(x)$ as $p$ tends to infinity[†]. If the vectors $\{\boldsymbol{\phi}(x) \mid x \in X\}$ are of full rank $n$, then $L(A_p, x)$ is uniquely determined. *We assume throughout this section that the set $\{\boldsymbol{\phi}(x) \mid x \in X\}$ contains at least one set of $n$ linearly independent vectors.* The reader may satisfy himself that the proof of Theorem 1–1 can be extended directly for any "well behaved" finite dimensional set $X$. We will not attempt to establish a general extension of the Polya algorithm.

The Corollary of Theorem 1–1 stated that, if the best Tchebycheff approximation $L(A^*, x)$ is uniquely determined, then

$$\lim_{p \to \infty} L(A_p, x) = L(A^*, x). \tag{12-8.1}$$

It is natural to ask whether the limit might exist even if the best Tchebycheff approximation is not uniquely determined. This was an open question for some time and the situation was clarified somewhat by Descloux, 1963. He was able to show that in certain situations, namely when $X$ is finite, the limit (12–8.1) does indeed always exist and that the limit is the strict approximation defined in the preceding section. This immediately raises the possibility that the Polya algorithm may provide the means of choosing the "best of the best" Tchebycheff approximations. However, an example given by Descloux rules out this possibility in the most interesting case, when $X$ is a simple region in Euclidean space, e.g. an interval, a square region, etc. The remainder of this section presents these two important results of Descloux.

**Theorem 12–11.** *Let $L(A_p, x)$ and $L(A^*, x)$ be the best $L_p$-approximation and the strict approximation, respectively, to $f(x)$ on a finite set $X$. Then*

$$\lim_{p \to \infty} L(A_p, x) = L(A^*, x).$$

*Proof.* The proof is based on the Corollary of Lemma 12–7. Thus we show that every convergent subsequence of $\{L(A_p, x)\}$ converges to a solution of (12–7.3). Since $\{L(A_p, x)\}$ is uniformly bounded and the unique solution of (12–7.3) is $L(A^*, x)$, this will establish the theorem.

The proof is by induction with the induction hypothesis

$$\lim_{p \to \infty} |r_p(x)| = |r^*(x)|, \qquad x \in \bigcup_{i=1}^{j} \mathscr{R}_i, \tag{12-8.2}$$

---

† We assume $X$ is such that we may integrate or sum functions defined on $X$.

where $r_p(x) = f(x) - L(A_p, x)$, $r^*(x) = f(x) - L(A^*, x)$. We first establish (12-8.2) for $j = 1$. The analysis is a simplified version of the proof of Theorem 1-1.

Suppose for some $x_0 \in \mathscr{R}_1$ and some sequence

$$\{p_i \mid p_i < p_{i+1}, \lim p_i = +\infty\}$$

we have

$$\lim_{p_i \to \infty} |r_{p_i}(x_0)| \neq |r^*(x_0)| = d_1.$$

Then, by (e) of Lemma 12-6, we have for some $x_1 \in \mathscr{R}_1$ and a sequence $\{p_i\}$ (one may have to choose a subsequence of $\{p_i\}$, and if so we denote it by $\{p_i\}$ also)

$$\lim_{p_i \to \infty} |r_{p_i}(x_1)| = z > d_1.$$

We now compare the $L_p$-norms of $L(A^*, x)$ and $L(A_{p_i}, x)$. Let $m$ denote the number of points in $X$, then

$$\sum_{x \in X} |f^*(x)|^{p_i} \leq m(d_1)^{p_i},$$

$$\sum_{x \in X} |r_{p_i}(x)|^{p_i} \geq \sum_{x \in \mathscr{R}_i} |r_{p_i}(x)|^{p_i} \geq |r_{p_i}(x_1)|^{p_i} = z^{p_i}.$$

Since $z > d_1$, there is an $M < \infty$ such that $p_i \geq M$ implies that $z^{p_i} > m(d_1)^{p_i}$. This contradicts the fact that $L(A_{p_i}, x)$ is a best $L_p$-approximation and the original supposition is untenable. This establishes the induction hypothesis for $j = 1$.

For the general induction step assume that (12-8.2) is valid for $j$. Suppose for some $x_0 \in \mathscr{R}_{j+1}$ and some sequence $\{p_i \mid p_i < p_{i+1}, \lim p_i = +\infty\}$ we have

$$\lim_{p_i \to \infty} |r_{p_i}(x_0)| \neq |r^*(x_0)| = d_{j+1}.$$

Then, by (e) of Lemma 12-6, we have for some $x_1 \in \mathscr{R}_{j+1}$ and a sequence $\{p_i\}$ (again a subsequence of the original may have to be taken)

$$\lim_{p_i \to \infty} |r_{p_i}(x_1)| = z > d_{j+1}.$$

Let $m$ denote the number of points in $X - X_j$, then

$$e^* = \sum_{x \in X} |r^*(x)|^{p_i} = \sum_{x \in X_j} |r^*(x)|^{p_i} + \sum_{x \in X - X_j} |r^*(x)|^{p_i},$$

$$e_{p_i} = \sum_{x \in X} |r_{p_i}(x)|^{p_i} = \sum_{x \in X_j} |r^*(x)|^{p_i} + \sum_{x \in X - X_j} |r_{p_i}(x)|^{p_i}.$$

The induction hypothesis has been used to conclude that $|r_{p_i}(x)| = |r^*(x)|$ for $x \in X_j$. We have

$$e^* - e_{p_i} \leq m(d_{j+1})^{p_i} - z^{p_i}$$

and for $p_i$ sufficiently large, $e^* - e_{p_i} < 0$ which contradicts the fact that $L(A_{p_i}, x)$ is a best $L_{p_i}$-approximation and the original supposition is untenable. We conclude then that any convergent subsequence of $\{L(A_{p_i}, x)\}$ satisfies (12–8.2) for $j = k$ and hence so does the whole sequence. Thus the sequence $\{L(A_{p_i}, x)\}$ converges to a solution of (12–7.3) and, by the Corollary of Lemma 12–7, the proof is complete.

Thus the Polya algorithm does pick out a unique "best of the best" Tchebycheff approximation when $X$ is a finite point set. Furthermore the approximation so determined is the strict approximation studied in the preceding section and this tends to justify further the strict approximation as the natural choice of the "best of the best".

The following example, also due to Descloux, shows that the Polya algorithm does not serve this purpose in all cases; in particular, in the case of an interval.

EXAMPLE 1. We define a function $h(x)$ on the interval $[-1, +1]$ which is a continuous polygonal (i.e. piecewise linear) function. Its general nature is illustrated in Fig. 12–3.

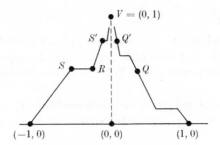

FIG. 12–3.   The function $h(x)$.

The graph of $h(x)$ is made up of lines which either pass through the point $V = (0, 1)$ or are horizontal. We have,

(1) $h(x)$ continuous on $[-1, 1]$,
(2) $h(x)$ increasing in $[-1, 0]$, decreasing in $[0, 1]$,
(3) $h(\pm 1) = 0$, $h(0) = 1$,
(4) $h(x) \geq 1 - |x|$.

We take as approximating function $L(A, x) = ax$.

The definition of the example is complicated and thus it is worthwhile to say something about the basic idea behind it. Above the $QS$ level we make $h(x)$ much "fatter" on the $Q$ side than the $S$ side. This causes the best $L_{p_1}$-approximation (for some judiciously chosen $p_1$) to tilt heavily up on the $Q$ side. Once this is accomplished, a small portion of $h(x)$ is redefined near the vertex $V$. This portion is so small that it does not affect the best

$L_{p_1}$-approximation significantly. In this small portion, $h(x)$ is now made much "fatter" on the other side, away from $Q$. This causes the best $L_{p_2}$-approximation (again for a certain $p_2$) to tilt heavily up on the $S$ side. This process is continued indefinitely to define $h(x)$. By the construction, the best $L_p$-approximations swing back and forth as $p$ tends to infinity and the Polya algorithm does not converge.

We start with $h(x)$ defined at the $QS$ level, i.e. in the intervals $[-1, -s]$ and $[q, 1]$ where $Q = (q, z)$, $S = (s, z)$. Its definition will be extended to the $Q'S'$ level. At that point the procedure is recycled. Let $-\beta$ denote the slope of the line $QV$ and choose $\alpha > \beta$ so that

$$(\beta + \tfrac{1}{4}) \left( \frac{1}{\beta + \tfrac{1}{2}} + \frac{1}{\alpha - \tfrac{1}{2}} \right) < 1.$$

Clearly this can be done. Let $R = (-r, z)$ be the point where the line through $V$ of slope $\alpha$ intersects the horizontal $QS$. Consider $g(x)$ as shown in Fig. 12–4, i.e. $g(x) = h(x)$ in $[-1, -s]$ and $[q, 1]$, and $g(x)$ is defined by the line segments $SR$, $RV$, $VQ$ in $[-s, q]$.

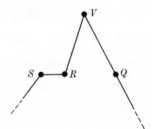

FIG. 12–4.   The function $g(x)$.

Define

$$L_p(f, a) = \int_{-1}^{1} |f(x) - ax|^p \, dx$$

and consider

$$L_p(g, \tfrac{1}{2}) = \left( \int_{-1}^{-r} + \int_{-r}^{0} + \int_{q}^{0} + \int_{q}^{1} \right) |g(x) - \tfrac{1}{2}x|^p \, dx$$

$$= I_1 + I_2 + I_3 + I_4.$$

These four integrals may be estimated as follows:

$$I_1 + I_4 \leq 4 \left( 1 - \frac{s}{2} \right)^p,$$

$$I_2 \leq \frac{1}{(p + 1)(\alpha - \tfrac{1}{2})},$$

$$I_3 \leq \frac{1}{(p + 1)(\beta + \tfrac{1}{2})}.$$

If $aq < z$, then

$$L_p(g, a) \geq \int_0^b |g(x) - ax|^p \, dx \geq \frac{1 - z^{p+1}}{(p+1)(\beta+a)}.$$

Recall that $1 - \beta q = z$. If $a \leq \frac{1}{4}$, we have

$$L_p(g, a) - L_p(g, \tfrac{1}{2})$$

$$\leq \frac{1 - z^{p+1}}{(p+1)(\beta+a)} - \frac{1}{(p+1)}\left[\frac{1}{\alpha - \frac{1}{2}} + \frac{1}{\beta + \frac{1}{2}}\right] - 4\left(1 - \frac{s}{2}\right)^p$$

$$= \frac{\beta+a}{p+1}\left[1 - (\beta+a)\left(\frac{1}{\alpha - \frac{1}{2}} + \frac{1}{\beta + \frac{1}{2}}\right)\right] - \frac{z^{p+1}}{(p+1)(\beta+a)}$$

$$- 4\left(1 - \frac{s}{2}\right)^p$$

$$\geq \frac{\beta+a}{p+1} - \frac{z^{p+1}}{(p+1)(\beta+a)} - 4\left(1 - \frac{s}{2}\right)^p.$$

Since both $z < 1$ and $1 - s/2 < 1$, there is a value, say $p_1$, of $p$ so that

$$L_{p_1}(g, a) - L_{p_1}(g, \tfrac{1}{2}) > 0, \qquad a \leq \tfrac{1}{4}.$$

It is clear that there is a value $z' < 1$ so that any function $h(x)$ with

$$h(x) = g(x), \qquad g(x) \leq z',$$
$$0 \leq h(x) \leq 1, \qquad g(x) > z',$$

satisfies

$$L_{p_1}(h, a) - L_{p_1}(h, \tfrac{1}{2}) > 0, \qquad a \leq \tfrac{1}{4}. \tag{12–8.3}$$

The situation is illustrated in Fig. 12–5.

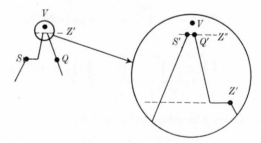

FIG. 12–5.   The second step in the definition of $h(x)$.

From the level of $z'$ to that of $z''$ or $Q'S'$ we define $h(x)$ analogously, except the definition is reflected about the line $x = 0$. Thus we arrive at a value $p_2$ and points $S'Q'$ for the definition of $h(x)$ so that

$$L_{p_2}(h, a) - L_{p_2}(h, -\tfrac{1}{2}) > 0, \qquad a \leq \tfrac{1}{4}. \tag{12–8.4}$$

We may assume that $p_2 \geq p_1 + 1$.

Let $a_p$ denote the best $L_p$-approximation to the function $f(x)$ constructed in this way. Then (12–8.3) and (12–8.4) imply that

$$a_{p_i} > \tfrac{1}{4}, \qquad i \text{ odd,}$$
$$a_{p_i} < -\tfrac{1}{4}, \qquad i \text{ even.}$$

Thus the sequence $\{L(A_{p_i}, x) \mid i = 1, 2, \ldots\}$ does not converge.

It is intuitively plausible that this example can be modified to obtain the following:

EXAMPLE 2. A function $h(x)$ analytic except at $x = 0$ for which the Polya algorithm does not converge.

EXAMPLE 3. A function $h(x)$ defined on a countable number of points with 0 as limit point for which the Polya algorithm does not converge.

EXAMPLE 4. A function $h(x, y)$ continuous on the unit square for which the Polya algorithm does not converge with the approximating function $a + bx + cy$.

Descloux has carried out the details for the last example.

## 12–9   COMPUTATION

In the remainder of this chapter we consider three distinct topics. They are (a) orthogonalization schemes, (b) exchange methods for Tchebycheff approximation, and (c) the structure of critical point sets of Tchebycheff approximation. The third topic is not computation in the strict sense, but the question is of some interest for computational work.

## 12–10   ORTHOGONALIZATION

The classical method of orthogonalizing a set of vectors is the *Gram-Schmidt* process. This method has been used extensively in applications (Davis, 1962, Davis and Rabinowitz, 1961). Let $\{\boldsymbol{\phi}_i \mid i = 1, 2, \ldots, n\}$ be a given set of linearly independent vectors and we wish to find an equivalent set $\{\boldsymbol{\psi}_i \mid i = 1, 2, \ldots, n\}$ which are orthogonal. Though we speak of $\boldsymbol{\phi}_i$ and $\boldsymbol{\psi}_i$ as vectors, they may in fact be elements of any Hilbert space. The classical *Gram-Schmidt* process is as follows, where, as usual, $\|\mathbf{v}\| = (\mathbf{v}, \mathbf{v})^{1/2}$.

$$\boldsymbol{\psi}_1' = \boldsymbol{\phi}_1, \qquad\qquad \boldsymbol{\psi}_1 = \boldsymbol{\psi}_1' / \|\boldsymbol{\psi}_1'\|$$
$$\boldsymbol{\psi}_2' = \boldsymbol{\phi}_2 - (\boldsymbol{\phi}_2, \boldsymbol{\psi}_1)\boldsymbol{\psi}_1, \qquad \boldsymbol{\psi}_2 = \boldsymbol{\psi}_2' / \|\boldsymbol{\psi}_2'\|$$
$$\cdot\ \cdot\ \cdot \qquad\qquad \cdot\ \cdot\ \cdot \qquad (12\text{–}10.1)$$
$$\boldsymbol{\psi}_k' = \boldsymbol{\phi}_k - \sum_{=1}^{k-1} (\boldsymbol{\phi}_k, \boldsymbol{\psi}_i)\boldsymbol{\psi}_i, \quad \boldsymbol{\psi}_k = \boldsymbol{\psi}_k' / \|\boldsymbol{\psi}_k'\|$$
$$\cdot\ \cdot\ \cdot$$

The process (12–10.1) in fact generates two matrices $D$, $T$ such that

$$\boldsymbol{\psi} = DT\boldsymbol{\phi}$$

where $\boldsymbol{\phi}$, $\boldsymbol{\psi}$ are the matrices $\{\boldsymbol{\phi}_1, \boldsymbol{\phi}_2, \ldots, \boldsymbol{\phi}_n\}$ and $\{\boldsymbol{\psi}_1, \boldsymbol{\psi}_2, \ldots, \boldsymbol{\psi}_n\}$. The matrices $D$ and $T$ are diagonal and triangular, respectively, and are given explicitly by

$$D = \begin{bmatrix} \|\boldsymbol{\psi}_1'\|^{-1} & & & & 0 \\ & \|\boldsymbol{\psi}_2'\|^{-1} & & & \\ & & \cdot & & \\ & & & \cdot & \\ 0 & & & & \|\boldsymbol{\psi}_n'\|^{-1} \end{bmatrix}$$

$$T = \begin{bmatrix} 1 & 0 & 0 & & & 0 \\ -(\boldsymbol{\phi}_2, \boldsymbol{\psi}_1) & 1 & 0 & & & \\ -(\boldsymbol{\phi}_3, \boldsymbol{\psi}_1) & -(\boldsymbol{\phi}_3, \boldsymbol{\psi}_2) & 1 & & & \\ \cdot & \cdot & \cdot & & & \\ & & & \cdot & & \\ & & & & 1 & 0 \\ -(\boldsymbol{\phi}_n, \boldsymbol{\psi}_1) & -(\boldsymbol{\phi}_n, \boldsymbol{\psi}_2) & -(\boldsymbol{\phi}_n, \boldsymbol{\psi}_3) \ldots & -(\boldsymbol{\phi}_n, \boldsymbol{\psi}_{n-1}) & 1 \end{bmatrix}$$

We see that (12–10.1) generates the matrix a row at a time.

The computations in (12–10.1) may be performed in a different order and the resulting process is called the *modified Gram-Schmidt* orthogonalization process. This process is defined explicitly as follows

$$\boldsymbol{\psi}_1' = \boldsymbol{\phi}_1, \qquad\qquad \boldsymbol{\psi}_1 = \boldsymbol{\psi}_1'/\|\boldsymbol{\psi}_1'\|,$$
$$\boldsymbol{\phi}_j^{(2)} = \boldsymbol{\phi}_j - (\boldsymbol{\phi}_j, \boldsymbol{\psi}_1)\boldsymbol{\psi}_1, \qquad j = 2, 3, \ldots, n;$$
$$\boldsymbol{\psi}_2' = \boldsymbol{\phi}_2^{(2)}, \qquad\qquad \boldsymbol{\psi}_2 = \boldsymbol{\psi}_2'/\|\boldsymbol{\psi}_2'\|,$$
$$\boldsymbol{\phi}_j^{(3)} = \boldsymbol{\phi}_j^{(2)} - (\boldsymbol{\phi}_j^{(2)}, \boldsymbol{\psi}_2)\boldsymbol{\psi}_2, \qquad j = 3, 4, \ldots, n; \tag{12–10.2}$$
$$\ldots$$
$$\boldsymbol{\psi}_k' = \boldsymbol{\phi}_k^{(k)}, \qquad\qquad \boldsymbol{\psi}_k = \boldsymbol{\psi}_k'/\|\boldsymbol{\psi}_k'\|,$$
$$\boldsymbol{\phi}_j^{(k+1)} = \boldsymbol{\phi}_j^{(k)} - (\boldsymbol{\phi}_j^{(k)}, \boldsymbol{\psi}_k)\boldsymbol{\psi}_k, \qquad j = k+1, k+2, \ldots, n$$

We see that (12–10.2) computes factors of the matrix $T$ a column at a time. Though the intermediate quantities in (12–10.1) and (12–10.2) are different, it is clear that they both lead to the same system $\{\boldsymbol{\psi}_i\}$ and involve the same amount of computation. The modified process requires less storage when carried out in a computer.

In spite of the apparent equivalence of the Gram-Schmidt and modified Gram-Schmidt processes, there is one distinct advantage to the modified process. This is that one can use *pivoting* during the orthogonalization. In the classical process the vectors $\{\boldsymbol{\phi}_i\}$ are ordered arbitrarily and this ordering may introduce unnecessary numerical instability. Consider the following example.

EXAMPLE. Let $\boldsymbol{\phi}_1, \boldsymbol{\phi}_2, \boldsymbol{\phi}_3$ be three vectors in $E_n$ which, for simplicity, differ in only the first three coordinates.

Those coordinates are

$$\boldsymbol{\phi}_1 = (1, 0, 0), \quad \boldsymbol{\phi}_2 = (1, \alpha, \beta), \quad \boldsymbol{\phi}_3 = (0, 1, 1).$$

We assume that $\alpha$ and $\beta$ are "small" numbers. This implies that $\boldsymbol{\phi}_1$ and $\boldsymbol{\phi}_2$ are nearly linearly dependent and hence the three-dimensional flat spanned by these three vectors is "poorly" defined in one direction. However, the two-dimensional flat spanned by $\boldsymbol{\phi}_1$ and $\boldsymbol{\phi}_3$ is well defined.

The first two steps of the Gram-Schmidt process give

$$\boldsymbol{\psi}_1 = (1, 0, 0)$$
$$\boldsymbol{\psi}_2 = (0, \alpha, \beta)/\sqrt{(\alpha^2 + \beta^2)}.$$

Now if $\alpha$ and $\beta$ are nearly equal, the vector $\boldsymbol{\psi}_2$ is nearly linearly dependent on $\boldsymbol{\psi}_3$. This implies that the vector $\boldsymbol{\psi}_3$ is also poorly defined. Thus the Gram-Schmidt process leads to one "well" defined vector $\boldsymbol{\psi}_1$ and two "poorly" defined vectors $\boldsymbol{\psi}_2$ and $\boldsymbol{\psi}_3$. This loss of accuracy in one of the directions may be eliminated by taking the vectors in the order $\boldsymbol{\phi}_1, \boldsymbol{\phi}_3, \boldsymbol{\phi}_2$.

At the end of the first step of the modified process, some information is known about the relationship of all of the vectors with $\boldsymbol{\psi}_1$. This information, which is $(\boldsymbol{\phi}_j, \boldsymbol{\psi}_1)$, may be used to make an advantageous choice of the second vector to be used in the orthogonalization. The choice that comes to mind first is the vector $\boldsymbol{\phi}_j$ which makes the largest angle $\theta_j$ with $\boldsymbol{\psi}_1$. Some information is known about this angle, indeed

$$\cos \theta_j = \frac{(\boldsymbol{\phi}_j, \boldsymbol{\psi}_1)}{\|\boldsymbol{\phi}_j\|}.$$

At the end of the $k$th step of this process, one would choose as the next vector, the one which makes the largest angle with the flat spanned by the first $k$ vectors. One may obtain this information fairly efficiently by the following *pivoting scheme*:

(1) *Normalize all vectors* $\boldsymbol{\phi}_j$ *to have length 1.*
(2) *Set* $c_j^{(i)} = (\boldsymbol{\phi}_j, \boldsymbol{\psi}_i)$, $i < j$. *Then choose the* $\boldsymbol{\phi}_j^{(k+1)}$ *which has the minimum value of*

$$\sum_{i=1}^{k} (c_j^{(i)})^2. \qquad (12\text{--}10.3)$$

Note that

$$\boldsymbol{\phi}_j = \boldsymbol{\phi}_j^{(k+1)} + \sum_{i=1}^{k} c_j^{(i)} \boldsymbol{\psi}_i$$

and, by orthogonality,

$$1 = \|\boldsymbol{\phi}_j^{(k+1)}\|^2 + \sum_{i=1}^{k} (c_j^{(i)})^2.$$

It is clear that the vector $\boldsymbol{\phi}_j$ which makes the largest angle with the flat spanned by $\boldsymbol{\psi}_1, \ldots, \boldsymbol{\psi}_k$ is the vector which maximizes $\|\boldsymbol{\phi}_j^{(k+1)}\|^2$ or, equivalently, minimizes (12–10.3).

It must be noted that computational experience using this pivoting scheme is limited, see Rice, 1966. It is likewise true that such a scheme will not ameliorate any near linear dependence that exists in the original set of vectors. The pivoting is simply designed to avoid introducing any artificial linear dependence at intermediate steps. This is exactly the same role that pivoting plays in the usual Gaussian elimination procedure.

## 12–11  THE ONE FOR ONE EXCHANGE ALGORITHM

There are two basic methods for computing Tchebycheff approximations —the method of descent and the method of ascent. These two methods are discussed in some detail in Chapter 6 for functions of one variable. The various methods of descent are not so much affected by the difficulties introduced in multivariate problems. This is due to the fact that these methods (at least the ones developed so far) do not exploit to any great extent the special characteristics of the Tchebycheff approximation problem. However, the methods of ascent do exploit these special characteristics and hence these methods must be modified when the characteristics are changed. In this section we will describe two variations of the one for one exchange algorithm. The first (Rice, 1963) allows one to compute the strict approximation, and the second (Descloux, 1961) allows one to compute a best Tchebycheff approximation. Both of these algorithms are discussed for approximation on a finite point set $X$.

The basic idea of the one for one exchange algorithm is as follows: Let $L(A_0, x)$ be an approximation to $f(x)$ which is a best approximation on $X_0 \subset X$ with critical point set $\mathcal{R}_0$. Locate $x_1 \in X$ such that

$$|L(A_0, x_1) - f(x_1)| = \max_X |L(A_0, x) - f(x)|.$$

One then determines $L(A_1, x)$ as the best approximation to $f(x)$ on $\mathcal{R}_0 \cup \{x_1\}$. One may then repeat the process with the critical point set $\mathcal{R}_1$. Normally $\mathcal{R}_0$ and $\mathcal{R}_1$ have the same number of points and a one for one exchange takes place. In the algorithm for strict approximations, this is not always the case. We now state formally the *exchange algorithm for strict approximation*:

0. *Assume that, at the kth step, one has determined a strict approximation* $L(A_k, x)$ *to* $f(x)$ *on a nondegenerate strict critical point set* $\mathscr{R}_k$ *with deviation vector* $\mathbf{d}_k$. *Let* $\mathscr{R}_k = \bigcup \mathscr{S}_{ik}$ *where* $\mathscr{S}_{ik}$ *is a critical point set with respect to* $\mathscr{L}_{i-1}$ *in Definition 11–4. The sets* $\mathscr{S}_{ik}$ *are ordered according to the corresponding deviation vector components* $d_{ik}$.

1. *Determine* $x_{k+1} \in X$ *such that* (a) $\boldsymbol{\phi}(x_{k+1}) \in [\boldsymbol{\phi}(\bigcup_j \mathscr{S}_{jk})]$ *for some set of indices* $j$. (b)

$$|L(A_k, x_{k+1}) - f(x_{k+1})| = d_0 > \min_j d_{jk}.$$

*If no such* $x_{k+1}$ *can be found then* $L(A_k, x)$ *is the strict approximation to* $f(x)$ *on* $X$.

2. *Determine* $L(A_{k+1}, x)$ *as the strict approximation to* $f(x)$ *on* $\mathscr{R}_k \cup \{x_{k+1}\}$ *and choose* $\mathscr{R}_{k+1}$ *as a strict critical point set of this approximation.*

The following lemma shows that this algorithm is indeed a method of ascent.

**Lemma 12–8.** *The deviation* $\mathbf{d}_{k+1}$ *determined by steps 1 and 2 above is larger than* $\mathbf{d}_k$.

*Proof.* Let $\mathscr{S}_p$ be the $\mathscr{S}_{jk}$ of step 1 with the smallest deviation component $d_{jk}$. If $d_{k+1}$ is not to be greater than $d_k$, then we must have

$$L(A_k, x) - L(A_{k+1}, x) = 0, \qquad x \in \bigcup_{j=1}^{p-1} \mathscr{S}_j. \qquad (12\text{–}11.1)$$

It is not possible for $L(A_{k+1}, x)$ to satisfy (12–11.1) and also

$$L(A_k - A_{k+1}, x) = 0, \qquad x \in \mathscr{S}_p,$$
$$L(A_k - A_{k+1}, x_{k+1}) \neq 0.$$

This would contradict the fact that $\boldsymbol{\phi}(x_{k+1}) \in [\boldsymbol{\phi}(\bigcup_j \mathscr{S}_{jk})]$. Consider then any $A_{k+1}$ satisfying (12–11.1) which is a candidate for best approximation on $\mathscr{S}_p \cup \{x_{k+1}\}$. If $L(A_{k+1}, x) = L(A_k, x)$ for $x \in \mathscr{S}_p$ then the deviation on $\mathscr{S}_p \cup \{x_{k+1}\}$ is $d_0 > d_p$. If, however, $L(A_{k+1}, x) \neq L(A_k, x)$ for $x \in \mathscr{S}_p$ then the deviation of $L(A_{k+1}, x)$ on $\mathscr{S}_p$ must be larger than $d_p$. This follows, for example, from the Corollary of Theorem 12–6 as applied to approximation on $\mathscr{S}_p \cup \{x_{k+1}\}$ by approximating functions $L(A, x)$ satisfying (12–11.1). This concludes the proof.

**Corollary.** *If* $X$ *is a finite set, then the one for one exchange algorithm converges to the strict approximation in a finite number of steps.*

If one is only interested in best approximation rather than strict approximation there is one obvious simplification possible. That is in step 1 to consider only those $x_{k+1}$ with

$$|L(A_k, x_{k+1}) - f(x_{k+1})| = d_0 > d_1.$$

It is, however, apparently difficult to avoid computing the strict approximation or making some other complicated computation. If one has merely the set $\mathscr{R}$ of critical point sets and $\boldsymbol{\phi}(x_{k+1}) \notin [\boldsymbol{\phi}(\mathscr{R})]$ then one must proceed with caution. One cannot merely decrease the deviation at $x_{k+1}$ and then discard $x_{k+1}$. This leads to a situation where the deviation is not decreased and the algorithm may cycle infinitely without reaching a best approximation. This is illustrated by the following

EXAMPLE. $L(A, x) = ax$, $X = \{-1, 0, +1\}$,

$$f(-1) = \tfrac{1}{2}, \quad f(0) = 1, \quad f(1) = \tfrac{1}{2}.$$

Suppose $L(A_0, x) = -\tfrac{3}{2}x$, then $x_1 = +1$. Suppose we decide to make $[L(A_1, x_1) - f(x_1)] = 1$. Then $L(A_1, x) = \tfrac{3}{2}x$, $x_2 = -1$. If we then decide to make $[L(A_2, x_2) - f(x_2)] = 1$, we have $L(A_2, x) = -\tfrac{3}{2}x = L(A_0, x)$.

An exchange algorithm which avoids this difficulty has been given by Descloux, 1961. At certain steps, called static exchanges, the deviation does not decrease. However, one has a set of auxiliary coefficients for those $x$'s such that $\boldsymbol{\phi}(x) \notin [\boldsymbol{\phi}(\mathscr{R})]$ where $\mathscr{R}$ is the current set of critical point sets. When a static exchange is made, these auxiliary coefficients are modified in such a way that an infinite sequence of static exchanges is not possible. We will not prove here that this is actually the case, and no proof is given in Descloux, 1961. It is contained in his thesis (Descloux, 1960). We now describe the *exchange algorithm for Tchebycheff approximation.*

0. Assume that, at the $k$th step, one has a set $\mathscr{P}_k\{x_i \mid i = 1, 2, \ldots, n + 1\}$ of dimension $n$ and which is an extremal point set of a best approximation $L(A_k, x)$ to $f(x)$ on $\mathscr{P}_k$ with deviation $d_k$. Let $\mathscr{R}_k$ be the set of critical point sets of this approximation (which we assume to be the first $p$ points of $\mathscr{R}_k$). There are coefficients $\alpha_i$ such that

$$\sum_{i=1}^{p} \alpha_i \boldsymbol{\phi}(x_i) = 0. \tag{12–11.2}$$

If $p < n + 1$ determine $n + 1 - p$ auxiliary coefficients

$$c_i = \operatorname{sgn}\left[L(A_k, x_i) - f(x_i)\right], \qquad i = p + 1, \ldots, n + 1. \tag{12–11.3}$$

1. Determine $x_0 \in X$ such that

$$|L(A_k, x_0) - f(x_0)| > d_k.$$

2. Calculate coefficients $\beta_i$ so that

$$\boldsymbol{\phi}(x_0) + \sum_{i=2}^{n+1} \beta_i \boldsymbol{\phi}(x_i) = 0$$

and set

$$\sigma = \operatorname{sgn}\left[\alpha_1\big(L(A_k, x_0) - f(x_0)\big)\right],$$

$$M = \min \frac{b_i}{c_i}, \qquad i = p + 1, \ldots, n + 1.$$

3. *Case 1 (Static Exchange):* $M < 0$. Assume, for concreteness that $M = \sigma b_{n+1}/c_{n+1}$. Then exchange $x_{n+1}$ and $x_0$, i.e. delete $x_{n+1}$ from $\mathscr{P}_k$ and add $x_0$ to form $\mathscr{P}_{k+1}$.

In $\mathscr{P}_{k+1}$, set $c_{n+1} = 0, b_{n+1} = 1$ and then modify all the auxiliary coefficients by

$$c_i' = c_i + b_i|M|, \qquad i = p + 1, \ldots, n + 1.$$

If, by accident, $c_i' = 0$ for some $i$, choose $c_i'$ arbitrarily and different from zero. Determine $L(A_{k+1}, x)$ so that (12–11.3) holds and $\mathscr{P}_{k+1}$ is an extremal point set. Return to step 1.

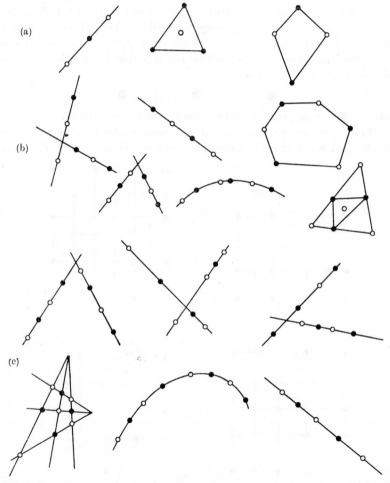

FIG. 12–6.  Some critical point sets for approximation in two variables by polynomials of (a) degree 1, (b) degree 2, (c) degree 3. Positive and negative points are denoted by $\bigcirc$ and $\bullet$, respectively. Not all possibilities are shown.

4. *Case 2 (Ordinary Exchange):* $M \geq 0$. One exchanges $x_0$ for a point of $\mathscr{P}_k$ such that a larger deviation occurs on $\mathscr{P}_{k+1}$. An approximation $L(A_{k+1}, x)$ is determined so that $\mathscr{P}_{k+1}$ is an extremal point set. As pointed out in Section 6–8, one does not have to choose the best approximation on $\mathscr{P}_k \cup \{x_0\}$. One need merely obtain an approximation with a larger deviation. Thus Descloux proposes the direct extension of the method due to Stiefel, 1959. One may use other rules for determining the point of $\mathscr{P}_k$ to be exchanged for $x_0$. In any case one returns to step 1.

## 12–12   CRITICAL POINT SETS

For approximation in one real variable, the nature of a critical point set and the error curve is very simply described. Thus if we examine the extremal points along with the sign of the error, $f(x)$ — approximation, the best approximation is characterized by the fact that these points contain a subset of $n + 1$ points in the order

where $\bigcirc$, $\bullet$ denote positive and negative points, respectively.

There is no natural ordering of the variables for functions of several variables and hence there is no simple geometric identification of a critical

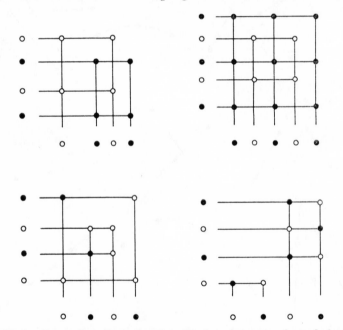

FIG. 12–7.   Some two-dimensional critical point sets formed by tensor products. The points on the axis (connected by dotted lines) are not part of the sets, but only indicate the construction.

point set. The possible arrangements of positive and negative points in a critical point set have been enumerated for approximation by the low degree polynomials in two variables (Collatz, 1965). Some of these are illustrated in Fig. 12–6. The number of possible configurations increases very rapidly with the number of parameters and only a selection is shown. One may interchange the positive and negative points to obtain other examples.

One often uses approximating functions which are tensor products (12–3.2) for approximation in higher dimensional spaces. In this situation, the critical points have special properties which have been investigated by Lawson, 1961, Newman and Shapiro, 1963, and Collatz, 1965.

The critical point sets in a product space must be products (in a certain sense) of critical point sets in the spaces entering into the product. We do not elaborate these upon the precise nature of the results but note that the proofs are surprisingly difficult. Some possibilities are illustrated in Fig. 12–7 for the two-dimensional case.

# 13

# Best Approximations and
# Interpolating Functions

## 13–1 INTRODUCTION

Historically there has been a close association between approximation and interpolation. In many situations an interpolation process is used to obtain approximations. The simple logic behind this process is that if an approximation agrees with $f(x)$ at some known points (points of interpolation), then it should come close to $f(x)$ at intermediate points. On the other hand it has long been recognized that the usual approximations used actually interpolate $f(x)$ as often as possible.

In order to discuss this relationship in more detail we define interpolation as follows: Assume that a function $F(A^*, x)$ has $n$ (effective) parameters at $A^*$, then $F(A^*, x)$ is said to be an *interpolating function* of $f(x)$ on $[0, 1]$ if $f(x) - F(A^*, x)$ has $n$ zeros on $[0, 1]$. A study of the relationship between approximation and interpolation should attempt to answer the following three questions:

QUESTION 1: What are the interpolation properties of the usual best approximations, and what are the approximation properties of the usual interpolating functions?

QUESTION 2: What are the exact properties of a norm $\delta$ and an approximating function $F(A, x)$ which force best approximations in the $\delta$ norm to also be interpolating functions?

QUESTION 3: Given an interpolating function $F(A^*, x)$, under what conditions on $F$ can we say that there exists a norm (perhaps from a restricted class of norms) so that $F(A^*, x)$ is also a best approximation?

It becomes apparent early in a study of these questions that it is natural to introduce three distinct types of interpolation. We begin with

**Definition 13–1.** *A function $g(x)$ is said to have $n$ weak sign changes on a*

260

set $X$ *if there are* $n + 1$ *points* $\{x_i \mid i = 1, 2, \ldots, n + 1,\ x_i < x_{i+1}\}$ *in $X$ so that*

$$g(x_i)(-1)^i \geq 0 \ or \ g(x_i)(-1)^{i+1} \geq 0.$$

*If strict inequality occurs at each point, then $g(x)$ is said to have $n$ strong sign changes on $X$.*

A varisolvent function $F(A, x)$ is said to be a *strongly interpolating function* of $f(x)$ on $X$ if $F(A, x) - f(x)$ has $m(A)$ strong sign changes on $X$. $F(A, x)$ is said to be a *weakly interpolating function* if $F(A, x) - f(x)$ has $m(A)$ weak sign changes on $X$. $F(A, x)$ is said to be an *exactly interpolating function* if $f(A, x) - f(x)$ has $m(A)$ zeros on $X$. This latter definition is useful only if $X$ contains isolated points. These definitions are illustrated in Fig. 13–1.

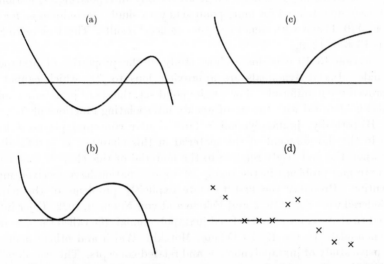

FIG. 13–1. Types of interpolation: (a) $g(x)$ has 3 strong sign changes; (b) $g(x)$ has 1 strong sign change and 3 weak sign changes; (c) $g(x)$ has no strong sign changes and infinitely many weak sign changes; (d) $g(x)$ has 1 strong sign change, 3 zeros and 5 weak sign changes.

If we interpret "usual" to mean linear approximating functions and weighted $L_p$-norms $(0 < p \leq \infty)$†, then Question 1 is completely answered in Section 13–9. The conclusion is that the sets of strong, weak and exact interpolating functions are identical with the sets of weighted $L_p$-approximations with $p \geq 1$, $p = 1$ and $1 > p > 0$, respectively.

The other two questions are somewhat less specific and considerably

---

† The values $0 < p < 1$ do not give norms in the usual sense but only distance functions. Even so, we use the terminology for uniformity. Care is taken not to assume the triangle inequality when $0 < p < 1$.

more difficult. Concerning Question 2 some general assumptions are made on an abstract norm $\delta$ and then conditions which imply that best approximations are weakly or strongly interpolating functions are investigated. There are distinct investigations for the interval $[0, 1]$ and a finite set $X$. The conditions studied are sufficient to show that varisolvent best approximations are interpolating functions. The necessity of these conditions, which is equivalent to Question 3, is not known. Only in the case of linear approximating functions and $L_p$-norms is Question 3 answered for the interval $[0, 1]$. These results are contained in the next three sections.

In general more can be done for a finite point set $X$ than for the interval $[0, 1]$. In Section 13–5 a theorem is established which shows with rather weak assumptions on the norm $\delta$ and approximating function $F$ that best approximations in the $\delta$ norm on $X$ are weakly interpolating. Questions 2 and 3 are investigated for finite point sets with similar techniques as for the interval $[0, 1]$ and with somewhat more general results. This is done in Sections 13–6 to 13–9.

Section 13–10 contains a short study of the properties of juxtapolynomials. Juxtapolynomials are approximations to $f(x)$ which cannot be improved upon uniformly. For a finite point set, the set of juxtapolynomials of $f(x)$ is identical with the set of weakly interpolating functions of $f(x)$.

Historically, juxtapolynomials (and similar concepts) played a large role in the development of the material in this chapter. It is difficult to say when the first study relative to the material of this chapter was made, for extremal problems in the theory of approximation have received much attention. Probably the first to state explicitly problems of the nature considered were Fejér, 1922, and Fekete and von Neuman, 1922. Fejér introduced an abstract norm and defined juxtapolynomials (he called them nearest polynomials). In the 1950's Fekete, Motzkin, Walsh and others made an intensive study of juxtapolynomials and related concepts. This was done for both real and complex functions, though the latter work is not considered here. It was from these studies that Motzkin and Walsh, 1959a, discovered the remarkable fact that linear $L_p$-approximations are interpolating functions and vice versa. Thus it has been possible to present the results in this chapter with little of the mathematics which led to these results in the first place. The first attempt to explore the limits of this phenomenon was made by Rice, 1961. He attempted to weaken the assumption on the norm $\delta$ and the approximating function $F$ as much as possible and still retain the interpolating properties of best approximations and vice versa.

The final section presents the Lawson algorithm (Lawson, 1961) for Tchebycheff approximation. It is an interesting computational method based on the results of Motzkin and Walsh (summarized in Section 13–9). The main attraction of this algorithm is not that it may be more efficient, but rather that it allows one to attack problems where other algorithms for

Tchebycheff approximations are completely unknown. For example, one can apply it for functions of a complex variable and to vector valued functions.

There is a general assumption made throughout this chapter that the function to be approximated (generally denoted by $f(x)$) is not identically equal to an approximating function on its domain of definition. This in particular implies that finite point sets contain more points than the number of parameters of $F$.

## 13–2  NORMS AND REGULARITY

If the function $|g(x)|$ is uniformly smaller than $|f(x)|$ on a set $X$, then it is natural to expect that

$$\delta_X(g) < \delta_X(f) \qquad (13\text{–}2.1)$$

where $\delta_X$ denotes a norm on the set of functions defined on $X$. This expectation may be carried further in that if $|g(x)| < |f(x)|$ on part of $X$ and $|g(x)| = |f(x)|$ on the remainder of $X$, then (13–2.1) is expected to be valid with equality admitted. These expectations do not follow from the abstract definition of the norm on a function space. Hence norms which do fulfill these expectations to some degree are of special interest. Such a norm is called a *monotonic norm*. Fejér, 1922, has defined a monotonic norm in the special context of the approximation problem by polynomials on a finite point set. It is particularly important in the abstract definition of a monotonic norm to be able to assert $\delta_X(g) < \delta_X(f)$ in a large variety of situations where intuition expects such a relationship. The definition given here is not the most flexible possible definition, but it suffices to illustrate the principle and to analyse the problems of this chapter.

A *monotonic norm* of $f(x)$ on $X$ is denoted by $\delta_X(f(x))$, and is assumed to have the following properties:

(1)  $\delta_X$ is defined for all piecewise continuous functions on $X$.
(2)  $\delta_X(f(x)) = \delta_X(|f(x)|)$
(3)  Given a continuous function $g(x)$ on $X$ let $\qquad\qquad (13\text{–}2.2)$
  $A(k) = \{x \mid |g(x)| \geq k \sup_X |g(x)|\}.$
  If $|f(x)| = |g(x)|$ for $x \notin A(k)$ and $|f(x)| < |g(x)|$ for $x \in A(k)$, then
  $$\delta_X(f(x)) < \delta_X(g(x))$$
  for all $0 < k < 1$.

If a sequence $\{f_n(x) \mid n = 1, 2, \ldots\}$ of functions converges to $f(x)$, the convergence is said to be *regular* if the rate of convergence is "uniform" with respect to $x$. This is stated precisely in the following definition.

**Definition 13–2.**  *Let $\bar{A}$ be the closure of the set*

$$A = \{x \mid f(x) = f_n(x) \text{ for some } n\}.$$

*Set $\epsilon_n = \sup_X |f(x) - f_n(x)|$ and let $I$ be a closed subset of $X$ such that*

$I \cap \bar{A}$ *is empty.* *The sequence* $\{f_n(x)\}$ *is said to converge regularly to* $f(x)$ *if*

$$\int_I |f_n(x) - f(x)| dx \geq K\epsilon_n$$

*for some positive* $K$ *which may depend on* $I$.

A varisolvent function $F(A, x)$ is said to be *regular* if

$$\lim_{n \to \infty} F(A_n, x) = F(A^*, x)$$

for each $x \in X$ implies that the convergence is regular. Regularity is a necessary requirement for most of the results of this chapter to be valid. All linear approximating functions of the form

$$L(A, x) = \sum_{i=1}^{n} a_i \phi_i(x)$$

are regular.

The following is a simple one parameter unisolvent functions which is not regular:

$$\phi(a, x) = \begin{cases} a^6 & 0 \leq x \leq \frac{1}{2} - a^2 \\ \dfrac{x}{a} + a + a^6 - \dfrac{1}{2a} & \frac{1}{2} - a^2 \leq x \leq \frac{1}{2} \\ -\dfrac{x}{a} + a + a^6 + \dfrac{1}{2a} & \frac{1}{2} \leq x \leq \frac{1}{2} + a^2 \\ a^6 & \frac{1}{2} + a^2 \leq x \leq 1 \end{cases}$$

This function is plotted for a few values of $a$ near zero in Fig. 13–2.

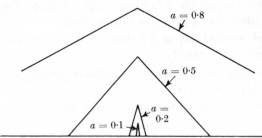

Fig. 13.2.   Plot of $\phi(a, x)$, $a = 0$, $a = 0 \cdot 1$, $a = 0 \cdot 2$, $a = 0 \cdot 5$, $a = 0 \cdot 8$.

In the study of the interpolating properties of best approximations there are three special types of monotonic norms which are of interest. Roughly speaking, a norm $\delta$ is said to be a Class 3 norm if $\delta$ emphasizes values near zero and a Class 2 norm if $\delta$ emphasizes values away from zero. Norms which emphasize all values equally are said to be Class 1 norms.

The motivating examples for these three classes are the following norms.

Class 1:  $\delta(f(x)) = \displaystyle\int_0^1 |f(x)| dx = \|f\|_1$

Class 2:  $\delta\big(f(x)\big) = \left[\displaystyle\int_0^1 |f(x)|^p\,dx\right]^{\frac{1}{p}} = \|f\|_p,\, p > 1$

Class 3:  $\delta\big(f(x)\big) = \left[\displaystyle\int_0^1 |f(x)|^p\,dx\right]^{\frac{1}{p}} = \|f\|_p,\, p < 1.$

In this chapter approximation is considered on only two types of sets. The first is a closed and bounded interval, which is taken as $[0, 1]$, and the second is a finite point set. The norm classes are precisely defined only for these two sets. The next section of this chapter deals with norm classes on $[0, 1]$ exclusively, and these classes are defined here. The norm classes for a finite point set are defined in Section 13–4.

In order to define the Class 1 and Class 2 norms precisely consider a continuous function $g(x)$ and a sequence $\{g_n(x)\}$ which converges regularly to $g(x)$. Let $r(n)$ be an arbitrary function such that

$$\lim_{n\to\infty} r(n) = 0$$

and set

$$R_n = \{x \mid |g(x)| \le |r(n)|\}.$$

Assume that

$$0 < g_n(x)/g(x) \le 1$$

for $x \notin R_n$. Further let $Y$ be a fixed subset of $[0, 1]$ with the following properties:

   (a)  $0 < g_n(x)/g(x) < 1$ for $x \in Y$ and all $n$

   (b)  $Y$ is the union of a finite number of closed intervals     (13–2.3)

   (c)  If $g(x_0) = \|g\|_\infty$ then $x_0$ is in the interior of $Y$.

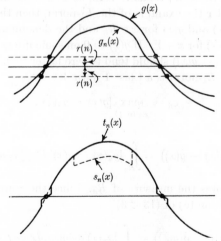

FIG. 13–3.   The functions $s_n(x)$ and $t_n(x)$.

Set

$$s_n(x) = \begin{cases} g_n(x), & x \in Y \\ g(x), & x \notin Y \end{cases}$$

$$t_n(x) = \begin{cases} g_n(x), & x \in R_n \\ g(x), & x \notin R_n \end{cases}$$

This construction is illustrated in Fig. 13–3. Both $t_n(x)$ and $s_n(x)$ are piecewise continuous and they agree on points not in either $Y$ or $R_n$.

**Definition 13–3.** $\delta$ *is a Class 2 norm if*

$$\lim_{n \to \infty} \frac{\delta(t_n(x) - g(x))}{\delta(s_n(x)) - \delta(g(x))} = 0. \qquad (13\text{–}2.4)$$

**Definition 13–4.** *Assume the measure of the set*

$$\{x \mid g(x) = 0\} \qquad (13\text{–}2.5)$$

*is zero.* $\delta$ *is a Class 1 norm if*

$$\lim_{n \to \infty} \frac{\delta(t_n(x) - g(x))}{\delta(s_n(x)) - \delta(g(x))} = 0.$$

The numerator of (13–2.4) is the effect on the norm of the difference between $g_n(x)$ and $g(x)$ on the set $R_n$, i.e. "near zero". If the norm is the Tchebycheff norm, then the numerator of (13–2.4) is identically zero. The denominator of (13–2.4) is the effect on the norm of the difference between $g_n(x)$ and $g(x)$ on the set $Y$, i.e. "away from zero".

In the definition of the Class 1 norms the numerator tends to zero because the measure of $R_n$ tends to zero, as well as because $\{g_n(x)\}$ tends to $g(x)$. If we consider the example of the $L_1$-norm, then the numerator is the area between $g_n(x)$ and $g(x)$ for $x \in R_n$ and the denominator is the area between $g_n(x)$ and $g(x)$ for $x \in Y$. If $g(x) \equiv 0$ on some interval, then there is no reason why $\delta(t_n(x) - g(x))$ should tend to zero faster than $\delta(s_n(x)) - \delta(g(x))$. To show that the $L_1$-norm is a Class 1 norm let

$$\epsilon_n = \max_{x \in [0,\, 1]} |g(x) - g_n(x)|.$$

Then

$$\delta(t_n(x) - g(x)) = \int_{R_n} |g_n(x) - g(x)| dx \le \epsilon_n \mu(R_n)$$

where $\mu(R_n)$ denotes the measure of $R_n$. Since the convergence is regular, we have by condition (a) of (13–2.3)

$$\delta(s_n(x)) - \delta(g(x)) = \int_Y |g_n(x) - g(x)| dx \ge K\epsilon_n \mu(Y).$$

where $K > 0$. Thus

$$\frac{\delta(t_n(x) - g(x))}{\delta(s_n(x)) - \delta(g(x))} \leq \frac{\mu(R_n)}{K\mu(Y)}$$

which tends to zero as $n$ tends to infinity if (13-2.5) holds.

## 13-3   VARISOLVENT APPROXIMATING FUNCTIONS ON AN INTERVAL

In this section the interpolating properties of best approximations on $[0, 1]$ by a varisolvent function are investigated. The basic tool of the investigation is the fact (Lemma 7-4) that a varisolvent function has Property $A$.

The proofs of these results are based on a simple construction. If a best approximation $F(A^*, x)$ to $f(x)$ does not interpolate $f(x)$ "enough" (i.e. $m(A^*)$ times) then Property $A$ allows one to "weave" another approximation $F(A_1, x)$ between $f(x)$ and $F(A^*, x)$. Except in the neighborhood of those points where

$$F(A^*, x) - f(x) = 0$$

$F(A_1, x)$ is uniformly closer to $f(x)$ than $F(A^*, x)$. One then investigates the norm of $F(A_1, x) - f(x)$ under the various hypotheses and shows that $F(A_1, x)$ is a better approximation than $F(A^*, x)$. This leads to a contradiction of the assumption that $F(A^*, x)$ is a best approximation to $f(x)$.

It should be remarked here that the results obtained in this section are considerably less complete than those in later sections where approximation on a finite point set is considered.

The assumption that $F$ is a regular varisolvent function is essential for these results, as shown by an example at the end of the section.

**Theorem 13-1.**   *Let $F$ be a regular varisolvent function and let the norm $\delta$ be of Class 1. If $F(A^*, x)$ is a best approximation to $f(x)$ on $[0, 1]$, then either $F(A^*, x) - f(x)$ vanishes identically on a set of positive measure or $F(A^*, x)$ strongly interpolates $f(x)$ on $[0, 1]$* (Rice, 1961a).

*Proof.* Assume that $F(A^*, x) - f(x)$ does not vanish on a set of positive measure and that $F(A^*, x) - f(x)$ has $k < m(A^*)$ simple zeros.

$$0 \leq y_1 < y_2 < \cdots < y_k \leq 1.$$

Since $F$ is varisolvent, $F$ has property $A$. Set $\epsilon = 2^{-n}$, $x_j = y_j$ (if $y_1 = 0$ take $x_1 = \epsilon$, if $y_k = 1$ take $x_k = 1 - \epsilon$) and by property $A$ determine $A_n$ such that

  (a)   $|F(A_n, x) - F(A^*, x)| < 2^{-n}$,
  (b)   $F(A_n, x_j) - F(A^*, x)$ changes sign in $[x_j - \epsilon, x_j + \epsilon]$ and has no other zeros, $j = 1, 2, \cdots, k$.
  (c)   $\|F(A^*) - f\|_\infty > \|F(A_m) - f\|_\infty$.

The last condition is equivalent to specifying the sign of $F(A^*, x)$ $- F(A_n, x)$ at one point, namely at a point where $\| F(A^*) - f \|_\infty$ is assumed. Let

$$R_n = \{x \mid | F(A^*, x) - f(x)| \le 2^{-n}\}.$$

Since $F(A^*, x) - f(x)$ vanishes on a set of measure zero, it follows that the measure of $R_n$ tends to zero as $n$ tends to infinity. $R_n$ includes points in a neighborhood of any double zeros of $F(A^*, x) - f(x)$. Further let

$$Y = \{x \mid | F(A^*, x) - f(x)| \ge \tfrac{1}{2} \| F(A^*) - f \|_\infty\}.$$

It is now shown that for $n$ sufficiently large

$$\delta\big(F(A^*, x) - f(x)\big) - \delta\big(F(A_n, x) - f(x)\big) \qquad (13\text{--}3.1)$$

is positive. Set

$$s_n(x) = \begin{cases} F(A_n, x) - f(x), & x \in Y \\ F(A^*, x) - f(x), & x \notin Y \end{cases}$$

$$t_n(x) = \begin{cases} F(A_n, x) - f(x), & x \in R_n \\ F(A^*, x) - f(x), & x \notin R_n. \end{cases}$$

Now consider (13–3.1) which is equal to

$$\delta\big(F(A^*, x) - f(x)\big) - \delta\big(s_n(x)\big) + \delta\big(s_n(x)\big) - \delta\big(s_n(x) + t_n(x)$$
$$+ f(x) - F(A^*, x)\big) + \delta\big(s_n(x) + t_n(x) + f(x) - F(A^*, x)\big)$$
$$\qquad\qquad - \delta\big(F(A_n, x) - f(x)\big) \quad (13\text{--}3.2)$$

Since

$$|s_n(x) + t_n(x) + f(x) - F(A^*, x)| \ge | F(A_n, x) - f(x)|$$

for all $x$, it follows that

$$\delta\big(s_n(x) + t_n(x) + f(x) - F(A^*, x)\big) - \delta\big(F(A_n, x) - f(x)\big) \ge 0. \quad (13\text{--}3.3)$$

It follows from the triangle inequality for norms that

$$\delta\big(t_n(x) + f(x) - F(A^*, x)\big)$$
$$\ge |\delta\big(s_n(x)\big) - \delta\big(s_n(x) + t_n(x) + f(x) - F(A^*, x)\big)|. \quad (13\text{--}3.4)$$

Since $\delta$ is a Class 1 norm, $F(A, x)$ is regular and the measure of $R_n$ tends to zero as $n$ tends to infinity, it is seen that

$$\lim_{n \to \infty} \frac{\delta\big(t_n(x) + f(x) - F(A^*, x)\big)}{\delta\big(F(A^*, x) - f(x)\big) - \delta\big(s_n(x)\big)} = 0. \qquad (13\text{--}3.5)$$

Furthermore,

$$\delta\big(F(A^*, x) - f(x)\big) - \delta\big(s_n(x)\big) > 0 \qquad (13\text{--}3.6)$$

since $\delta$ is a monotonic norm.

Thus expression (13–3.2) has been separated into three parts; the first part (13–3.6) is positive and the third part (13–3.3) is nonnegative. From (13–3.4) and (13–3.5) it follows that for $n$ sufficiently large the second part is less than the first part. These facts combined establish that

$$\delta\big(F(A^*, x) - f(x)\big) - \big(F(A_n, x) - f(x)\big) > 0$$

for $n$ sufficiently large. This contradicts the assumption that $F(A^*, x)$ is a best approximation to $f(x)$. Thus the original assumption is false, and the theorem is established.

There are two simple corollaries of Theorem 3–1 which may be stated. The first of these is a much weaker result, but it will be instructive to compare it with results obtained for approximation on a finite point set.

**Corollary 1.** *Let $F$ be a regular varisolvent function and let the norm $\delta$ be of Class 1. If $F(A^*, x)$ is a best approximation to $f(x)$ on $[0, 1]$, then $F(A^*, x)$ weakly interpolates $f(x)$ on $[0, 1]$.*

Let $L(A, x)$ be a linear varisolvent function, i.e.

$$L(A, x) = \sum_{i=1}^{n} a_i \phi_i(x).$$

**Corollary 2.** *Let the norm $\delta$ be of Class 1. If $L(A^*, x)$ is the best approximation to $f(x)$ on $[0, 1]$, then either $L(A^*, x) - f(x)$ vanishes on a set of positive measure or $L(A^*, x) - f(x)$ has $n$ strong sign changes on $[0, 1]$.*

The first theorem of the type of Theorem 13–1 was established by Jackson, 1921. He considered the special case of approximation by polynomials in the $L_1$-norm. The $L_1$-norm is the best known Class 1 norm which is not also a Class 2 norm. In the special case of the $L_1$-norm a stronger result than Theorem 13–1 may be established.

We define a function $p(A, A^*)$ as follows:

$$p(A, A^*) = \| F(A) - F(A^*) \|_1 / \| F(A) - F(A^*) \|_\infty.$$

Set

$$p_k(A^*) = \inf_{A \in P} \{ p(A, A^*) | F(A, x) - F(A^*, x) \text{ has exactly } k \text{ zeros} \}$$

The next theorem gives an estimate of the measure of the subset upon which $F(A^*, x) - f(x)$ must vanish if $F(A^*, x)$ does not strongly interpolate $f(x)$. This problem was first considered by Motzkin and Walsh, 1959.

**Theorem 13–2.** *Let $F$ be a varisolvent function, and let $F(A^*, x)$ be a best approximation to $f(x)$ in the $L_1$-norm. If $F(A^*, x) - f(x)$ has exactly $k$ strong sign changes, then $F(A^*, x) - f(x)$ must vanish on a subset of $[0, 1]$ of measure at least $p_k(A^*)/2$.*

The assumption of regularity does not appear explicitly in this theorem. However, for nonregular approximating functions Theorem 13–2 probably has less significance for it is likely that there are $A$ for which $p_k(A) = 0$, $k = 1, 2, \ldots, m(A)$.

The calculation of the $p_k$ is quite difficult and only a few values are known. For polynomial approximation it may be shown that

$$p_0 = 1, \, p_1 = \sqrt{2} - 1$$

independently of the polynomial chosen. One may show that $p_0(A^*) > 0$ for regular varisolvent functions as follows. Since $F(A, x) - F(A^*, x)$ has no zeros, one may choose the interval $I$ of Definition 13–1 to be $[0, 1]$. Since $F$ is regular, there exists a constant $k(A^*) > 0$ such that

$$\| F(A) - F(A^*) \|_1 \geq k(A^*) \, \| F(A) - F(A^*) \|_\infty.$$

This implies that

$$p_0(A^*) \geq k(A^*) > 0.$$

It is likely that one can show $p_k(A^*) > 0$, $k < m(A^*)$ for any regular varisolvent function.

It is not known how good an estimate $\frac{1}{2}p_k(A^*)$ is of the measure of the interval in question. Due to the difficulty of computing $p_k(A^*)$ and to the lack of an application of the estimate at present, this is not a pressing problem.

*Proof of Theorem 13–2.* Choose $F(A_n, x)$ by Property $A$ so that
(a)  $F(A_n, x) - F(A^*, x)$ has $k < m(A^*)$ strong sign changes in $[0, 1]$. $F(A_n, x) - f(x)$ has weakly the same sign as $F(A^*, x) - f(x)$ except in $k$ intervals of arbitrarily small length, say $2^{-n}$.
(b)  $\| F(A_n) - F(A^*) \|_\infty \leq 2^{-n}$.
(c)  $\| F(A_n) - f \|_\infty < \| F(A^*) - f \|_\infty$

Set

$$R_n = \{ x \mid |F(A^*, x) - f(x)| \leq 2^{-n} \}$$

and let $\eta_n$ be the measure of $R_n$. Then $\eta_\infty = \lim_{n \to \infty} \eta_n$ is the measure of the set

$$R = \{ x \mid |F(A^*, x) - f(x)| = 0 \}.$$

Let $I_n$ denote the set $[0, 1] - R_n$.

We now estimate the difference in the norm of $F(A^*, x) - f(x)$ and $F(A_n, x) - f(x)$.

$$\int_{I_n} |F(A^*, x) - f(x)| dx - \int_{I_n} |F(A_n, x) - f(x)| dx = \int_{I_n} |F(A^*, x) - F(A_n, x)| dx$$

$$= \int_0^1 |F(A^*, x) - F(A_n, x)| dx - \int_{R_n} |F(A^*, x) - F(A_n, x)|$$

$$\geq \int_0^1 |F(A^*, x) - F(A_n, x)| dx - \eta_n \| F(A^*) - F(A_n) \|_\infty.$$

Also

$$\int_{R_n} |F(A_n, x) - f(x)| dx = \int_R |F(A^*, x) - F(A_n, x)| dx$$

$$+ \int_{R_n - R} |F(A_n, x) - f(x)| dx$$

$$\leq (2\eta_{n} - \eta_{\infty}) \|F(A^*) - F(A_n)\|_{\infty}.$$

Hence

$$\|F(A^*) - f\|_1 - \|F(A_n) - f\|_1$$

$$\geq \|F(A^*) - F(A_n)\|_1 - (3\eta_n - \eta_{\infty}) \|F(A^*) - F(A_n)\|_{\infty}.$$

Since $F(A^*, x)$ is a best approximation to $f(x)$, it follows that

$$\|F(A^*) - F(A_n)\|_1 - (3\eta_n - \eta_{\infty}) \|F(A^*) - F(A_n)\|_{\infty} \geqslant 0$$

or

$$3\eta_n - \eta_{\infty} \geq p_k(A^*).$$

This implies that

$$\eta_{\infty} \geq \tfrac{1}{2} p_k(A^*)$$

which establishes the theorem.

It should be remarked that the subset (denoted by $R$ in the proof) in question in Theorem 13–2 need not contain an interval. This is seen from the following example: choose $R$ to be a set in $[0, 1]$ of measure $\tfrac{1}{2}$ and define $f(x)$ by

$$f(x) = \inf_{y \,\in\, R} |x - y|.$$

Thus $f(x)$ is the distance of the point $x$ to the set $R$ and is a continuous function. Consider the best constant approximation to $f(x)$ in $[0, 1]$. The constant zero is the best approximation for

$$\frac{d}{dc} \int_0^1 |f(x) - c| dx = \text{meas } \{x \mid f(x) \leq c\} - \text{meas } \{x \mid f(x) > c\} > 0.$$

Thus for $0 < c < \max |f(x)|$ the norm is an increasing function of $c$. Since the only assumption on $R$ is that it be of measure $\tfrac{1}{2}$, it can, for example, be a Cantor set containing no interval.

If one assumes the norm of Class 2 rather than Class 1, then the same argument as used in the proof of Theorem 13–1 may be used to show that best approximations are strongly interpolating functions. This is what one would intuitively expect. For a Class 1 norm, the fact that $F(A^*, x) - f(x) = 0$ on a large interval has a large effect on the value of $\delta(F(A^*, x) - f(x))$. Indeed Theorem 13–2 shows that if the interval is large enough this is the dominant factor. However, for a Class 2 norm one can reduce the norm by reducing $F(A^*, x) - f(x)$ in a small neighborhood of the points where

$\|F(A^*) - f\|_\infty$ is attained, even if this means an equal increase in $F(A^*, x)$ $- f(x)$ on a large interval where $F(A^*, x) = f(x)$.

**Theorem 13–3.** *Let $F$ be a regular varisolvent function and let the norm $\delta$ be of Class 2. If $F(A^*, x)$ is a best approximation to $f(x)$ on $[0, 1]$, then $F(A^*, x)$ is a strongly interpolating function of $f(x)$ on $[0, 1]$.*

*Proof.* Assume that $F(A^*, x) - f(x)$ has $k < m(A^*)$ strong sign changes and let $0 < y_1 < y_2 < \cdots < y_k < 1$ be the simple zeros of $F(A^*, x)$ $- f(x)$ (if $F(A^*, x) - f(x)$ has a strong sign change accompanied by an interval where $F(A^*, x) - f(x) \equiv 0$, then one point is chosen from that interval). From Property $A$ determine $A_n$ such that

(a)   $F(A_n, x) - F(A^*, x)$ changes sign from $y_j - 2^{-n}$ to $y_j + 2^{-n}$ and has no other zeros.

(b)   $\|F(A_n) - F(A^*)\|_\infty \le 2^{-n}$

(c)   $\|F(A_n) - f\|_\infty < \|F(A^*) - f\|_\infty.$

Set

$$R_n = \{x \mid |F(A^*, x) - f(x)| \le 2^{-n}\}$$

$$Y = \{x \mid |F(A^*, x) - f(x)| \ge \tfrac{1}{2} \|F(A^*) - f\|_\infty\}.$$

As in the proof of Theorem 13–1 define

$$s_n(x) = \begin{cases} F(A_n, x) - f(x), & x \in Y \\ F(A^*, x) - f(x), & x \notin Y \end{cases}$$

$$t_n(x) = \begin{cases} F(A_n, x) - f(x), & x \in R_n \\ F(A^*, x) - f(x), & x \notin R_n. \end{cases}$$

We now consider the difference between $\delta(F(A^*, x) - f(x))$ and $\delta(F(A_n, x)$ $- f(x))$. This is given by (13–3.2). Inequalities (13–3.3) and (13–3.4) are still valid; and since $\delta$ is a Class 2 norm and $F(A, x)$ is regular it follows that

$$\lim_{n \to \infty} \frac{\delta(t_n(x) + f(x) - F(A^*, x))}{\delta(F(A^*, x) - f(x)) - \delta(s_n(x))} = 0.$$

The same argument as in the proof of Theorem 13–1 shows

$$\delta(F(A^*, x) - f(x)) - \delta(F(A_n, x) - f(x)) > 0$$

for $n$ sufficiently large, which leads to a contradiction. This establishes the theorem.

A theorem of this type was first established by Jackson, 1921, for the special case of approximation by polynomials in the $L_p$-norm, $1 < p < \infty$.

EXAMPLE. Consider approximation to

$$f(x) = |x - \tfrac{1}{2}|$$

in the $L_2$-norm on $[0, 1]$ by the nonregular approximating function $\phi(a, x)$ given in the previous section. By direct evaluation we have

$$\frac{3}{2} \int_0^1 [|x - \tfrac{1}{2}| - \phi(a, x)]^2 \, dx = \tfrac{1}{8} + a^4 - a^5 - 3a^6/4 - 3a^9 + 6a^{10} + 3a^{12}/2.$$

Clearly the minimum of the norm is attained for $a = 0$, and $\phi(0, x) \equiv 0$ is the best approximation to $|x - \tfrac{1}{2}|$ on $[0, 1]$. It is seen that $|x - \tfrac{1}{2}| - \phi(0, x)$ has one zero, two weak sign changes and no strong sign changes in the interval $[0, 1]$. Thus this simple nonregular unisolvent function does not satisfy Theorem 13–3

## 13–4  LINEAR INTERPOLATING FUNCTIONS ON AN INTERVAL

In the preceeding section we showed that best approximations by varisolvent functions are interpolating functions. The nature of the interpolation depended upon some characteristics of the norm involved. In this section the converse problem is considered. This problem is: *supposing that $F(A^*, x)$ interpolates $f(x)$, is $F(A^*, x)$ a best approximation to $f(x)$ in some sense?* We are not able to treat this problem with the same generality that is considered in Section 13–5. We restrict ourselves in this section to the much simpler

PROBLEM. *Suppose a linear approximating function*

$$L(A^*, x) = \sum_{i=1}^{n} a_i \phi_i(x)$$

*interpolates a continuous function $f(x)$ on $[0, 1]$. Is $L(A^*, x)$ a best approximation to $f(x)$ in some weighted $L_p$-norm?*

The question raised here is answered in the affirmative by the analysis of this section.

The analysis of this problem is based on the following theorem due to Motzkin and Walsh, 1960, which characterizes best $L_p$-approximations in terms of a certain integral inequality. For $p > 1$, this theorem is due to Jackson, 1921. For the following theorem let

$$I = [0, 1]$$
$$I_0 = \{x \mid f(x) - L(A^*, x) = 0\}.$$

**Theorem 13–4.** *A necessary and sufficient condition that $L(A^*, x)$ be a best approximation to $f(x)$ in the weighted $L_p$-norm*

$$\delta_p[f(x)] = \left[ \int_0^1 |f(x)|^p \, w(x) \, dx \right]^{1/p} \qquad p \geq 1$$

*is that*

$$\int_{I-I_0} [L(A^*, x) - L(A, x)] |f(x) - L(A^*, x)|^{p-1} \operatorname{sgn} [f(x) - L(A^*, x)] w(x) \, dx$$

$$\leq \begin{cases} \int_{I_0} |L(A, x) - L(A^*, x)| w(x) \, dx, & p = 1 \\ 0, & p > 1 \end{cases} \qquad (13\text{–}4.1)$$

*for every* $L(A, x)$.

*Proof.* For simplicity of notation let

$$g(x) = f(x) - L(A^*, x)$$
$$\Delta(x) = L(A^*, x) - L(A, x)$$
$$I_\epsilon = \{x | 0 < |g(x)| \leq \epsilon |\Delta(x)|\}.$$

Since (13–4.1) is homogeneous in $\Delta(x)$, we may further assume that $\|\Delta(x)\| = 1$.

First assume that $L(A^*, x)$ is a best approximation to $f(x)$, then

$$\int_0^1 |g(x) - \epsilon \Delta(x)|^p \, w(x) \, dx - \int_0^1 |g(x)|^p \, w(x) \, dx \geq 0 \qquad (13\text{–}4.2)$$

is valid for all $\epsilon$ and $\Delta(x)$. Inequality (13–4.2) is divided into three parts, corresponding to integration over $I_0$, $I_\epsilon$ and $I - I_0 - I_\epsilon$. We first consider

$$I_1 = \int_{I_\epsilon} [|g(x) - \epsilon \Delta(x)|^p - |g(x)|^p] w(x) \, dx.$$

The mean value theorem for derivatives may be applied for each $x \in I_\epsilon$ to obtain

$$I_1 = \int_{I_\epsilon} p |\alpha(x)|^{p-1} \epsilon \Delta(x) w(x) \, dx, \qquad p > 1$$

where $\alpha(x)$ is an intermediate value with $|\alpha(x)| \leq |\epsilon \Delta(x)|$. Thus

$$I_1 \leq p \epsilon^p \int_{I_\epsilon} w(x) \, dx, \qquad p \geq 1.$$

The measure of $I_\epsilon$ tends to zero as $\epsilon$ tends to zero. This is due to the fact that $I_\epsilon$ contains no points where $|g(x)| = 0$, yet if $x \in I_\epsilon$, then $|g(x)| \leq \epsilon$. Thus we may conclude that $I_1 = o(\epsilon^p)$. Again by the mean value theorem we have for $p > 1$

$$I_2 = \int_{I-I_0-I_\epsilon} [|g(x) - \epsilon \Delta(x)|^p - |g(x)|^p] w(x) \, dx$$

$$= - \int_{I-I_0-I_\epsilon} p \epsilon \Delta(x) |\beta(x)|^{p-1} \operatorname{sgn} [g(x)] w(x) \, dx \qquad (13\text{–}4.3)$$

where $|g(x) - \beta(x)| < \epsilon$. If $p \geq 1$, then

$$I_3 = \int_{I_0} |\epsilon \Delta x|^p \, w(x) \, dx \leq \epsilon^p \int_{I_0} w(x) \, dx.$$

Inequality (13-4.2) implies that

$$I_1 + I_2 + I_3 \geq 0.$$

If we divide by $\epsilon$ and let $\epsilon$ tend to zero, we have for $p > 1$, $\lim_{\epsilon \to 0} I_1 = \lim_{\epsilon \to 0} I_3 = 0$ and hence

$$-\int_{I-I_0} p\Delta(x)|g(x)|^{p-1} \operatorname{sgn}[g(x)]w(x) \, dx \geq 0, \qquad p > 1.$$

If $p = 1$, then the limit of $I_3$ is no longer zero, and we obtain

$$-\int_{I-I_0} \Delta(x) \operatorname{sgn}[g(x)]w(x) \, dx + p \int_{I_0} |\Delta x| w(x) \, dx \geq 0.$$

This concludes the proof of the necessity of (13-4.1).

To show that (13-4.1) is sufficient for $L(A^*, x)$ to be a best approximation to $f(x)$ we note that

$$\int_0^1 |f(x) - L(A_0, x) - \eta[L(A^*, x) - L(A_0, x)]|^p \, w(x) \, dx \qquad (13\text{-}4.4)$$

is a convex and differentiable function of $\eta$. Thus the derivative of (13-4.4) with respect to $\eta$ ($p > 0$) is positive if $L(A^*, x)$ is not a best approximation to $f(x)$. On the other hand inequality (13-4.1) implies that

$$\frac{\int_0^1 [|g(x) - \epsilon \Delta x|^p - |g(x)|^p]w(x) \, dx + o(\epsilon)}{\epsilon} \geq 0 \qquad (13\text{-}4.5)$$

for any $\Delta(x)$. If we take $\Delta(x) = L(A^*, x) - L(A_0, x)$, (13-4.5) implies that

$$\frac{d}{d\epsilon} \int_0^1 |f(x) - L(A^*, x) - \epsilon[L(A^*, x)]|^p \, w(x) \, dx \geq 0 \qquad (13\text{-}4.6)$$

at $\epsilon = 0$. This is precisely the derivative of (13-4.4) with respect to $\eta = 1 - \epsilon$ evaluated at $\eta = 1$. Since $\dfrac{d\eta}{d\epsilon} = -1$, the derivative of (13-4.4) and (13-4.6) must be of opposite signs, which contradicts the assumption leading to (13-4.6). This concludes the proof.

As a first step towards showing that linear interpolating functions are also best approximations, we show that if $f(x) - L(A^*, x)$ vanishes on a set $I_0$ of positive measure, then there is a positive continuous weight function $w(x)$ such that $L(A^*, x)$ is the best weighted $L_1$-approximation to $f(x)$.

The idea is very simple, and one makes $w(x) = 1$ on $I_0$ and very small on the remaining portion of $[0, 1]$.

**Theorem 13–5.** *Let $f(x) - L(A^*, x)$ vanish on a set $I_0$ of positive measure. Then there is a positive continuous weight function $w(x)$ such that $L(A^*, x)$ minimizes*

$$\int_0^1 |f(x) - L(A^*, x)|w(x)\, dx$$

*among all functions $L(A, x)$.*

Proof. It is seen that

$$\int_{I-I_0} \Delta(x)\, \mathrm{sgn}\,[f(x) - L(A^*, x)]w(x)\, dx \leq \int_{I-I_0} |\Delta(x)|w(x)\, dx$$

$$\leq \|\Delta(x)\|_\infty \int_{I-I_0} w(x)\, dx.$$

Thus it is sufficient to construct $w(x)$ so that

$$\|\Delta(x)\|_\infty \int_{I-I_0} w(x)\, dx \leq \int_{I_0} |\Delta(x)|w(x)\, dx \qquad (13\text{--}4.7)$$

for all $\Delta(x)$ (recall that $\Delta(x)$ is just another $L(A, x)$). Let

$$\sigma = \min_A \frac{\displaystyle\int_{I_0} |L(A, x)|\, dx}{\|L(A, x)\|_\infty}.$$

Since the measure of $I_0$ is positive, $\sigma$ exists and is positive. We set $w(x) \equiv 1$ on $I_0$, and (13–4.7) becomes

$$\int_{I-I_0} w(x)\, dx \leq \int_{I_0} |\Delta(x)|\, dx / \|\Delta(x)\|_\infty. \qquad (13\text{--}4.8)$$

Inequality (13–4.8) is satisfied if we choose $w(x)$ on $I - I_0$ so that

$$\int_{I-I_0} w(x)\, dx \leq \sigma. \qquad (13\text{--}4.9)$$

The set $I_0$ is closed, and $I - I_0$ is the union of a countable number of mutually disjoint open subintervals of $[0, 1]$. Two of these subintervals may be half open if they include the end points 0 or 1. We denote this collection of intervals as $\{I_j \mid j = 1, 2, \ldots\}$. On the $j$th subinterval $I_j$ we define $w(x)$ so as to be continuous and positive, to take on the value $+1$ at the end points of $I_j$ and so that

$$\int_I w(x)\, dx = \sigma 2^{-j}.$$

The weighting function $w(x)$ thus defined is continuous and positive on the interval $[0, 1]$ and

$$\int_{I-I_0} w(x)dx = \sum_j \int_{I_j} w(x)dx \leq \sigma \sum_{j=1}^{\infty} 2^{-j} = \sigma.$$

Thus (13–4.9) is satisfied, and the proof is completed.

This theorem is a partial converse of Theorem 13–1 for the norm and approximating functions being considered. To obtain a complete converse, it is necessary to show that if $L(A^*, x)$ strongly interpolates $f(x)$ on $[0, 1]$, then $L(A^*, x)$ is a best approximation to $f(x)$ in the $L_1$-norm. The next theorem is the converse of Theorem 13–1. The following lemma from the theory of functions is established by Motzkin and Walsh, 1960.

**Lemma 13–1.** *Suppose the function $\phi(x)$ is bounded and integrable on $[0, 1]$ and at $n + 1$ ordered points $0 < x_1 < x_2 < \cdots < x_n < 1$ is continuous and alternately positive and negative. Then there exists a positive continuous function $w(x)$ such that for each $L(A, x)$*

$$I(A) = \int_0^1 \phi(x)L(A, x)w(x)\, dx = 0.$$

Note that the hypothesis on $\phi(x)$ implies that $\phi(x)\phi_i(x)$ changes sign at least once in $[0, 1]$ for $i = 1, 2, \ldots, n$. This lemma then states that there is a positive $w(x)$ orthogonal to each of these $n$ functions $\phi(x)\phi_i(x)$.

**Theorem 13–6.** *Suppose that $L(A^*, x)$ interpolates $f(x)$ strongly on $[0, 1]$. Then given $p \geq 1$ there exists a positive continuous weight function $w(x)$ such that $L(A^*, x)$ minimizes*

$$\int_0^1 |f(x) - L(A^*, x)|^p w(x)\, dx. \tag{13–4.10}$$

*Proof.* We have that

$$|f(x) - L(A^*, x)|^{p-1} \operatorname{sgn}[f(x) - L(A^*, x)] = \phi(x)$$

is bounded, integrable and is continuous at $n + 1$ points $\{x_i\}$ such that sgn $[\phi(x_i)] = -\operatorname{sgn}[\phi(x_{i+1})]$, $i = 1, 2, \ldots, n$. Thus the lemma can be invoked to establish the existence of a weight function $w(x)$ so that

$$\int_0^1 L(A_1, x)\phi(x)w(x)dx = 0$$

for any $A_1$, in particular for $A_1 = A^* - A$. Now $\phi(x) = 0$ on $I_0$ since sgn $[0] = 0$ and we have

$$\int_{I-I_0} L(A_1, x)\phi(x)w(x)\, dx = 0.$$

It follows from Theorem 13–4 that $L(A^*, x)$ minimizes (13–4.10). This concludes the proof.

## 13–5  VARISOLVENT APPROXIMATIONS ON A FINITE POINT SET

In this section a very general result is established concerning best approximations on a finite point set $X$. The result is (Rice, 1961a)

**Theorem 13–7.**  *Let $F$ be a varisolvent function and let $\delta$ be a monotonic norm. If $F(A^*, x)$ is a best approximation to $f(x)$ on a finite point set $X$, then $F(A^*, x)$ is a weakly interpolating function of $f(x)$ on $X$.*

Theorem 13–7 is in sharp contrast with Corollary 1 of Theorem 13–1. The conclusion drawn is the same but the hypotheses of Theorem 13–7 are much weaker. Nothing is said in Theorem 13–7 about the class of the norm or the regularity of $F(A, x)$. Furthermore, the proof of Theorem 13–7 is relatively simple and carries over directly to approximation on $[0, 1]$ *except* for one small but essential point. This point will be indicated after the proof.

From this discussion it is natural to conjecture that a theorem analogous to Theorem 13–7 is valid without the assumptions of regularity and of a Class 1 norm. At least one expects that the hypotheses of Corollary 1 of Theorem 13–1 can be weakened to some extent. However, this has not yet been done.

*Proof of Theorem 13–7.*  Assume that $F(A^*, x) - f(x)$ has $k < m(A^*)$ weak sign changes on $X$. Let

$$d = \min_{x \in X} \{|F(A^*, x) - f(x)| \,\big|\, |F(A^*, x) - f(x)| \neq 0\}$$

and by solvency determine $A_1$ such that

(a)  $\displaystyle \max_{x \in X} |F(A_1, x) - F(A^*, x)| \leq d/2$

(b)  $F(A^*, x_0) - f(x_0) = 0$ for $x_0 \in X$ implies $F(A_1, x_0) - f(x_0) = 0$.

(c)  $F(A_1, x) - f(x)$ has weakly the same sign as $F(A^*, x) - f(x)$, for $x \in X$.

It is clear that if $F(A^*, x_0) - f(x_0) \neq 0$, $x_0 \in X$, then

$$|F(A^*, x_0) - f(x_0)| > |F(A_1, x_0) - f(x_0)|.$$

Since the norm $\delta$ is monotonic, it follows that

$$\delta\big(F(A^*, x) - f(x)\big) > \delta\big(F(A_1, x) - f(x)\big).$$

This implies that $F(A^*, x)$ is not a best approximation to $f(x)$ on $X$, and hence a best approximation must weakly interpolate $f(x)$ on $X$. This concludes the proof.

The difficulty in extending this proof to best approximations on $[0, 1]$ is in the choice of $d$. Since both $f(x)$ and $F(A^*, x)$ are continuous

$$\inf_{x \in [0, 1]} \{|F(A^*, x) - f(x)| \mid F(A^*, x) - f(x) \neq 0\} = 0.$$

It is clear that a best approximation by a varisolvent function must interpolate once. On the other hand, one could set

$$I_n = \{x \mid |F(A^*, x) - f(x)| \geq 2^{-n}\}$$

and then choose $F(A_n, x)$ so that

$$|F(A^*, x) - f(x)| > |F(A_n, x) - f(x)|, \qquad x \in I_n.$$

Then $F(A_n, x)$ is uniformly closer to $f(x)$ except on an arbitrarily small interval. Furthermore $F(A_n, x) - f(x)$ is arbitrarily small in this interval. This, however, does not appear to be a strong enough conclusion to establish the analog of Theorem 13–6 for approximations on the interval $[0, 1]$. The monotonicity of the norm does not (at least without further argument) imply that for some $n$, $F(A_n, x)$ is a better approximation to $f(x)$ than $F(A^*, x)$. It does indicate that a monotonic norm $\delta$ must be of a pathological nature in order for a best approximation on $[0, 1]$ not to be a weakly interpolating function.

## 13–6 NORM CLASSES FOR FINITE POINT SETS

Let $X$ denote a finite set of distinct points contained in the interval $[0, 1]$,

$$X = \{x_j \mid j = 1, 2, \ldots, M\}.$$

It is assumed that the approximating functions are defined for every point in $[0, 1]$, even though $f(x)$ may be defined only on $X$. The norms of course, depend only on function values on $X$. It is further assumed that $f(x)$ is not identically equal on $X$ to any approximating function.

The definitions of the norm classes are somewhat simpler for finite point sets than for the interval $[0, 1]$. Let a continuous function $g(x)$ and a sequence $\{g_n(x)\}$ of continuous functions which converges regularly to $g(x)$ be given. Set

$$R = \{x \mid g(x) = 0\}.$$

It is assumed that

$$0 < g_n(x)/g(x) < 1, \qquad x \notin R.$$

Define the functions $s_n(x)$ and $t_n(x)$ as follows:

$$s_n(x) = \begin{cases} g_n(x), & x \notin R \\ g(x), & x \in R \end{cases}$$

$$t_n(x) = \begin{cases} g_n(x), & x \in R \\ g(x), & x \notin R \end{cases}$$

**Definition 13–5.** *$\delta_X$ is a Class 2 norm if, for any choice of $g(x)$, $\{g_n(x)\}$ satisfying the above conditions,*

$$\lim_{n \to \infty} \frac{\delta_X\big(g(x) - t_n(x)\big)}{\delta_X\big(g(x)\big) - \delta_X\big(s_n(x)\big)} = 0. \qquad (13\text{–}6.1)$$

**Definition 13–6.** *$\delta_X$ is a Class 1 norm if, for any choice of $g(x)$, $\{g_n(x)\}$ satisfying the above conditions, there exists a constant $K < \infty$ such that*

$$\frac{\delta_X\big(g(x) - t_n(x)\big)}{\delta_X\big(g(x)\big) - \delta_X\big(s_n(x)\big)} \leq K \qquad (13\text{–}6.2)$$

These definitions are the direct analogs of Definitions 13–3 and 13–4, and perhaps they show the intuitive nature of Class 1 and 2 norms more clearly.

If it is assumed that

$$\delta_X\big(g(x)\big) \neq \delta_X\big(t_n(x)\big) \qquad (13\text{–}6.3)$$

except for possibly a finite number of $n$, then a third class of norms may be defined.

**Definition 13–7.** *$\delta_X$ is a Class 3 norm if, for any choice of $g(x)$, $\{g_n(x)\}$ satisfying the above conditions*

$$\lim_{n \to \infty} \frac{\delta_X\big(g(x)\big) - \delta_X\big(s_n(x)\big)}{\delta_X\big(g(x) - t_n(x)\big)} = 0. \qquad (13\text{–}6.4)$$

Class 3 norms could be defined for the interval $[0, 1]$; however, no special properties of this general class of norms are known at the present. Motzkin and Walsh, 1959, have given a result in a special case which indicates that the properties of Class 3 norms on $[0, 1]$ are quite complex. Even for finite point sets, the results for Class 3 norms are less complete than for Class 1 and 2 norms.

In addition to the very general result, Theorem 13–6, of the previous section, one can obtain more specialized results for the Class 1, 2 and 3 norms. Naturally the results are closely related to results obtained in Section 13–3 for approximation on an interval.

Corresponding to Theorems 13–1 and 13–2 there is a result, Problem 13–8, which relates the number of strong sign changes of $F(A^*, x) - f(x)$ with the number of zeros of $F(A^*, x) - f(x)$ on $X$. The proof of this result follows approximately the same line of argument as the proof of Theorem 13–2. The quantities $\mu_k$ which estimate the number of zeros of $F(A^*, x) - f(x)$ in $X$ are even less available in practice than the quantities $p_k$ defined in Theorem 13–2.

A direct analog of Theorem 13–3 may be established (Rice, 1961a).

**Theorem 13–8.** *Let $F$ be a regular varisolvent function and let the norm $\delta$*

be of Class 2. *If* $F(A^*, x)$ *is a best approximation to* $f(x)$, *then* $F(A^*, x)$ *is a strongly interpolating function of* $f(x)$ *on* $X$.

*Proof.* Assume that $F(A^*, x) - f(x)$ has $k < m(A^*)$ strong sign changes in $X$. A set $\{y_i \mid i = 1, 2, \ldots, k\}$ is chosen in the following manner. If $F(A^*, x) - f(x)$ has a strong sign change between $x_j$ and $x_{j+1}$, choose a point $y_i$ in the interior of the interval $[x_j, x_{j+1}]$. If

$$F(A^*, x_j) - f(x_j) = 0, \qquad j = l, l+1, \ldots, p$$

and $F(A^*, x_j) - f(x)$ changes sign from $x_{l-1}$ to $x_{p+1}$, choose a point $y_i$ in the interior of the interval $[x_{l-1}, x_{p+1}]$.

The proof may now be completed along the lines of the proof of Theorem 13–3.

The natural companion of Theorem 13–8 for Class 3 norms is the statement: *Let* $F$ *be a regular varisolvent function and let the norm* $\delta_X$ *be of Class 3. If* $F(A^*, x)$ *is a best approximation to* $f(x)$ *on* $X$, *then* $F(A^*, x)$ *is an exactly interpolating function of* $f(x)$ *on* $X$. It is not known whether this is a true statement.

Up to this point in this section we have been concerned with showing that best approximations are interpolating functions of various types. We now consider the converse problem, namely showing that interpolating functions are best approximations.

**Definition 13–8.** $F(A^*, x)$ *is said to be a local best approximation to* $f(x)$ *if there is a neighborhood* $N(A^*)$ *of* $A^*$ *in* $P$ *such that* $A \in N(A^*)$ *implies*

$$\delta_X\big(F(A^*, x) - f(x)\big) < \delta_X\big(F(A, x) - f(x)\big). \qquad (13\text{–}6.5)$$

Note that Definition 13–8 has a strict inequality in (13–6.5). This implies that the local best approximations are isolated from one another.

**Theorem 13–9.** *Let* $F$ *be a regular varisolvent function and let the norm* $\delta_X$ *be of Class 3 with the additional assumption that if* $|g(x)| \leq |h(x)|$ *for all* $x \in X$ *and* $|g(x)| < |h(x)|$ *for some* $x \in X$ *then* $\delta_X(g(x)) < \delta_X(h(x))$. *If* $F(A^*, x)$ *is an exactly interpolating function of* $f(x)$ *on* $X$, *then* $F(A^*, x)$ *is a local best approximation to* $f(x)$ *on* $X$.

The additional hypothesis about $\delta_X$ in Theorem 13–9 is another hypothesis on the monotonicity of the norm. This hypothesis is not satisfied by some well-known norms, but those norms defined by the means of weighted sums generally satisfy this portion of the hypothesis of Theorem 13–9.

*Proof.* Assume that $F(A^*, x)$ exactly interpolates $f(x)$ on $X$ and set

$$R = \{x_j \mid F(A^*, x_j) - f(x_j) = 0\}.$$

The set $R$ contains at least $m(A^*)$ points. Define

$$d = \min \{|F(A^*, x_j) - f(x_j)| \mid x_j \notin R\} > 0.$$

Let the neighborhood $N_1(A^*)$ be such that $A \in N_1(A^*)$ implies

$$|F(A^*, x_j) - F(A, x_j)| \leq d/2, \qquad x_j \in X$$

If there exists a sequence $\{A_n \mid A_n \in N_1(A^*), A_n \neq A^*\}$ such that

$$\lim_{n \to \infty} A_n = A^*$$

$$\delta_X(F(A^*, x) - f(x)) \geq \delta_X(F(A_n, x) - f(x)), \qquad (13\text{-}6.6)$$

then set

$$s_n(x) = \begin{cases} F(A_n, x) - f(x), & x \notin R \\ F(A^*, x) - f(x), & x \in R \end{cases}$$

$$t_n(x) = \begin{cases} F(A_n, x) - f(x), & x \in R \\ F(A^*, x) - f(x), & x \notin R . \end{cases}$$

An elementary argument on the monotonicity of $\delta_X$ and (13–6.6) shows that

$$\delta_X(t_n(x)) \geq \delta_X(F(A^*, x) - f(x)) \geq \delta_X(F(A_n, x) - f(x))$$
$$\geq \delta_X(s_n(x)). \qquad (13\text{-}6.7)$$

Consider the quantity

$$\delta_X(F(A^*, x) - f(x)) - \delta_X(F(A_n, x) - f(x))$$
$$= \delta_X(F(A^*, x) - f(x)) - \delta_X(s_n(x)) + \delta_X(s_n(x)) - \delta_X(F(A_n, x) - f(x)). \qquad (13\text{-}6.8)$$

For some $x \in R$ we have

$$0 = |s_n(x)| < |F(A_n, x) - f(x)|, \qquad (13\text{-}6.9)$$

for if (13–6.9) does not hold for at least one point in $R$, then $F(A^*, x) - F(A_n, x)$ has at least $m(A^*)$ zeros. This would imply $A^* = A_n$ by Property $Z$ of varisolvent functions. Inequality (13–6.9) together with the additional hypothesis on the monotonicity of $\delta_X$ imply that

$$\delta_X(s_n(x)) - \delta_X(F(A_n, x) - f(x)) < 0. \qquad (13\text{-}6.10)$$

From (13–6.7) it follows that

$$\left| \frac{\delta_X(F(A^*, x) - f(x)) - \delta_X(s_n(x))}{\delta_X(F(A_n, x) - f(x)) - \delta_X(s_n(x))} \right| \leq \left| \frac{\delta_X(F(A^*, x) - f(x)) - \delta_X(s_n(x))}{\delta_X(F(A^*, x) - f(x)) - \delta_X(t_n(x))} \right| \qquad (13\text{-}6.11)$$

It follows from (13–6.10) that the denominator of (13–6.11) is non-zero. From the fact that $\delta_X$ is a Class 3 norm and $F(A, x)$ is regular it is seen that the right hand side of (13–6.11) tends to zero as $n$ tends to infinity. Thus for $n$ sufficiently large the quantity in (13–6.8) is negative. This, however, contradicts the assumption in (13–6.6). This completes the proof.

Theorem 13–9 naturally raises the question of companion theorems for Class 1 and 2 norms. However, no such theorems have been established in situations of this generality. Thus the properties of the Class 3 norms which make it difficult to show that best approximations are interpolating functions seem to have made it possible to establish the result that interpolating functions are, in some sense, best approximations. In the next section it is seen that, with linear approximating functions and $L_p$-norms, a complete discussion of the relationship between best approximations and interpolating functions can be given.

## 13–7  LINEAR APPROXIMATION AND $L_p$-NORMS

In this section all approximating functions are assumed to be linear approximating functions, i.e.

$$L(A, x) = \sum_{i=1}^{n} a_i \phi_i(x), \qquad |a_i| < \infty$$

where $\{\phi_i(x) \mid i = 1, 2, \ldots, n\}$ is a Tchebycheff set. Furthermore only approximation and interpolation on a finite point set $X$

$$X = \{x_i \mid i = 1, 2, \ldots, M\}$$

is considered with $M \geq n + 1$.

The main problem considered here is to show that interpolating functions of $f(x)$ are also best approximations to $f(x)$ in some weighted $L_p$-norm, $0 < p < \infty$,

$$\left[ \sum_{i=1}^{M} \mu_i |L(A, x) - f(x)|^p \right]^{1/p}$$

This is accomplished by an explicit construction of the required set $\{\mu_i\}$ of positive weights.

This construction consists of three distinct steps. The first is a representation (Lemma 13–2) of exactly, weakly and strongly interpolating functions on a set of $n + 1$ points. The second step is to use this representation to compute explicitly the set $\{\mu_i\}$ for approximation on a set of $n + 1$ points. The final step is to combine these weights to form a set $\{\mu_i\}$ of weights for approximations on the entire set $X$.

Relative to any set

$$Y = \{y_i \mid y_i < y_{i+1}, y_i \in X, i = 1, 2, \ldots, n + 1\}$$

of $n + 1$ points, a function $\phi_Y(x)$ may be found such that $\{\phi_i(x)\} \cup \{\phi_Y(x)\}$ forms a Tchebycheff set of $n + 1$ functions on the set $Y$. In order to simplify the notation, the function $\phi_Y(x)$ is denoted by $\phi_{n+1}(x)$, and the possible dependence of $\phi_{n+1}(x)$ on the set $Y$ is not indicated in the notation. For the set $\{\phi_i(x) \mid i = 1, 2, \ldots, n + 1\}$ we may determine a set of coefficients $\{(A_k, c_k) \mid k = 1, 2, \ldots, n + 1\}$ so that

$$L(A_k, y_j) + c_k\phi_{n+1}(y_j) = \begin{cases} 0, & j \neq k \\ (-1)^k, & j = k. \end{cases} \tag{13-7.1}$$

That such a set of coefficients exists follows from the fact $\{\phi_i(x) \mid i = 1, 2, \ldots, n + 1\}$ is a Tchebycheff set. This same fact implies that the $c_k$ are all non-zero.

The "basis functions" $w_k(x)$ to be used in the representation of interpolating functions on $Y$ are defined by

$$w_k(x) = L(A_k, x)/c_k + \phi_{n+1}(x), \qquad x \in Y. \tag{13-7.2}$$

The sign of $c_k$ is denoted by $\sigma_k$, i.e.

$$|\sigma_k| = 1, \qquad \sigma_k c_k > 0.$$

The following lemma gives a representation of exactly, strongly and weakly interpolating functions in terms of the basis functions $w_i(x)$.

**Lemma 13-2.** *The functions $T(x)$ of the form $L(A, x) + \phi_{n+1}(x)$ which weakly interpolate zero on $Y$ are exactly the functions*

$$T(x) = \sum_{j=1}^{n+1} \lambda_j \sigma_j w_j(x) \tag{13-7.3}$$

*where*

$$\lambda_j \geq 0, \qquad \sum_{j=1}^{n+1} \lambda_j = 1. \tag{13-7.4}$$

*Those which strongly interpolate zero on $Y$ are exactly the functions* (13-7.3) *with*

$$\lambda_j > 0, \qquad \sum_{j=1}^{n+1} \lambda_j = 1. \tag{13-7.5}$$

*Those which exactly interpolate zero on $Y$ are exactly the functions* (13-7.3) *with*

$$\lambda_j = \begin{cases} 0, j \neq k \\ 1, j = k \end{cases} \qquad \sum_{j=1}^{n+1} \lambda_j = 1. \tag{13-7.6}$$

*Proof.* By direct evaluation of (13-7.3) we have

$$T(y_k) = \sum_{i=1}^{n+1} \lambda_j \frac{\sigma_j}{c_j} [L(A_j, y_k) + c_j\phi_{n+1}(y_k)] = \lambda_k(-1)^k.$$

Thus every function of the form (13-7.3) with the $\lambda_j$ determined by (13-7.4), (13-7.5) or (13-7.6) is a weakly, strongly or exactly interpolating function of zero, respectively.

Assume now that a function $T(x)$ of the form $L(A, x) + \phi_{n+1}(x)$ has $n$ strong sign changes in $Y$. Then $T(x)$ changes sign from $y_j$ to $y_{j+1}$, and on $Y$ we have

$$T(y) = \sum_{i=1}^{n+1} \lambda_i \sigma_i w_i(y)$$

where $\lambda_i = \pm |c_i T(y_i)| \neq 0$. All the $\lambda_i$ must have the same sign, and since the coefficient of $\phi_{n+1}(x)$ is 1, we have

$$\sum_{i=1}^{n+1} \lambda_i = 1.$$

This implies that the $\lambda_i$ are positive, and the conditions (13–7.5) follow.

If $T(x)$ has $n$ weak sign changes on $Y$, then again

$$T(y) = \sum_{i=1}^{n+1} \lambda_i \sigma_i w_i(y)$$

where $\lambda_i = \pm |c_i T(y_i)|$. All of the $\lambda_i$ must have the same sign or be zero. Since the coefficient of $\phi_{n+1}$ is 1, we have

$$\sum_{i=1}^{n+1} \lambda_i = 1$$

and the conditions (13–7.4) follow.

A similar argument establishes conditions (13–7.6).

The next lemma establishes that weakly interpolating functions of $\phi_{n+1}(x)$ on a set $Y$ of $n + 1$ points are best approximations to $\phi_{n+1}(x)$ on $Y$ in some weighted $L_1(Y)$-norm.

**Lemma 13–3.** *If $L(A^*, x)$ weakly interpolates $-\phi_{n+1}(x)$ on $Y$, then there is a set $\{\mu_i \mid i = 1, 2, \ldots, n + 1\}$ of positive weights such that $L(A^*, x)$ minimizes the $L_1(Y)$-norm*

$$\sum_{i=1}^{n+1} \mu_i |L(A, y_i) + \phi_{n+1}(y_i)|. \tag{13–7.7}$$

*Proof.* If $L(A^*, x) + \phi_{n+1}(x)$ has $n$ weak sign changes on $Y$, then by Lemma 13–2

$$L(A^*, x) + \phi_{n+1}(x) = \sum_{i=1}^{n+1} \lambda_i^* \sigma_i w_i(x),$$

where $\lambda_i^* \geq 0$ and $\sum_{i=1}^{n+1} \lambda_i^* = 1$. The weights $\mu_i$ are chosen in the following manner. If $\lambda_i^* \neq 0$, set $\mu_i = |c_i|$; and if $\lambda^* = 0$, set $\mu_i = 2|c_i|$.

The norm (13–7.7) may be directly evaluated for $L(A^*, x)$, and it is seen that

$$\sum_{i=1}^{n+1} \mu_i |L(A^*, y_i) + \phi_{n+1}(y_i)| = 1.$$

For any other approximation $L(A, x)$ divide the sum (13–7.7) into two parts $\sum^1$ and $\sum^2$ where an index is included in $\sum^1$ if $\lambda_j^* > 0$ and in $\sum^2$ if $\lambda_j^* = 0$. Then

$$\sum_{i=1}^{n+1} \mu_i |L(A, y_i) + \phi_{n+1}(y_i)| = \sum_{i=1}^{n+1} \mu_i |\lambda_i \sigma_i w_i(y_i)|$$

$$= \sum_{i=1}^{n+1} \mu_i \frac{\lambda_i}{|c_i|} = \sum^1 \lambda_i + 2\sum^2 \lambda_i \geq 1.$$

Thus $L(A^*, x)$ is a best approximation to $-\phi_{n+1}(x)$ in the weighted $L_1$-norm (13–7.7) with the weights defined above.

With the aid of Lemma 13–3 one is able to construct a set of weights for any finite set $X$ so that a weakly interpolating function $L(A, x)$ of $f(x)$ is a best approximation to $f(x)$ in a weighted $L_1$-norm. The resulting theorem is the exact converse of Theorem 13–7 for the special case considered in this section.

**Theorem 13–10.** *If $L(A^*, x)$ is a weakly interpolating function of $f(x)$ on $X$, then there is a set $\{\mu_i \mid i = 1, 2, \ldots, M\}$ of positive weights such that $L(A^*, x)$ is a best approximation to $f(x)$ in the weighted $L_1$-norm*

$$\sum_{i=1}^{M} \mu_i |L(A^*, x) - f(x)|. \tag{13–7.8}$$

*Proof.* If $L(A^*, x) - f(x)$ has $n$ weak sign changes on $X$, then it is easy to show that every point of $X$ belongs to a subset $Y$ of $n + 1$ points such that $L(A^*, x) - f(x)$ has $n$ weak sign changes on $Y$. This is not shown here.

Consider any such set $Y$. There is a $K$ and a set of parameters $A_1$ such that, on $Y$

$$L(A^*, y) - f(y) = K[L(A_1, y) + \phi_{n+1}(y)], \qquad y \in Y.$$

It follows from Lemma 13–3 that, since $L(A_1, x) + \phi_{n+1}(x)$ has $n$ weak sign changes on $Y$, there are positive weights $\{\mu_i^{(1)} \mid i = 1, 2, \ldots, n + 1\}$ such that $L(A_1, x)$ is a best approximation to $-\phi_{n+1}(x)$ on $Y$ in the weighted $L_1$-norm. Since $L(A^*, y) - f(y)$ is proportional to $L(A_1, y) + \phi_{n+1}(y)$ on $Y$, it follows that $L(A^*, y) - f(x)$ minimizes the same $L_1$-norm with the same weights.

It is now shown how the weights may be found to make $L(A^*, x) - f(x)$ a best approximation in a weighted $L_1$-norm on the union of two sets $Y_1$ and $Y_2$. Let $\{\mu_i^{(1)}\}$ and $\{\mu_i^{(2)}\}$ be the weights associated with $Y_1$ and $Y_2$, respectively. The weights $\mu_i^{(3)}$ are computed as follows:

$$\begin{aligned}
\mu_i^{(3)} &= \tfrac{1}{2}(\mu_i^{(1)} + \mu_i^{(2)}), & x_i &\in Y_1 \cap Y_2 \\
\mu_i^{(3)} &= \tfrac{1}{2}\mu_i^{(1)}, & x_i &\in Y_1 - Y_1 \cap Y_2 \\
\mu_i^{(3)} &= \tfrac{1}{2}\mu_i^{(2)}, & x_i &\in Y_2 - Y_1 \cap Y_2.
\end{aligned} \tag{13–7.9}$$

Since $X$ has a finite number of subsets of $n + 1$ points, equations (13–7.9) can be used recursively to compute a set $\{\mu_i \mid i = 1, 2, \ldots, M\}$ such that $L(A^*, x) - f(x)$ minimizes the norm (13–7.8). This concludes the proof.

The same method of analysis may be used to establish the analogy of Theorem 13–10 for $L_p$-norms $(1 < p < \infty)$ and strongly interpolating functions. In Lemma 13–2 an explicit representation of strongly interpolating functions was obtained. This representation is used in Lemma 13–5 to determine the required set of weights on a set $Y$ of $n + 1$ points. Then in Theorem 13–11 these weights are combined to determine the required set of weights for the entire set $X$.

The proof of the following lemma is left as an exercise.

**Lemma 13–4.** *Let $p > 1$ and a set $\{\mu_i \mid \mu_i > 0, i = 1, 2, \ldots, m\}$ be given. Define*

$$\mu(\lambda) = \sum_{i=1}^{m} \mu_i \lambda_i^p.$$

*The minimum value of $\mu(\lambda_i)$ for $\lambda_i \geq 0$ and $\sum_{i=1}^{m} \lambda_i = 1$ is given by*

$$\lambda_i = \mu_i^{1/(1-p)} \Big/ \sum_{j=1}^{m} \mu_j^{1/(1-p)}. \tag{13–7.10}$$

For the next lemma $Y$, as usual in this section, denotes a subset of $X$ containing $n + 1$ distinct points.

**Lemma 13–5.** *Let $p > 1$ be given. If $L(A^*, x)$ strongly interpolates $-\phi_{n+1}(x)$ on $Y$, then there is a set $\{\mu_i \mid i = 1, 2, \ldots, n + 1\}$ of positive weights such that $L(A^*, x)$ minimizes the $L_p$-norm*

$$\left[ \sum_{i=1}^{n+1} \mu_i |L(A^*, y_i) + \phi_{n+1}(y_i)|^p \right]^{1/p} \tag{13–7.11}$$

*Proof.* It follows from Lemma 13–2 that $L(A^*, x) + \phi_{n+1}(x)$ has the explicit representation

$$\phi_{n+1}(y) + L(A^*, y) = \sum_{i=1}^{n+1} \lambda_i^* \sigma_i w_i(x), \qquad y \in Y$$

where

$$\lambda_i^* > 0, \qquad \sum_{i=1}^{n+1} \lambda_i^* = 1.$$

Set $\mu_i = |c_i|^p (\lambda_i^*)^{1-p}$. For any approximation $L(A, x)$ to $-\phi_{n+1}(x)$ the norm (13–7.11) may be explicitly evaluated as

$$\sum_{i=1}^{n+1} \mu_i |\lambda_i \sigma_i w_i(x)|^p = \sum_{i=1}^{n} \mu_i |\lambda_i |c_i||^p = \sum_{i=1}^{n} (\lambda_i^*)^{1-p} \lambda_i^p.$$

It follows from (13–7.10) that $\lambda_i = \lambda_i^*$ minimizes (13–7.11), and hence

$L(A^*, x)$ is a best approximation to $-\phi_{n+1}(x)$ in the weighted $L_p$-norm (13–7.11).

**Theorem 13–11.** *If $L(A^*, x)$ is a strongly interpolating function of $f(x)$ on $X$, then for any $p > 1$ there is a set $\{\mu_i \mid i = 1, 2, \ldots, M\}$ of positive weights such that $L(A^*, x)$ is a best approximation of $f(x)$ in the weighted $L_p$-norm*

$$\left[ \sum_{i=1}^{M} \mu_i |L(A^*, x_i) - f(x_i)|^p \right]^{1/p} \tag{13–7.12}$$

*Proof.* Set

$$R = \{x \mid x \in X, \, |L(A^*, x) - f(x)| > 0\}.$$

Every point of $R$ belongs to a subset $Y$ such that $L(A^*, x) - f(x)$ has $n$ strong sign changes on $Y$. For any such subset $Y$ there is a constant $K$ and an $A_1$ such that

$$L(A^*, x) - f(x) = K[L(A_1, x) + \phi_{n+1}(x)].$$

It follows from Lemma 13–5 that there is a set $\{\mu_i\}$ of weights such that $L(A^*, x)$ is a best approximation to $f(x)$ in the weighted $L_p$-norm (13–7.11).

If $L(A^*, x)$ *minimizes*

$$\sum \mu_i^{(1)} |L(A^*, y_i) + f(y_i)|^p, \qquad y_i \in Y_1$$

and

$$\sum \mu_i^{(2)} |L(A^*, y_i) + f(y_i)|^p, \qquad y_i \in Y_2,$$

then clearly $L(A^*, x)$ minimizes

$$\sum \mu_i^{(3)} |L(A^*, y_i) + f(y_i)|^p, \qquad y_i \in Y_1 \cup Y_2$$

where the $\mu_i^{(3)}$ are computed by (13–7.9). Since $R$ has a finite number of subsets, a set $\{\mu_i\}$ may be computed so that $L(A^*, x)$ is a best approximation to $f(x)$ on $R$ in the weighted $L_p$-norm with weights $\{\mu_i\}$.

Since $|L(A^*, x) - f(x)| = 0$ for points of $X$ not in $R$, the weights $\mu_i$ may be assigned arbitrarily there, and then $L(A^*, x)$ is a best approximation in the norm (13–7.12).

The analysis for $L_p$-norms, $0 < p < 1$, follows the same pattern as for $p \geq 1$. The proof of the following lemma is omitted.

**Lemma 13–6.** *Let $0 < p < 1$ and a set $\{\mu_i \mid \mu_i > 0, i = 1, 2, \ldots, m\}$ be given. Define*

$$\mu(\lambda_i) = \sum_{i=1}^{m} \mu_i \lambda_i^p.$$

*The minimum value of $\mu(\lambda_i)$ for $\lambda_i \geq 0$ and $\sum\limits_{i=1}^{m} \lambda_i = 1$ is given by*

$$\lambda_i = \begin{cases} 0 \text{ if } \mu_i > \min\limits_{j} \mu_j \\ p_i \text{ if } \mu_i = \min\limits_{j} \mu_j \end{cases}$$

*where $p_i \neq 0$ for only one value of $i$.*

**Lemma 13–7.** *Let $0 < p < 1$ be given. If $L(A^*, x)$ exactly interpolates $-\phi_{n+1}(x)$ on $Y$, then there is a set $\{\mu_i \mid i = 1, 2, \ldots, n + 1\}$ of positive weights such that $L(A^*, x)$ minimizes the $L_p$-norm (13–7.11).*

*Proof.* At one point of $Y$ we have $L(A^*, x) + \phi_{n+1}(x) = 0$. Set $\mu_i = |c_i|^p$ at that point. At each of the other points of $Y$ set $\mu_i = 2|c_i|^p$. If (13–7.11) is evaluated for $L(A^*, x) + \phi_{n+1}(x)$, it follows from Lemma 13–6 that $L(A^*, y) + \phi_{n+1}(y)$ minimizes (13–7.11) with the weights $\{\mu_i\}$.

**Theorem 13–12.** *If $L(A^*, x)$ is an exactly interpolating function of $f(x)$ on $X$, then for any $p$, $0 < p < 1$, there is a set $\{\mu_i \mid i = 1, 2, \ldots, M\}$ of positive weights such that $L(A^*, x)$ is a best approximation to $f(x)$ in the weighted $L_p$-norm (13–7.12).*

*Proof.* Every point of $X$ belongs to a subset $Y$ of $n + 1$ points such that $L(A^*, x) - f(x)$ has $n$ exact sign changes on $Y$. For any such subset $Y$ there is a constant $K$ and an $A_1$ such that

$$L(A^*, x) - f(x) = K[L(A_1, x) + \phi_{n+1}(x)].$$

By Lemma 13–7 a set $\{\mu_i\}$ of positive weights may be determined so that $L(A^*, x) - f(x)$ minimizes the $L_p$-norm (13–7.11).

By the construction (13–7.9) previously employed it follows that a set $\{\mu_i\}$ exists so that $L(A^*, x)$ minimizes the weighted $L_p$-norm (13–7.12).

The converse theorems of Theorems 13–10 and 13–11 are special cases of Theorems 13–7 and 13–8 respectively. No converse to Theorem 13–12 has been established in a general situation, and we consider such a theorem now. The proof of this theorem is based on a remark by Dvoretzky. It is an entirely different type of proof from the ones so far encountered in this section.

**Theorem 13–13.** *Let $p$, $0 < p < 1$, be given. If $L(A^*, x)$ is a best approximation to $f(x)$ in a weighted $L_p$-norm, then $L(A^*, x)$ is an exactly interpolating function of $f(x)$ on $X$.*

*Proof.* Suppose that $L(A^*, x)$ minimizes the $L_p$-norm (13–7.12) and that $L(A^*, x) - f(x)$ has exactly $m < n$ zeros in $X$. Set

$$R = \{z_i \mid z_i \in X, L(A^*, z_i) = f(z_i), i = 1, 2, \ldots, m\}$$

and determine $A_1$ so that

$$L(A_1, z_i) = 0, \qquad i = 1, 2, \ldots, m$$

$$L(A_1, x) \not\equiv 0.$$

The function $L(A^*, x) + \sigma L(A_1, x)$ is a linear approximating function. Consider (13–7.12) evaluated for $L(A^*, x) + \sigma L(A_1, x)$

$$\sum_{i=1}^{M} \mu_i |L(A^*, x) + \sigma L(A_1, x) - f(x)|^p. \tag{13–7.13}$$

The sum (13–7.13) has $m$ terms which vanish, and others may be independent of $\sigma$. Each of the remaining terms is of the form

$$|A + \sigma B|^p. \tag{13–7.14}$$

The graph of (13–7.14) as a function of $\sigma$ is concave downward unless $B = 0$ or $A + \sigma B = 0$. For at least one point we have $B \neq 0$. If there is a $\sigma_0 > 0$ such that $\sigma < \sigma_0$ implies $|A + \sigma B| > 0$, then (13–7.13) is the sum of concave downward functions plus a constant. Such a sum cannot have a local minimum for $\sigma = 0$. Thus at least one of the terms $|A + \sigma B|$ must vanish for $\sigma = 0$. This implies that $L(A^*, x) - f(x)$ has $m + 1$ zeros in $X$, contrary to the definition of $m$.

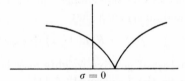

Fig. 13–4.    Plot of $|A + \sigma B|^p$ for $0 < p < 1$, $B \neq 0$, $A \neq 0$.

## 13–8  THE TCHEBYCHEFF NORM

The Tchebycheff norm is of such a nature that it is relatively easy to show that strongly interpolating functions are best approximations in a weighted Tchebycheff norm. Not only are the proofs easier, but the results are general. The following theorem is analogous to Theorem 13–10 and Theorem 13–6 with the generalization to varisolvent functions (without a regularity assumption).

**Theorem 13–14.**  *Let $F$ be a varisolvent function and $f(x)$ a continuous function. If $F(A^*, x) - f(x)$ has $m(A^*)$ strong sign changes in $[0, 1]$, then there is a positive continuous weight function $\mu(x)$ such that $F(A^*, x)$ is the best approximation to $f(x)$ in the weighted Tchebycheff norm.*

$$\max_{x \in [0, 1]} [\mu(x) |F(A, x) - f(x)|]. \tag{13–8.1}$$

*Proof.* Choose a set $Y$ of $m(A^*) + 1$ points such that $F(A^*, x) - f(x)$ has $m(A^*)$ strong sign changes on $Y$. For $y_i \in Y$ the value of $\mu(x)$ is determined by

$$\mu(y_i)|F(A^*, y_i) - f(y_i)| = 1, \qquad i = 1, 2, \ldots, m(A^*) + 1.$$

For $x \notin Y$ $\mu(x)$ is determined so as to be continuous and so that

$$\mu(x)|F(A^*, x) - f(x)| < 1. \tag{13–8.2}$$

Thus $\mu(x)[F(A^*, x) - f(x)]$ alternates $m(A^*)$ times on $[0, 1]$ and by Theorem 7–3, $F(A^*, x)$ is the best approximation to $f(x)$ in the norm (13–8.1). This concludes the proof.

It is seen that there is great latitude in the choice of the weight function $\mu(x)$. First there are nondenumerably many choices for the set $Y$, and once $Y$ is determined, there are nondenumerably many ways to define $\mu(x)$ so that (13–8.2) is valid.

**Corollary 1.** *If $F(A^*, x)$ strongly interpolates $f(x)$ on a finite point set $X$, then there is a set $\{\mu_i\}$ of positive weights such that $F(A^*, x)$ is the best approximation to $f(x)$ in the weighted Tchebycheff norm*

$$\max_{x_i \in X} [\mu_i|F(A^*, x_i) - f(x_i)|].$$

## 13–9 SUMMARY FOR $L_p$-NORMS AND LINEAR FUNCTIONS

Some of the results concerning $L_p$-norms obtained in the preceeding sections can be consolidated into the following theorem. This theorem shows clearly the equivalence of linear interpolating functions and best approximations in weighted $L_p$-norms.

**Theorem 13–15.** *Let $\{\phi_i(x)\}$ be a Tchebycheff set and $X$ be a finite point set. Define*

$$L(A, x) = \sum_{i=1}^{n} a_i \phi_i(x).$$

*Then given $0 < q < 1 < p < \infty$ and $f(x)$ we have three pairs of identical sets:*

(a) $\{A \mid L(A, x) - f(x)$ *minimizes a weighted $L_p$-norm on $X\}$*
    $\{A \mid L(A, x)$ *strongly interpolates $f(x)$ on $X\}$;*
(b) $\{A \mid L(A, x) - f(x)$ *minimizes a weighted $L_1$-norm on $X\}$*
    $\{A \mid L(A, x)$ *weakly interpolates $f(x)$ on $X\}$;*
(c) $\{A \mid L(A, x) - f(x)$ *minimizes a weighted $L_q$-norm on $X\}$*
    $\{A \mid L(A, x)$ *exactly interpolates $f(x)$ on $X\}$.*

*Proof.* The equivalence of the first pair follows from Theorem 13–8,

Theorem 13–11 and Theorem 13–14. The equivalence of the second pair follows from Theorem 13–7 and Theorem 13–10. The equivalence of the third pair follows from Theorem 13–12 and Theorem 13–13.

We have the following corollaries of this theorem.

**Corollary 1.** *Let $L(A, x)$, $X$ and $f(x)$ be as given in Theorem 13–15. Then for any $p$, $q$, $1 < p < q \leq \infty$ the following sets are identical:*
*$\{A \mid L(A, x) - f(x)$ minimizes a weighted $L_p$-norm on $X\}$*
*$\{A \mid L(A, x) - f(x)$ minimizes a weighted $L_q$-norm on $X\}$.*

**Corollary 2.** *Let $L(A, x)$, $X$ and $f(x)$ be as given in Theorem 13–15. Then for any $p$, $q$, $0 < p < q < 1$, the following sets are identical:*
*$\{A \mid L(A, x) - f(x)$ minimizes a weighted $L_p$-norm on $X\}$*
*$\{A \mid L(A, x) - f(x)$ minimizes a weighted $L_q$-norm on $X\}$.*

For the interval $[0, 1]$ similar results are true, except that $L_p$-norms, $0 < p < 1$, and exact interpolation are not present.

**Theorem 13–16.** *Let $\{\phi_i(x)\}$ be a Tchebycheff set and define $L(A, x)$ by (13–9.1). Then given $1 < q < p \leq \infty$ and $f(x)$ continuous on $[0, 1]$ we have three pairs of identical sets:*

(1)   $\{A \mid L(A, x) - f(x)$ *minimizes a weighted $L_p$-norm on $[0, 1]\}$*
       $\{A \mid L(A, x)$ *strongly interpolates $f(x)$ on $[0, 1]\}$;*
(2)   $\{A \mid L(A, x) - f(x)$ *minimizes a weighted $L_1$-norm on $[0, 1]\}$*
       $\{A \mid L(A, x)$ *weakly interpolates $f(x)$ on $[0, 1]$*
       or $f(x) - L(A, x)$ *vanishes on a set of positive measure$\}$;*
(3)   $\{A \mid L(A, x) - f(x)$ *minimizes a weighted $L_p$-norm on $[0, 1]\}$*
       $\{A \mid L(A, x) - f(x)$ *minimizes a weighted $L_q$-norm on $[0, 1]\}$.*

*Proof.* The equivalence of the first pair follows from Theorem 13–3, Theorem 13–14 and Theorem 13–6. The equivalence of the second pair follows from Theorem 13–1, Theorem 13–5 and Theorem 13–6. The equivalence of the third pair follows from the equivalence of the first pair.

One of the main conclusions to be drawn from Theorem 13–15 and Theorem 13–16 is that there is little significance to the statement: "$L(A, x)$ is a best approximation to $f(x)$ in a weighted $L_p$-norm." This statement only implies that $L(A, x)$ is in the general neighborhood of $f(x)$—at least for part of the interval $[0, 1]$ or the set $X$. This fact is illustrated by the examples

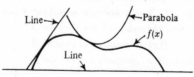

FIG. 13–5.   Some best weighted $L_1$-approximations to $f(x)$.

given in Figs. 13–5 and 13–6. These examples show that one must use considerable care in chosing a weight function in the actual use of approximations.

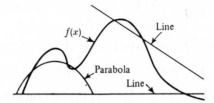

FIG. 13–6.    Some best weighted least squares approximations to $f(x)$.

## 13–10    JUXTAPOLYNOMIALS

So far in this chapter we have been concerned with two types of approximations; those that interpolate $f(x)$ and those that minimize some norm. In this section another type of approximation is considered. Let $X$ be any subset of the interval $[0, 1]$ and let a function $f(x)$ be given. Then the linear approximating function $L(A_1, x)$ is *closer to* $f(x)$ than $L(A_2, x)$ if

$$|L(A_1, x) - f(x)| < |L(A_2, x) - f(x)| \qquad (13\text{–}10.1)$$

for those $x \in X$ such that the right hand side of (13–10.1) is positive and if

$$L(A_1, x) = L(A_2, x)$$

for those $x \in X$ such that $L(A_2, x) = f(x)$.

**Definition 13–9.** $L(A^*, x)$ *is a juxtapolynomial of $f(x)$ on $X$ if there exists no polynomial closer to $f(x)$ than $L(A^*, x)$ on $X$.*

If $L(A^*, x)$ is a juxtapolynomial of $f(x)$ on $X$, then $L(A^*, x)$ is a juxtapolynomial of $f(x)$ on any set $X'$ containing $X$.

The property given by Definition 13–9 is essentially different from either best approximation in a norm, or interpolation. It is shown that if $X$ is a finite point set that the set of juxtapolynomials is identical with the set of weakly interpolating functions. However, if $X$ is the interval $[0, 1]$, this is no longer the case; and the set of juxtapolynomials is a distinct entity.

The following lemma shows that the set of juxtapolynomials contains a large class of approximations.

**Lemma 13–8.** *If $L(A^*, x)$ is a best approximation to $f(x)$ on $X$ in a monotonic norm $\delta$, then $L(A^*, x)$ is a juxtapolynomial of $f(x)$.*

*Proof.* Assume that there exists a linear approximating function $L(A_1, x)$ which is closer to $f(x)$ on $X$ than $L(A^*, x)$. Let

$$Y = \left\{ x \,\middle|\, |L(A^*, x) - f(x)| \geq \tfrac{1}{2} \sup |L(A^*, x) - f(x)| \right\}.$$

Then for $x \in Y$, $|L(A_1, x) - f(x)| < |L(A^*, x) - f(x)|$ by (13–10.1). Define the auxiliary function

$$h(x) = \begin{cases} L(A^*, x) - f(x), & x \notin Y \\ L(A_1, x) - f(x), & x \in Y \end{cases}$$

then by the definition of a monotonic norm (13–2.2)

$$\delta\big(L(A_1, x) - f(x)\big) \leq \delta\big(h(x)\big) < \delta\big(L(A^*, x) - f(x)\big).$$

This implies that $L(A^*, x)$ is not a best approximation to $f(x)$ on $X$ and establishes the lemma.

If one assumes that $X$ is a finite point set, then a converse result to Lemma 13–8 may be established. The proof is based on the fact that if $L(A, x) - f(x)$ does not have $n$ weak sign changes on $X$, then one can find an $L(A_1, x)$ such that

$$\text{sgn } L(A_1, x) = -\text{sgn}\,[L(A, x) - f(x)], \quad x \in X;$$

and hence $L(A, x) + \epsilon L(A_1, x)$ is closer to $f(x)$ than $L(A, x)$ for $\epsilon$ suitably chosen.

**Theorem 13–17.**   *Let $f(x)$ and a finite point set $X$ be given. Then the following sets of linear approximating functions are identical:*

(a)  $\{L(A, x) \mid L(A, x)$ *is a juxtapolynomial to $f(x)$ on $X\}$*
(b)  $\{L(A, x) \mid L(A, x)$ *weakly interpolates $f(x)$ on $X\}$.*

*Proof.* By Theorem 13–15 the set (b) is identical with the set of linear approximating functions which minimize a weighted $L_1$-norm. From Lemma 13–8 it follows that this set is contained in (a). Thus the set (b) is contained in (a).

It is now shown that (a) is contained in (b). Assume that a juxtapolynomial $L(A^*, x) - f(x)$ has less than $n$ weak sign changes on $X$. Then $L(A_1, x)$ may be determined so that $L(A_1, x)$ vanishes when $L(A^*, x) - f(x)$ vanishes on $X$ and otherwise has the opposite sign on $X$ to $L(A^*, x) - f(x)$. If $L(A^*, x) - f(x)$ vanishes at $x_0$ and has the same sign at the points of $X$ adjacent to $x_0$, then $L(A_1, x)$ is chosen to have another zero between $x_0$ and one of the adjacent points. Thus we have that

$$|L(A^*, x) + \epsilon L(A_1, x) - f(x)| \qquad\qquad (13\text{–}10.2)$$

vanishes whenever $L(A^*, x) - f(x)$ vanishes on $X$ and that for $\epsilon$ sufficiently small (13–10.2) is less than $|L(A^*, x) - f(x)|$. This contradicts the assumption that $L(A^*, x)$ is a juxtapolynomial and concludes the proof.

Thus for a finite point set the study of juxtapolynomials reverts to the study of best approximations. This is not the case for the interval $[0, 1]$ as is seen in the following example:

EXAMPLE. $f(x) = x^2$. There is no constant closer to $f(x)$ than 0, hence 0 is a juxtapolynomial to $f(x)$. However

$$\frac{d}{da} \int_0^1 \mu(x)|x^2 - a|\, dx = \int_{x^2 > a} \mu(x)\, dx - \int_{x^2 < a} \mu(x)\, dx. \quad (13\text{–}10.3)$$

Since $\mu(x)$ is a continuous and positive function, it follows that (13–10.3) is negative for $a = 0$; and hence $a = 0$ is not a best weighted $L_1$-approximation to $x^2$ for any weight function $\mu(x)$.

For the special case of approximation by polynomials $P_n(x)$,

$$P_n(x) = \sum_{i=0}^{n-1} a_i x^{i-1},$$

Motzkin and Walsh, 1959, have obtained some characteristic properties of juxtapolynomials on an interval. The following definition is required.

**Definition 13–10.** *Let $f(x)$ be continuous on $[0, 1]$. We say that $f(x)$ has a zero of order $\lambda$ at $x = x_0$ if $\lambda$ is the largest number such that for some $\delta > 0$ and some $M > 0$ we have*

$$\frac{f(x)}{|(x - x_0)|^\lambda} \leq M < \infty, \qquad 0 < |x - x_0| < \delta. \quad (13\text{–}10.4)$$

*If (13–10.4) is valid for no positive $\lambda$, then we set $\lambda = 0$. If (13–10.4) is valid for all $\lambda$, then we set $\lambda = \infty$.*

**Lemma 13–9.** *If $f(x)$ is continuous on $[0, 1]$ and if $L(A_1, x)$ is closer to $f(x)$ than $L(A_2, x)$ on $[0, 1]$, then $L(A_1, x) - L(A_2, x)$ has a zero of at least order $\lambda$ whenever $f(x) - L(A_2, x)$ has a zero of order $\lambda$.*

*Proof.* Let $x_0$ be a zero of $f(x) - L(A_2, x)$. Then in a neighborhood of $x_0$

$$|L(A_1, x) - L(A_2, x)| \leq |f(x) - L(A_1, x)| + |f(x) - L(A_2, x)|$$

$$\leq 2|f(x) - L(A_2, x)| \leq 2M|x - x_0|^\lambda.$$

**Definition 13–11.** *A zero $x_0$ of a continuous function $f(x)$ is said to be a plus zero (or minus zero) if there is a $\delta > 0$ such that*

$$f(x) > 0, \quad ((x - x_0)f(x) > 0), \quad 0 < |x - x_0| < \delta,$$

*or*

$$f(x) < 0, \quad ((x - x_0)f(x) < 0), \quad 0 < |x - x_0| < \delta).$$

A function may have a zero which is neither plus or minus, e.g. $x \sin(1/x)$ at $x = 0$.

**Lemma 13–10.** *If $f(x)$ is continuous on $[0, 1]$ and if $L(A_1, x)$ is closer to $f(x)$ than $L(A_2, x)$ on $[0, 1]$, then if $f(x) - L(A_2, x)$ has a zero at $x_0$, $L(A_1, x) - L(A_2, x)$ has a zero at $x_0$ of the same sign.*

*Proof.* It follows from (13–10.1) that the value of $f(x)$ is nearer to $L(A_1, x)$ than $L(A_2, x)$. Thus

$$\text{sgn}[f(x) - L(A_2, x)] = \text{sgn}[L(A_1, x) - L(A_2, x)]$$

which establishes the lemma.

There is a particular property of ordinary polynomials

$$p_n(x) = \sum_{i=1}^{n-1} a_i x^{i-1}$$

which is used to characterize juxtapolynomials. This is the fact that the sum of the orders of the zeros of $P_n(x)$ must be less than $n - 1$. This may be stated more exactly if we define the plus and minus orders of a zero. The *plus order* $\lambda^+$ associated with a zero $x_0$ of $P_n(x)$ or order $\lambda$ is the smallest number $\lambda^+$ such that $\lambda^+ \geq \lambda$ and such that there is a polynomial $P_n^+(x)$ which has a zero at $x_0$ of order $\lambda^+$, and $P_n^+(x)$ does not change sign in a neighborhood of $x_0$. The *minus order* $\lambda^-$ is defined similarly except that $P_n^-(x)$ does change sign at $x_0$. These definitions could have been stated more simply as: $\lambda^+$ is the smallest even integer larger than $\lambda$, and $\lambda^-$ is the smallest odd integer larger than $\lambda$. The more complex definition is given to expose the exact characteristic of polynomials being described, namely that a polynomial cannot have a zero of odd order without changing sign.

Thus if $f(x) - P_n'(x)$ has a zero of order 2.5 at $x_0$ and if $f(x) - P_n'(x)$ is positive in a neighborhood of $x_0$, then a closer polynomial $P_n''(x)$ to $f(x)$ than $P_n'(x)$ must be such that $P_n''(x) - P_n'(x)$ has a zero of order 4 at $x_0$.

Polynomials have a stronger property than Property $Z$, which only implies that $P_n(x)$ has at most $n - 1$ zeros regardless of order. Polynomials have the property that the *sum of the signed orders* of the zeros of a polynomial cannot exceed $n - 1$. With this property we may characterize juxtapolynomials by the following theorem.

**Theorem 13–18.** *A necessary and sufficient condition that the polynomial $P_n^*(x)$ be a juxtapolynomial to a continuous function $f(x)$ on $[0, 1]$ is that $f(x) - P_n^*(x)$ has zeros on $[0, 1]$ of total signed order at least $n - 1$.*

*Proof.* Assume that $P_n^1(x)$ is closer to $f(x)$ than $P_n^*(x)$. It follows from Lemma 13–9 that $P_n^1(x) - P_n^*(x)$ has the same zeros as $f(x) - P_n^*(x)$ with orders at least as large. From Lemma 13–10 it follows that the zeros of $P_n^1(x) - P_n^*(x)$ and $f(x) - P_n^*(x)$ have the same sign. Thus $P_n^1(x) - P_n^*(x)$ has zeros of total signed order at least as large as $f(x) - P_n^*(x)$. Thus if the total signed order of the zeros of $f(x) - P_n^*(x)$ is at least $n - 1$, then $f(x)$ can have no closer polynomial. This establishes the sufficiency part of the proof.

Assume that $f(x) - P_n(x)$ has zeros $\{x_i \mid i = 1, 2, \ldots, p\}$ of total signed order less than $n - 1$. It will now be shown that $f(x)$ possesses a closer polynomial $P_n^*(x)$ than $P_n(x)$. Let $\lambda_i$ be the order of the zero of $f(x) - P_n(x)$

at $x_i$. Choose a polynomial $Q_n(x)$ such that $Q_n(x)$ has a zero of order $\lambda_i^+$ or $\lambda_i^-$ according to whether $x_i$ is a plus or minus zero. Further choose the sign of $Q_n(x)$ so that

$$\text{sgn}\,[Q_n(x)] = \text{sgn}\,[f(x) - P_n(x)].$$

Since polynomials are linear in the coefficients $a_i$, there is an $\epsilon > 0$ such that

$$|f(x) - P_n(x) - \epsilon Q_n(x)| < |f(x) - P_n(x)|, \qquad x \neq x_i; \; i = 1, 2, \ldots, p.$$

Thus $P_n^*(x) = P_n(x) + \epsilon Q_n(x)$ is closer to $f(x)$ than $P_n(x)$.

This establishes the necessity part.

An examination of the proof of Theorem 13–18 shows that two properties of polynomials were used. The first of these is that the total of the signed order of the zeros of $P_n(x)$ cannot exceed $n - 1$. The second property used is that the zeros of a polynomial may be assigned arbitrarily with assigned signs as long as the total of the signed order of the zeros does not exceed $n - 1$. Theorem 13–18 is valid for any linear approximating function $L(A, x)$ which has these two properties.

It should be remarked that though the properties alluded to above are common among the functions met in the usual course of analysis, they are actually very special. First, this whole development tacitly requires some degree of differentiability. Otherwise, zeros will be of order 1 or 2 only, in which case the definition of the order loses significance. Second, the ability to assign the order and sign of a zero as well as its location is a rare property. For example, if one is approximating with

$$L(A, x) = a_1 + a_2 x + a_2 x^2 + a_3 x^2 |x - \tfrac{1}{2}| + a_4 |x - \tfrac{1}{2}|,$$

one may have plus or minus zeros of orders both 1 and 2. There are, however, definite limitations on the location of these zeros.

It is likely that a more general characterizing property than that given in Theorem 13–18 can be described, at the expense of making it more complicated. Theorem 13–18 does make it clear that any characteristic property of juxtapolynomials for general approximating functions which is given in terms of zeros of $f(x) - L(A, x)$ must take into account the possible coalescing (which is equivalent to high order zeros) of the zeros.

One might also consider at this point whether the original definition of an interpolating function might be modified to take into account the coalescing of the points of interpolation. At this point it is not clear which is the more natural definition. Since the limitation of differentiability was not desired for this study, no attempt was made to use such a definition in this chapter.

### 13-11  THE LAWSON ALGORITHM

This algorithm is designed to exploit computationally the results summarized in Theorem 13-15. It is normally much easier to compute $L_2$-approximations than $L_p$-approximations and thus we can find $L_p$-approximations by this easier $L_2$-computation *provided we know the appropriate weight function.* Lawson's algorithm is designed to generate such a weight function to obtain $L_\infty$-approximations.

Lawson, 1961, considered the computation of $L_\infty$-approximations by means of weighted $L_p$, $p < \infty$, approximations for functions defined on finite point sets. We consider only the use of $L_2$-approximations here.

Before proceeding with the development of the algorithm, we briefly indicate some of its advantages, an open question and a possible extension. The main attraction of this algorithm is not that it may be more efficient computationally (this point has not been settled,) but rather that it allows one to attack problems which lack algorithms for Tchebycheff approximation. Examples of this investigated by Lawson are approximations in the complex plane and to vector valued functions. Further, the computational procedure involves only a rather small addition to the usual $L_2$-procedure.

Convergence of this algorithm has only been established for approximation on finite point sets. It is not difficult to extend the definition of the algorithm for approximation on more general sets, but it appears that the proof of convergence (if the algorithm does converge) becomes considerably more difficult.

There are two directions for extending this algorithm which suggest themselves. The first is to approximation by varisolvent and other nonlinear approximating functions. This direction is of lesser interest because it is not clear at this time that it is easier to compute nonlinear $L_2$-approximations than it is to compute nonlinear Tchebycheff approximations. The other direction of extension is toward the computation of other $L_p$-approximations for $p < \infty$. This extension is discussed in Rice and Usow, 1968, along with computation.

We begin by establishing some notation. We wish to approximate the values $f(x_i) = f_i$, $i = 1, 2, \ldots, m$ on the set $X \equiv \{x_i \mid i = 1, 2, \ldots, m\}$ by the approximating function

$$L(A, x) = \sum_{i=1}^{n} a_i \phi_i(x)$$

where $\{\phi_i(x)\}$ is a Tchebycheff set. We define a sequence of weight functions $w^k(x)$ on $X$ and a corresponding sequence $\{L(A_k, x)\}$ of best $L_2$-approximations to $f(x)$ with the weights $w^k(x)$. All weight functions are normalized so that

$$\sum_{x \in X} w(x) = 1.$$

**Definition 13–12.** *The Lawson algorithm is defined by the recursive relation*

$$w^{k+1}(x) = w^k(x)|f(x) - L(A_k, x)| \bigg/ \sum_{x \in X} w^k(x)|f(x) - L(A_k, x)| \quad (13\text{--}11.1)$$

*where $w^1(x)$ is a positive weight function and $L(A_k, x)$ is the best $L_2$-approximation to $f(x)$ with weights $w^k(x)$.*

One would normally take $w^1(x) = 1/m$, but we will see later that we might wish to choose other initial weight functions. Due to its frequent use, we introduce the notation

$$e^k(x) = f(x) - L(A_k, x), \qquad x \in X$$

for the *error* and set

$$\sigma^k = \left[ \sum_{x \in X} w^k(x)[e^k(x)]^2 \right]^{1/2}.$$

The definition (13–11.1) does not force $w^k(x)$ to remain positive and we set

$$Z_k = \{x \mid x \in X, \quad e^k(x) = 0\},$$
$$W_k = W_{k-1} - Z_k, \qquad W_0 = X.$$

**Lemma 13–11.** *The numbers $\sigma^k$ are positive for all $k$ if $\sigma^1 \neq 0$.*

If $\sigma^1 = 0$ then $f(x)$ is of the form of $L(A, x)$, a situation which we exclude from consideration in this chapter.

*Proof.* The proof is by induction, i.e. assume that $\sigma^k > 0$. This implies that $W_k$ is not empty. If $W_{k+1} = W_k$, then no function $L(A, x)$ agrees with $f(x)$ on $W_{k+1} = W_k$ and hence $\sigma^{k+1} > 0$. If $W_k - W_{k+1}$ is not empty, then it is seen that $L(A_k, x)$ is a best $L_2$-approximation to $f(x)$ on $W_{k+1}$ as well as $W_k$ with the weight $w^k(x)$. Again $\sigma^k > 0$ implies that $f(x)$ is not of the form $L(A, x)$ on $W_{k+1}$ and $\sigma^{k+1} > 0$. This concludes the proof.

Note that this implies that

$$W = \bigcap_k W_k$$

is not empty and, indeed, contains at least $n + 1$ points.

**Lemma 13–12.** *If for some $k$ we have $|e_k(x)|$ constant on $W_k$ then $L(A_{k+j}, x) = L(A_k, x)$ for all $j$. Otherwise*

$$\sigma^k < \sigma^{k+1} \leq \zeta^* = \max_{x \in X} |f(x) - L(A^*, x)| \quad (13\text{--}11.2)$$

*where $L(A^*, x)$ is the best Tchebycheff approximation to $f(x)$ on $X$.*

*Proof.* The first statement is clear. For the second part we introduce the inner product

$$(f, g)_w = \sum_{x \in W_k} w(x)f(x)g(x).$$

Then

$$\sigma^k = [(e^k, e^k)_{w^k}]^{1/2}$$

or

$$\sigma^k = \left(f - L(A_k), \frac{e^k}{\sigma^k}\right)_{w^k} = \left(f, \frac{e^k}{\sigma^k}\right)_{w^k}.$$

We have

$$\sigma^{k+1} = \left(f, \frac{e^{k+1}}{\sigma^{k+1}}\right)_{w^{k+1}} > (f, \text{sgn } (e^k(x)))_{w^{k+1}} > \left(f, \frac{e^k}{\sigma^k}\right)_{w^k} = \sigma^k.$$

$$(13\text{--}11.3)$$

The first inequality in (13–11.3) is due to the fact that $g = e^{k+1}$ maximizes $(f, g)_{w^{k+1}}$ among those $g$ with $(g, g)_{w^{k+1}} = 1$ and $(g, L(A, x))_{w^{k+1}} = 0$ for all $A$. Equality would imply that $|e^{k+1}(x)|$ is constant on $X$. The second inequality in (13–11.3) follows from the definitions (13–11.1) of $w^{k+1}$ in Lawson's algorithm and the fact that $[\sum e^k w^k]^2 \le \sum (e^k)^2 w^k$. That $\sigma^{k+1} \le \zeta^*$ is clear and the proof is complete.

Let

$$\sigma^* = \lim_{k \to \infty} \sigma^k$$

$X_1 = \{x| \ w^k(x) \ge \epsilon > 0 \text{ for infinitely many } k \text{ and some } \epsilon\},$

$X_2 = \{x \ | \ \lim_{k \to \infty} w^k(x) = 0 \text{ and } w^k(x) > 0\},$

$$Z = \bigcup_k Z_k.$$

**Theorem 13–19.**  *The sequence $\{L(A_k, x)\}$ converges to $L(A_0, x)$ which is a best Tchebycheff approximation to $f(x)$ on $X_1$ with*

$$|f(x) - L(A_0, x)| = \sigma^*$$

*for all $x \in X_1$.*

*Proof.* Since $X$ is finite and $L(A, x)$ has a finite number of parameters, it is possible to choose sequences $\{k_\mu\}$ of integers so that $L(A_{k_\mu}, x)$ and $w^{k_\mu}$ are convergent. We denote such subsequences by $L(A_\mu, x)$ and $w^\mu(x)$ to simplify the notation and let $L(A', x)$ and $w'(x)$ denote the corresponding limits. The following assertion establishes some facts about the limits of any such subsequence. Let

$$W' = \{x \ | \ w'(x) > 0\}.$$

*Assertion.*  $L(A', x)$ is a best Tchebycheff approximation to $f(x)$ on $W'$ and $|f(x) - L(A', x)| = \sigma^*$ for all $x \in W'$.

The set $W'$ is not empty since $\displaystyle\sum_{x \in X} w^k(x) = 1$ and

$$\sigma^* = \lim_{\mu \to \infty} \sigma^\mu = \lim_{\mu \to \infty} (e^\mu, e^\mu)_{w^\mu}^{1/2} \ne 0$$

implies that $W'$ contains at least $n + 1$ points. It is seen that $w^{\mu+1}$, $\sigma^{\mu}$ are continuous functions of $w^{\mu}$. This implies that $\sigma^2 = \sigma^1$ (for this new sequence) and from Lemma 13-12 it follows that $|e^1(x)| = |f(x) - L(A', x)|$ is constant on $W'$. Thus Lawson's algorithm starting with $w^1 = w'$ must have $w^2 = w^1 = w'$.

This may be restated by saying that Lawson's algorithm defines a descent mapping $\Psi$ from $(w^k(x), L(A_k, x), -\sigma^k)$ into $(w^{k+1}(x), L(A_{k+1}, x), -\sigma^{k+1})$. The mapping $\Psi$ is continuous and hence the limit of any convergent sequence defined by $\Psi$ is a fixed point of $\Psi$ (see Theorem 6-2).

It remains only to show that $L(A', x)$ is a Tchebycheff approximation. If there is a better Tchebycheff approximation $L(A'', x)$, then

$$|f(x) - L(A'', x)| < |f(x) - L(A', x)|$$

for all $x \in W'$. This contradicts the fact that $L(A', x)$ is a best weighted $L_2$-approximation to $f(x)$ on $W'$ and establishes the assertion.

We now show that

$$\lim_{k \to \infty} w^{k+1}(x) - w^k(x) = 0. \tag{13-11.4}$$

Consider any subsequence so that $\{w^{\mu}(x)\}$ and $\{w^{\mu+1}(x) - w^{\mu}(x)\}$ converge. Then

$$\lim_{\mu \to \infty} w^{\mu+1}(x) = \lim_{\mu \to \infty} \frac{w^{\mu}(x)|e^{\mu}(x)|}{\sum\limits_{x \in X} w^{\mu}(x)|e^{\mu}(x)|} = \frac{w'(x)|e'(x)|}{\sigma^*}$$

$$= \begin{cases} 0 \text{ if } w'(x) = 0 \\ \dfrac{w'(x)\sigma^*}{\sigma^*} = w'(x) \text{ if } x \in W'. \end{cases}$$

Thus (13-11.4) is established for all such subsequences and hence the entire sequence satisfies (13-11.4).

Denote by $\mathscr{W}$ the limit points of $w^k(x)$. It is clear that $\mathscr{W}$ is not empty, closed and bounded, i.e. $\mathscr{W}$ is compact. Furthermore, (13-11.4) shows that $\mathscr{W}$ is a connected set.

*Assertion. Every $w(x) \in \mathscr{W}$ gives the same $L_2$-approximation to $f(x)$.*

The set $\mathscr{W}$ may be decomposed into equivalence classes by saying two weight functions are equivalent if they give rise to the same approximation to $f(x)$. If $L(A, x)$ is a best approximation to $f(x)$ with weight $w(x)$ then it is the uniquely determined best Tchebycheff approximation to $f(x)$ on the set $W'$ where $w(x) > 0$. This follows from the previous assertion. Thus there is at most a finite number of equivalence classes, each is compact and distinct. Since $\mathscr{W}$ is connected, there is at most one such set and the assertion is established.

We establish the last

*Assertion. The sequence* $\{L(A_k, x)\}$ *converges.*

It is clear that $\{L(A_k, x)\}$ is bounded and hence contains convergent subsequences. If there are two such subsequences with different limits, consider the corresponding sequences of weight functions. These sequences have convergent subsequences which, according to the previous assertion, give rise to the same $L_2$-approximation to $f(x)$. This contradicts the assumption of two different limits and establishes the assertion.

The first assertion may now be applied to complete the proof.

**Corollary.**  $L(A_0, x)$ *is a best Tchebycheff approximation to* $f(x)$ *on* $X_1 \cup X_2$.

Suppose that $y \in X_2$ and

$$|f(y) - L(A_0, y)| = \sigma_0 > \sigma^*.$$

Then, at $y$,

$$w^{k+1}(y) = \frac{|e^k(y)| w^k(y)}{\sum\limits_x w^k(x) |e^k(x)|}$$

and $|e^k(y)|$ converges to $\sigma_0 = \rho \sigma^*$ where $\rho > 1$. Thus

$$\lim_{k \to \infty} \frac{w^{k+1}(y)}{w^k(y)} = \rho > 1$$

if $w^k(y) > 0$ for all $k$, which is the case. This implies that $\{w^k(y)\}$ diverges, but this is impossible.

This corollary used the fact that $w^k(y) \neq 0$ and, so far, we are not yet able to conclude that $L(A_0, x)$ is the best Tchebycheff approximation $L(A^*, x)$. The following example shows that, in fact, $L(A_0, x)$ might not be the best Tchebycheff approximation $L(A^*, x)$.

EXAMPLE.  $X = \{0, 1, 2, 3, 6.5\}$, $L(A, x) = a_1 + a_2 x$, $f(x) = \{0, 10, 1, 1, 0\}$.

We see that $L(A^*, x) = 5$. Let us apply Lawson's algorithm with $w^1(x) = \frac{1}{5}$. Then we have $L(A_1, x) = 3.9 - 0.6x$ and

$$w^2(x) = \{0.291, 0.500, 0.127, 0.082, 0\}.$$

If the algorithm is carried out it may be verified that

$$L(A_0, x) = \tfrac{29}{6} + \tfrac{1}{3}x$$
$$e_0(x) = \{\tfrac{1}{3}, \tfrac{1}{2}, 0, \tfrac{1}{6}, 0\}$$
$$f(x) - L(A_0, x) = \{-\tfrac{29}{6}, \tfrac{29}{6}, -\tfrac{27}{6}, -\tfrac{29}{6}, -7\}.$$

In this example $L(A_1, x)$ interpolates $f(x)$ at $x = 6.5$ and $w^k(6.5) = 0$ for $k \geq 2$. Thus this point does not enter into the determination of $L(A_0, x)$. We have

$$X_1 = \{0, 1, 3\}$$
$$X_2 = \{2\}$$
$$Z = \{6.5\}.$$

This phenonomen is a serious (though infrequently occurring) drawback to Lawson's algorithm. There appear to be two possible ways to remedy this situation. The first of these is to modify definition (13–11.1) so that an "accidental" zero value of $e^k(x)$ does not set $w^k(x) = 0$ permanently. The second of these is to devise a procedure to reinitialize the algorithm if $L(A_0, x)$ $\neq L(A^*, x)$ in such a way that the resulting $\sigma^*$ is increased. The second remedy is presented by Lawson. He proceeds as follows: Let $z \in Z$ be a point such that

$$|f(z) - L(A_0, z)| > \sigma^*.$$

Set $u(x) = 0$ if $x \neq z$, $u(z) = 1$ and form

$$w(\lambda, x) = \lambda u(x) + (1 - \lambda)w'(x) \qquad (13\text{–}11.5)$$

One may show that for a value $\lambda_0$ sufficiently small and positive, the corresponding value $\sigma(\lambda_0)$ of $\sigma$ is greater than $\sigma^*$. Thus if the algorithm is initialized with $w^1(x) = w(\lambda_0, x)$, it must lead to a Tchebycheff approximation $L(A_0^{(2)}, x)$ with deviation larger than $\sigma^*$. Of course, this second $L(A_0^{(2)}, x)$ might also not equal $L(A^*, x)$. However, a finite number of repetitions of this procedure leads to $L(A^*, x)$ since $X$ is finite.

We now discuss some possible variants of this algorithm which appear interesting. It must be kept in mind that these variations have neither been studied analytically nor experimentally. First we consider the problem of modifying the algorithm to avoid the trouble that occurs when $w^k(x) = 0$ for some value of $x$. Two types suggest themselves.

$$w^{k+1}(x) = \begin{cases} w^k(x)|e^k(x)|, & |e^k(x)| \neq 0 \\ w^k(x), & |e^k(x)| = 0 \end{cases} \qquad (13\text{–}11.6)$$

$$w^{k+1}(x) = \begin{cases} w^k(x)|e^k(x)|, & |e^k(x)| \neq 0 \\ a(k), & |e^k(x)| = 0. \end{cases} \qquad (13\text{–}11.7)$$

In (13–11.6) one could choose for $a(k)$ functions such as $1/k$, $1/k^4$, $2^{-k}$, etc. The objective of both of these modifications is always to assure that $w^k(x)$ $> 0$ and yet not keep $w^k(x)$ from tending to zero rapidly. The present convergence proofs break down at (13–11.3) for both of these modifications.

While one is interested in preventing $w^k(x) = 0$ by accident, one is also concerned with making $w^k(x)$ tend to zero as rapidly as possible except at the critical points of the Tchebycheff approximation. Let $e^*(x) = f(x)$ $- L(A^*, x)$; then one sees that $w^k(x)$ is asymptotically proportional to

$$[e^*(x)]^k.$$

Thus at those points where $|e^*(x)|$ is nearly maximized, the weight function $w^k(x)$ does not tend to zero too rapidly. Indeed let

$$\rho^* = \max \left\{ \rho = \frac{|e^*(x)|}{\max_{x \in X} |e^*(x)|} \, \middle| \, \rho < 1 \right\}.$$

12

Lawson reports that the algorithm appears to converge linearly with ratio $\rho^*$. The ratio $\rho^*$ also determines the slowest rate at which $w^k(x)$ tends to zero. Thus one might hope to achieve faster convergence by modifying the algorithm so as to make $w^k(x)$ tend to zero faster. Such modifications might be

$$w^{k+1}(x) = w^k(x)|e^k(x)|^2 \tag{13-11.8}$$

$$w^{k+1}(x) = [w^k(x)]^2|e^k(x)|. \tag{13-11.9}$$

These modifications make $w^k(x)$ tend to zero like $(\rho^*)^{2k}$ and $(\rho^*)^{2^k}$, respectively, provided that the resulting algorithm converges. It has been observed that (13-11.8) sometimes leads to divergence.

Lawson notes that the algorithm tends to distinguish rather quickly those points which are likely to be the critical points. He suggests that it may be efficient to do a few steps of this algorithm and then set $w^k(x) = 0$ except at those $n + 1$ points which are candidates for a critical point set. A variant of this is studied by Rice and Usow, 1968, and is said to increase efficiency greatly. He notes that if $X$ has exactly $n + 1$ points then $L(A_2, x)$ $= L(A^*, x)$, i.e. the algorithm converges in one step.

### PROBLEMS

13-1.  Every juxtapolynomial $P_n(x)$ to a real function $f(x)$ on a real finite point set $X$ containing at least $n + 1$ points is also real. (Motzkin and Walsh, 1959.)

13-2.  Given a real finite set $X$ containing at least $n + 1$ points and $f(x)$ defined on $X$, the set of juxtapolynomials of degree $n$ to $f(x)$ on $X$ is bounded on every finite set. (Motzkin and Walsh, 1959.)

13-3.  Given a real finite set $X$ containing at least $n + 1$ points, the set of juxtapolynomials of degree $n$ to $f(x)$ on $X$ is closed. (Motzkin and Walsh, 1959.)

13-4.  Given a real finite set $X$ containing at least $n + 1$ points and $f(x)$ defined on $X$, represent a polynomial in the space $E_n$ by its coefficients. The set of coefficients of juxtapolynomials of degree $n$ to $f(x)$ on $X$ is connected. (Motzkin and Walsh, 1959.)

13-5.  Let

$$\delta_\tau(f(x)) = \int_0^1 \tau(|f(x)|)w(x)\,dx$$

where $\tau(t)$ is defined for all $t$, $0 \le t < \infty$, and $\dfrac{d^2\tau(t)}{dt^2} \ge 0$, is continuous for such $t$. $w(x)$ is a weight function. Show that

    (a)   $\delta_\tau$ is a monotonic norm

    (b)   $\delta_\tau$ is a Class 1 norm

    (c)   If $\tau'(0) = 0$, the $\delta_\tau$ is a Class 2 norm

    (d)   Analogous to Theorem 13-4 we have the condition

$$\int_{I-I_0} [L(A^*, x) - L(A, x)]\tau'(|f(x) - L(A^*, x)|)\,\mathrm{sgn}\,[f(x) - L(A^*, x)]w(x)\,dx$$
$$\le \tau(0) \int_{I_0} |L(A^*, x) - L(A, x)|w(x)\,dx.$$

13–6. Let $Y = \{y_i \mid i = 1, 2, \ldots, n + 1\}$. Define $w(x) = \prod_{i=1}^{n} (x - y_i)$. Show that the basis functions of Section 13–8 for polynomials are the function

$$w_1(x) = \frac{w(x)}{x - y_i}.$$

13–7. Let $f(x)$ be a nonpolynomial function of Class $C^\infty$ on $[0, 1]$. Let $P_n^*(x)$ be a polynomial of degree $n$ which for some $p$, $0 < p < 1$, is a best weighted $L_p[0, 1]$-approximation to $f(x)$. Let $f(x) - P^*(x)$ have zeros of multiplicities $k_j$, $1 \le j \le r$ and let $k_j^*$ be the smallest integer larger than or equal to $(1 - p)k_j$ which has the same parity as $k_j$ if the zero is not $x = 0$ or $x = 1$. Then

$$\sum_{j=1}^{r} k_j^* \ge n + 1.$$

(Motzkin and Walsh, 1959.)

13–8. We refer to the constructions made in the proof of Theorem 13–9.

Set

$$k_f(\{A_n\}) = \inf \left\{ k \left| \left| \frac{\delta\big(F(A_n, x) - f(x)\big) - \delta\big(s_n(x)\big)}{\delta\big(F(A^*, x) - f(x)\big) - \delta\big(s_n(x)\big)} \right| \le k \text{ for all } n \right. \right\}.$$

$k_f(\{A_n\})$ is positive for each $f(x)$ and each sequence $\{A_n\}$. Set

$$k_f = \inf \{k_f(\{A_n\})\}$$

where the infimum is taken over all $\{A_n\}$ as described in the first part of the construction of Theorem 13–9. Let

$$k(l, m) = \inf \{k_f\}$$

where the infimum is taken over all $f(x)$ such that $F(A^*, x) - f(x)$ has $l$ strong sign changes and $m$ zeros in $X$. Set

$$\mu_k = \min \{m \mid k(l, m) \ge 1\}.$$

*Conclusion:* Let $F$ be a regular varisolvent function, and let the norm be of Class 1. If $F(A^*, x)$ is a best approximation to $f(x)$ on $X$ and $F(A^*, x) - f(x)$ has exactly $k$, $k \le m(A^*)$, strong sign changes on $X$, then $F(A^*, x) - f(x)$ has at least $\mu_k$ zeros in $X$ (Rice, 1961a).

# Bibliography

# BIBLIOGRAPHY

ACHIESER, N. I.
  1956   *Theory of Approximation.* New York: Frederick Ungar Publishing Co.

ACHIESER, N. I. and KREIN, M. G.
  1938   *Some questions in the theory of moments.* Kharkov. (Amer. Math. Soc. Translation, 1962.)

AHLBERG, J. H. *See* WALSH, J. L.

AHLBERG, J. H. and NILSON, E. N.
  1963   *Convergence properties of the spline fit.* J. Soc. Indust. Appl. Math., **11**, pp. 95–104.
  1966   *The approximation of linear functionals.* SIAM J. Numer. Anal., **3**, pp. 173–182.

AHLBERG, J. H., NILSON, E. N. and WALSH, J. L.
  1964   *Fundamental properties of generalized splines.* Proc. Nat. Acad. Sci. USA, **52**, pp. 1412–1419.
  1965   *Best approximation and convergence properties of higher-order spline approximations.* J. Math. Mech., **14**, pp. 231–244.
  1965a  *Orthogonal properties of spline functions.* J. Math. Anal. Appl., **11**, pp. 321–337.
  1965b  *Extremal, orthogonality and convergence properties of multi-dimensional splines.* J. Math. Anal. Appl., **12**, pp. 27–48.
  1965c  *Convergence properties of generalized splines.* Proc. Nat. Acad. Sci. USA, **54**, pp. 344–350.

ATTEIA, M.
  1965   *Généralization de la définition et des propriétés des "spline fonctions".* C. R. Acad. Sci. Paris, **260**, pp. 3550–3553.
  1965a  *"Spline Fonctions" Généralisés.* C. R. Acad. Sci. Paris, **261**, pp. 2149–2152.
  1966   *Existence et détermination des fonctions "spline" à plusieurs variables.* C. R. Acad. Sci. Paris, **262**, pp. 575–578.

AUSLANDER, L. and MACKENSIE, R. E.
  1960   *Introduction to Differentiable Manifolds.* New York: McGraw-Hill.

BARRONDALE, I. and YOUNG, A.
  1966   *Algorithms for best $L_1$ and $L_\infty$ linear approximations on a discrete set.* Numer. Math., **8**, pp. 295–306.

BAUER, F. L.
  1965   *Nonlinear sequence transformations.* From "Approximation of Functions", edited by H. L. Garabedian, Elsevier, Amsterdam, pp. 135–151.

BECKENBACH, E. F. and BING, R. H.
  1945   *On generalized convex functions.* Trans. Amer. Math. Soc., **48**, pp. 220–230.

BERMAN, D. L.

1959   *On the impossibility of constructing a linear polynomial operator giving an approximation of best order.* Usp. Mat. Nauk SSSR, **14**, pp. 141–142.

BERNSTEIN, S. N.

1912   *Sur l'ordre de la meilleure approximation des fonctions continues par des polynomes.* Acad. Roy. Belg., Cl. Sci. Memoires 4°, ser. II.

1926   *Leçons sur les Propriétés Extrémales et la Meilleure Approximation des Fonctions Analytiques d'une Variable Réelle.* Paris: Gauthier-Villars.

BING, R. H.   *See* BECKENBACH, E. F.

BIRKHOFF, G. and DE BOOR, C.

1964   *Error bounds for cubic spline interpolation.* J. Math. Mech., **13**, pp. 827–835.

1965   *Piecewise polynomial interpolation and approximation.* From "Approximation of Functions", edited by H. L. Garabedian, Elsevier, Amsterdam, pp. 164–190.

BIRKHOFF, G. and GARABEDIAN, H. L.

1960   *Smooth surface interpolation.* J. Math. and Phys., **39**, pp. 258–268.

BOEHM, B.

1964   *Existence, Characterization and Convergence of best Rational Tchebycheff Approximations.* Thesis, UCLA.

1965   *Existence of best rational Tchebycheff approximations.* Pac. J. Math., **15**, pp. 19–28.

DE BOOR, C.

1962   *Bicubic spline interpolation.* J. Math. and Phys., **41**, pp. 212–218.

1963   *Best approximation properties of spline functions of odd degree.* J. Math. Mech., **12**, pp. 747–750.

*See* BIRKHOFF, G.

DE BOOR, C. and LYNCH, R. E.

1966   *On splines and their minimum properties.* J. Math. Mech., **15**, pp. 953–970.

DE BOOR, C. and RICE, J. R.

1969   *Least squares cubic spline approximation. I: fixed knots* (to appear).

1969   *Least squares cubic spline approximation. II: variable knots* (to appear).

BRAESS, D.

1967   *Approximation mit Exponentialsummen.* Computing, **2**, pp. 309–321.

BRONDSTED, A.

1965   *Convex sets and Chebyshev sets.* Math. Scand., **17**, pp. 5–16.

1966   *Convex sets and Chebyshev sets II.* Math. Scand., **18**, pp. 5–15.

BROSOWSKI, B.

1965   *Über Extremalsignatures linearer Polynome in n Veränderlichen.* Numer. Math., **7**, pp. 396–405.

1965a   *Über Tschebyscheffsche Approximationen mit linearen Nebenbedingungen.* Math. Zeit., **88**, pp. 105–128.

1965b   *Über die Eindeutigkeit der rationalen Tschebyscheff-Approximationen.* Numer. Math., **7**, pp. 176–186.

1965c   *Über Tschebyscheffsche Approximationen mit verallgemeinerten rationalen Funktionen.* Math. Zeit., **90**, pp. 140–151.

BUCK, R. C.

1958   *Preferred optimal strategies.* Proc. Amer. Math. Soc., **9**, pp. 312–314.

1959   *Linear spaces and approximation theory.* From "On Numerical Approximation", edited by R. E. Langer, Univ. of Wisc. Press, pp. 11–23.

1959a   *Survey of recent Russian literature on approximation.* From "On Numerical Approximation", edited by R. E. Langer, Univ. of Wisc. Press, pp. 341–359.

1965   *Application of duality in approximation theory.* From "Approximation of functions", edited by H. L. Garabedian, Elsevier, Amsterdam, pp. 27–42.

BUROV, V. N.

1961   *The approximation of functions by polynomials satisfying nonlinear relations.* Dokl. Akad. Nauk SSSR, **138**, pp. 515–517.

BUSEMAN, H.

1947   *Note on a theorem on convex sets.* Mat. Tidsskr., pp. 32–34.

1950   *The foundations of Minkowskian geometry.* Comm. Math. Helv., **24**, pp. 156–186.

1955   *The Geometry of Geodesics.* New York: Academic Press.

BUTZER, P. L.

1964   *Saturation and approximation.* SIAM J. Numer. Anal., **1**, pp. 2–10.

1964a   *Integral transform methods in the theory of approximation.* ISNM **5**, Birkhauser Verlag, Basel, pp. 12–23.

CARVER, W. B.

1922   *Systems of linear inequalities.* Ann. Math., **23**, pp. 212–220.

CÉSARO, E.

1904   *Elementares Lehrbuch der algebraischen Analysis und der Infinitesimalrechnung.* Leipzig, pp. 77–79.

CHAND, D. R.

1965   *Approximation of curves by piece-wise continuous functions.* Thesis, Boston University.

CHENEY, E. W.

1965   *Approximation by generalized rational functions.* From "Approximation of Functions", edited by H. L. Garabedian, Elsevier, Amsterdam, pp. 101–110.

1966   *Introduction to Approximation Theory.* New York: McGraw-Hill.

CHENEY, E. W. and GOLDSTEIN, A. A.

1958   *A finite algorithm for the solution of consistent linear equations and inequalities and for the Tchebycheff approximation of inconsistent linear equations.* Pac. J. Math., **8**, pp. 415–427.

1962   *Tchebycheff approximation in locally convex spaces.* Bull Amer. Math. Soc., **68**, pp. 449–450.

1965   *Tchebycheff approximation and related extremal problems.* J. Math. Mech., **14**, pp. 87–98.

1967   *Mean-square approximation by rational functions.* Math. Zeit., **95**, pp. 232–241.

CHENEY, E. W. and LOEB, H. L.
  1962  *On rational Chebyshev approximation*. Numer. Math., **4**, pp. 124–127.
  1964  *Generalized rational approximation*. SIAM J. Num. Anal., **1**, pp. 11–25.
  1966  *On the continuity of rational approximation operators*. Arch Rat. Mech. Anal., **21**, pp. 391–401.

CHENEY, E. W. and SOUTHARD, T. H.
  1963  *A survey of methods for rational approximation*. SIAM Rev., **5**, pp. 219–231.

CLENSHAW, C. W.
  1962  *Chebyshev series for mathematical functions*. NPL Math. Tables, **5**, Her Majesty's Stationery Office, London.
  1964  *A comparison of "best" polynomial approximations with truncated Chebyshev series expansions*. SIAM J. Num. Anal., **1**, pp. 26–37.

CLENSHAW, C. W. and HAYES, J. G.
  1965  *Curve and surface fitting*. J. Inst. Maths. Applics., **1**, pp. 164–183.

CODY, W. T. and HILLSTROM, K. E.
  *Chebyshev approximations for the natural logarithm of the real Gamma function*. Math. Comp., **21**, pp. 198–203.

CODY, W. T. and STOER, J.
  1966  *Rational Chebyshev approximation using interpolation*. Numer. Math., **9**, pp. 177–188.

CODY, W. J. and THACHER, H. C.
  1967  *Approximations to Fermi–Dirac Integrals of Orders $-\frac{1}{2}$, $\frac{1}{2}$ and $\frac{3}{2}$*. Math. Comp., **21**, pp. 30–40.

COLLATZ, L.
  1956  *Approximation von Funktionen bei einer und bei mehreren unabhängigen Veränderlichen*. Z. Angw. Math. Mech., **36**, pp. 198–211.
  1960  *Tschebyscheffsche Annäherung mit rational Funktionen*. Abh. Math. Sem. Univ. Hamburg, **24**, pp. 70–78.
  1965  *Inclusion theorems for the minimal distance in rational Tschebyscheff approximation with several variables*. From "Approximation of Functions", edited by H. L. Garabedian, Elsevier, Amsterdam, pp. 43–56.

COLLATZ, L. and QUADE, W.
  1938  *Zur interpolations Theorie der reellen periodischen Funktionen*. Sitz. ber. Berliner Akad. Wiss. Phys-Math., **30**.

CURTIS, A. R. and POWELL, M. J. D.
  1966  *On the convergence of exchange algorithms for calculating minimax approximations*. Computer J., **9**, pp. 78–80.

CURTIS, P. C.
  1959  *n-Parameter families and best approximation*. Pac. J. Math., **9**, pp. 1013–1027.

CURTIS, P. C. and FRANK, W. L.
  1959  *An algorithm for the determination of the polynomial of best minimax approximation*. J. Ass. Comp. Mach., **6**, pp. 395–404.

DAVIS, P. J.
  1963  *Interpolation and Approximation*. New York, Blaisdell.
  1965  *Approximation theory in the first two decades of electronic computers*, in "Approximation of Functions", edited by H. L. Garabedian, Elsevier, Amsterdam, pp. 152–163.

DAVIS, P. J. and RABINOWITZ, P.
  1961  *Advances in orthonormalization computation*. From "Advances in Computers", vol. II, edited by F. L. Alt, Academic Press, New York.

DESCLOUX, J.
  1960  *Contribution au Calcul des Approximations de Tschebyscheff*. Thesis, École Polytechnique Federal, Zurich.
  1961  *Dégénérescence dans les approximations de Tschebycheff linéaires et discrètes*. Numer. Math., **3**, pp. 180–187.
  1963  *Approximation in $L_p$ and Tchebycheff approximation*. SIAM J. Appl. Math., **11**, pp. 1017–1026.

DOLBY, J. L.
  1963  *A quick method for choosing a transformation*. Technometrics, **5**, pp. 317–325.

DUGUNDJI, J.
  1966  *Topology*. New York: Allyn and Bacon.

DUNHAM, C. B.
  1965  *Convergence problems in Maehly's second method*. J. Assoc. Comp. Mach., **12**, pp. 181–186.
  1966  *Convergence problems in Maehly's second method: Part II*. J. Assoc. Comp. Mach., **13**, pp. 108–113.

EFIMOV, N. V. and STECKIN, S. B.
  1958  *Chebyshev sets in Banach spaces*. Dokl. Akad. Nauk SSSR, **121**, pp. 582–585.
  1959  *Some supporting properties of sets in Banach spaces as related to Chebyshev sets*. Dokl. Akad. Nauk SSSR, **127**, pp. 254–257.
  1961  *Approximative compactness and Chebyshev sets*. Dokl. Akad. Nauk SSSR, **140**, pp. 522–524.

ERDÖS, P.
  1945  *Some remarks on the measurability of certain sets*. Bull. Amer. Math. Soc., **51**, pp. 728–731.

FAN, K.
  1956  *On systems of linear inequalities, linear inequalities and related systems*. Annals of Mathematics Studies No. 38, Princeton Univ. Press, Princeton, N.J., pp. 94–156.

FAN, K. and GLICKSBERG, I.
  1958  *Some geometric properties of the spheres in a normed linear space*. Duke Math. J., **25**, pp. 553–568.

FAVARD, J.
  1949  *Sur l'approximation dans les espaces vectoriels*. Ann. Mat. Pura Appl., **29**, pp. 259–291.

FEDERER, H.
1959  *Curvature measures.* Trans. Amer. Math. Soc., **93**, pp. 418–491.

FEJÉR, L.
1922  *Über die Lage der Nullstellen von Polynomen, die aus Minimumforderungen gewisser Art entspringen.* Math. Ann., **85**, pp. 41–48.

FEKETE, M.
1951  *On the structure of extremal polynomials.* Proc. Nat. Acad. Sci., **37**, pp. 95–103.
1955  *On the structure of polynomials of least deviation.* Bull Res. Council Israel, **5A**, pp. 11–19.

FEKETE, M. and WALSH, J. L.
1956  *On restricted infrapolynomials.* J. d'Analyse Math., **5**, pp. 47–76.

FEKETE, M. and VON NEUMAN, J.
1922  *Über die Lage der Nullstellen gewisser minimum Polynome.* Jber. Deut. Math. Verein., **31**, pp. 19–22.

FISHER, W. D.
1961  *A note on curve fitting with minimum deviations by linear programming.* J. Amer. Stat. Assoc., **56**, pp. 359–362.

FORSYTHE, G. E.
1957  *Generation and use of orthogonal polynomials for data-fitting with a digital computer.* SIAM J. Appl. Math., **5**, pp. 74–88.

FOX, P., GOLDSTEIN, A. A., and LASTMAN, G.
1965  *Rational approximations on finite point sets.* From "Approximation of Functions", edited by H. L. Garabedian, Elsevier, Amsterdam, pp. 56–67.

FRANK, W. L.  *See* CURTIS, P. C.

FRASER, W.
1965  *A survey of methods of computing minimax and near-minimax polynomial approximations for functions of a single independent variable,* J. Assoc. Comp. Mach., **12**, pp. 295–314.

FRASER, W. and HART, J. F.
1962  *On the computation of rational approximations to continuous functions.* Comm. Assoc. Comp. Mach., **5**, pp. 401–403.

FREUD, G.
1958  *Eine Ungleichung für Tschebyscheffsche Approximationspolynome.* Acta Aci. Math (Szeged), **19**, pp. 162–164.

GARABEDIAN, H. L.
1965  *Approximation of Functions*, Elsevier, Amsterdam.
*See* BIRKHOFF, G.

GATLINBURG CONFERENCE
1964  *Proceedings.* SIAM J. Num. Anal., **1**.

GLICKSBERG, I.  *See* FAN, K.

GOFFMAN, G.
1953  *Real Functions*, Chapter 7. New York: Rinehart.

GOLDSTEIN, A. A.
1963  *On the stability of rational approximation.* Numer. Math., **5**, pp. 431–438.

*See* CHENEY, E. W.
*See* FOX, P.

GOLDSTEIN, A. A., LEVINE, N., and HERESHOFF, J. B.
1957  *On the "best and least Qth" approximation of an overdetermined system of linear equations.* J. Ass. Comp. Mach., **4**, pp. 341–347.

GOLOMB, M.
1962  *Lectures on Theory of Approximation.* Argonne National Labs.
1965  *Optimal and nearly optimal linear approximation.* From "Approximation of Functions", edited by H. L. Garabedian, Elsevier, Amsterdam, pp. 83–100.

GOLOMB, M. and WEINBERGER, H. W.
1959  *Optimal approximation and error bounds.* From "On Numerical Approximation", edited by R. E. Langer, Univ. of Wisc. Press, pp. 117–190.

GOLUB, G. H.
1965  *Numerical methods for solving linear least squares problems.* Numer. Math., **7**, pp. 206–216.

GREBENYUK, D. G.
1960  *Polynomials of best approximation with linearly related coefficients.* Izdat. Akad. Nauk Uzbek, SSR, Tashkent.

GREVILLE, T. N. E.
1964  *Numerical procedures for interpolation by spline functions.* SIAM J. Num. Anal., **1**, pp. 53–68.
1966  *Spline functions, interpolation and numerical quadrature.* From "Mathematical Methods for Digital Computers", Vol. 2, edited by A. Ralston and H. Wilf, New York: John Wiley.

HAMMER, P. C.
1964  *Topologies of approximation.* SIAM J. Num. Anal., **1**, pp. 69–75.

HANDBOOK OF MATHEMATICAL FUNCTIONS
1964  N.B.S. Applied Math. Ser., **55**, U.S. Gov't Printing Office.

HART, J. F., *et al.*
1968  *Computer Approximations.* New York: John Wiley.

*See* FRASER, W.

HASTINGS, C. B.
1955  *Approximations for Digital Computers.* Princeton University Press.

HAVINSON, S. YA.
1958  *On uniqueness of functions of best approximation in the metric of the space $L^1$.* Izv. Akad. Nauk SSSR, **22**, pp. 243–270.

HAYES, J. G. *See* CLENSHAW, C. W.

HERESHOFF, J. B. *See* GOLDSTEIN, A. A.

HILDEBRAND, F. B.
  1956 *Introduction to Numerical Analysis.* Chapters 7 and 9. New York: McGraw-Hill.

HILLSTROM, K. E. *See* CODY, W. T.

HITOTUMATU, S.
  1964 *Some considerations on the best-fit polynomial approximations, I.* Comment. Math. Univ. St. Pauli, **12**, pp. 59–73.
  1966 *Some considerations on the best-fit polynomial approximations, II.* Comment. Math. Univ. St. Pauli, **14**, pp. 71–83.

HOBBY, C. R. and RICE, J. R.
  1965 *A moment problem in $L_1$ approximation.* Proc. Amer. Math. Soc., **16**, pp. 665–670.
  1967 *Approximation from a curve of functions.* Arch. Rat. Mech. Anal., **24**, pp. 91–106.

HOLLADAY, J. C.
  1957 *Smoothest curve approximation.* MTAC, **11**, pp. 233–243.

HORNECKER, G.
  1960 *Méthodes pratiques pour la détermination approchée de la meilleure approximation polynomial ou rationelle.* Chiffres, **3**, pp. 143–228.

JACKSON, D.
  1921 *On functions of closest approximation.* Trans. Amer. Math. Soc., **22**, pp. 117–128.
  1921a *Note on a class of polynomials of approximation.* Trans. Amer. Math. Soc., **22**, pp. 320–326.

JAMES, R. C.
  1957 *Reflexivity and the supremum of linear functionals.* Ann. Math., **66**, pp. 159–169.

JESSEN, B.
  1940 *To satninger om konvekse Punktmangder.* Mat. Tidsskrift B, pp. 66–70.

JOHNSON, R. S.
  1960 *On monosplines of least deviation.* Trans. Amer. Math. Soc., **96**, pp. 458–477.

JURKAT, W. B. and LORENTZ, G. G.
  1961 *Uniform approximations by polynomials with positive coefficients.* Duke Math. J., **28**, pp. 463–474.

KARLIN, S.
  1963 *Representation theorems for positive functions.* J. Math. Mech., **12**, pp. 599–618.
  1968 *Total Positivity.* Stanford University Press.

KARLIN, S. and SCHUMAKER, L.
  1966 *The fundamental theorem of algebra for Tchebycheffian splines.* J. d'Anal. Math., **20**, pp. 233–270.

KARLIN, S. and STUDDEN, W. J.
1966 *Tchebycheff Systems with Applications in Analysis and Statistics.* New York: Interscience.

KARLIN, S. and ZIEGLER, Z.
1966 *Chebyshevian spline functions.* SIAM J. Num. Anal., **3**, pp. 514–534.

KLEE, V. L.
1953 *Convex bodies and periodic homeomorphisms in Hilbert space.* Trans. Amer. Math. Soc., **74**, pp. 10–43.
1961 *Convexity of Chebyshev sets.* Math. Ann., **142**, pp. 292–304.

KOROVKIN, P. P.
1959 *Linear Operators and Approximation Theory.* English translation 1960. Delhi: Hindustan Pub. Corp.

KREIN, M. G.
1938 *The L-problem in an abstract linear normed space.* From "Some questions in the theory of moments", Achieser, N. I. and Krein, M. G., Kharkov, pp. 175–204.
1951 *The ideas of P. L. Chebyshev and A. A. Markov in the theory of limiting values of integrals and their further development.* Usp. Math. Nauk SSSR, **6**, pp. 3–120. Amer. Math. Soc. Translations (II) **12**, pp. 1–122.
*See* ACHIESER, N. I.

KRIPKE, B. R. and RIVLIN, T. J.
1965 *Approximation in the metric $L^1$ $(x, \mu)$.* Trans. Amer. Math. Soc., **119**, pp. 101–122.

KUHN, H.
1964 *Ein elementarer Beweis des Weierstrasschen Approximationssatzes.* Arch. Math., **15**, pp. 316–317.

LAASONEN, P.
1949 *Einige Sätze über Tschebyscheffsche Funktionensysteme.* Ann. Acad. Scient. Fennicae, **52**, pp. 3–24.

LANCZOS, C.
1956 *Applied Analysis.* New Jersey: Prentice Hall.
1964 *Evaluation of noisy data.* SIAM J. Num. Anal., **1**, pp. 76–85.

LANGER, R. E.
1959 *On Numerical Approximation.* University of Wisconsin Press.

LASTMAN, G. *See* FOX, P.

LAWSON, C. L.
1961 *Contributions to the Theory of Linear Least Maximum Approximations.* Thesis, UCLA.
1964 *Characteristic properties of the segmented rational minmax approximation problem.* Numer. Math., **6**, pp. 293–301.

LEBEDEN, L. P.
1962 *An efficient method of constructing best approximation procedures.* Dokl. Akad. Nauk SSSR, **142**, pp. 530–533.

LEFCHETZ, S.
1949   *Introduction to Topology.* Princeton, N.J.: Princeton Univ. Press.

LEVINE, N. *See* GOLDSTEIN, A. A.

LOEB, H. L.
1960   *Algorithms for Chebycheff approximation using the ratio of linear forms.* J. Soc. Indust. Appl. Math., **8**, pp. 458–465.
1965   *Contributions to Rational Approximation.* Thesis, UCLA.
*See* CHENEY, E. W.

LORENTZ, G. G.
1962   *Metric entropy, widths, and superpositions of functions.* Amer. Math. Monthly, **69**, pp. 469–485.
1965   *Russian literature on approximation in 1958–1964.* From "Approximation of Functions", edited by H. L. Garabedian, Elsevier, Amsterdam, pp. 191–215.
1966   *Approximation of Functions.* New York: Holt, Rinehart, and Winston.
*See* JURKAT, W. B.

LUKE, Y. L.
1958   *The Padé table and the τ-method.* J. Math. Phys., **37**, pp. 110–127.

LYNCH, R. E. *See* DE BOOR, C.

LYSTERNIK, L. A. *et al.*
1965   *Handbook for Computing Elementary Functions.* Moscow, 1963. English translation: Pergamon, London, 1965.

MACKENSIE, R. E. *See* AUSLANDER, L.

MAEHLY, H. J.
1960   *Methods for fitting rational approximations I: Telescoping procedures for continued fractions.* J. Assoc. Comp. Mach., **7**, pp. 150–162.
1962   *Numerical solution of a certain transcendental equation involving exponentials.* J. Soc. Ind. Appl. Math., **10**, pp. 30–39.
1963   *Methods for fitting rational approximations II and III:* J. Assoc. Comp. Mach., **10**, pp. 257–277.

MAEHLY, H. J. and WITZGALL, CH.
1960   *Tschebyscheff-Approximationen in kleinen Intervallen II: Stetigkeitssatze fur gebrochen rationale approximationen.* Numer. Math., **2**, pp. 293–307.

MAIRHUBER, J. C.
1956   *On Haar's theorem concerning Chebychev approximation problems having unique solutions.* Proc. Amer. Math. Soc., **7**, pp. 609–615.

MALINI, V. *See* SANKAR, R.

MARQUARDT, D. W.
1963   *An algorithm for least squares estimation of nonlinear parameters.* J. Soc. Indust. Appl. Math., **11**, pp. 431–441.

MEINARDUS, G.
1962 *Über Tschebyscheffsche Approximation.* Arch. Rat. Mech. Anal., **9**, pp. 329–351.
1963 *Über den Haarschen Eindeutigkeitssatze aus der Theorie der linearen Approximationen.* Arch. Math., **14**, pp. 47–54.
1964 *Approximation von Funktionen und ihre numerische Behandlung.* Berlin: Springer-Verlag.

MEINARDUS, G. and SCHWEDT, D.
*Nicht-lineare Approximationen.* Arch. Rat. Mech. Anal., **17**, pp. 297–326.

MEINARDUS, G. and STRAUER, H. D.
1963 *Über Tschebyscheffsche Approximationen der Losungen linear Differential- und Integralgleichungen.* Arch. Rat. Mech. Anal., **14**, pp. 184–195.

MEIR, A. and SHARMA, A.
1966 *Degree of approximation of spline interpolation.* J. Math. Mech., **15**, pp. 759–767.

MEYERS, L. F. and SARD, A.
1950 *Best interpolation formulas.* J. Math. Physics, **29**, pp. 198–206.

MILNOR, J. W.
1963 *Morse Theory.* Princeton, N.J.: Princeton Univ. Press.

MOTZKIN, T. S.
1935 *Sur quelques propriétés caractéristiques des ensembles convexes.* Atti R. Acad. Lincei, Red. VI, **21**, pp. 562–567.
1949 *Approximation by curves of a unisolvent family.* Bull. Amer. Math. Soc., **55**, pp. 789–793.
1966 *Approximation in the sense of a deviator integral.* SIAM J. Numer. Anal., **3**, pp. 276–286.

MOTZKIN, T. S., STRAUSS, E. G. and VALENTINE, F. A.
1953 *The number of farthest points.* Pac. J. Math., **3**, pp. 221–232.

MOTZKIN, T. S. and WALSH, J. L.
1955 *Least pth power polynomials on a real finite point set.* Trans. Amer. Math. Soc., **78**, pp. 67–81.
1957 *Underpolynomials and infrapolynomials.* Illinois J. Math., **1**, pp. 406–426.
1959 *Polynomials of best approximation on an interval.* Proc. Nat. Acad. Sci., **45**, pp. 1523–1528.
1959a *Polynomials of best approximation on a real finite point set I.* Trans. Amer. Math. Soc., **91**, pp. 231–245.
1960 *Best approximations within a linear family on an interval.* Proc. Nat. Acad. Sci., **46**, pp. 1225–1233.

MOURSUND, D. G.
1964 *Chebyshev approximation for a function and its derivative.* Math. Comp., **18**, pp. 382–389.

MURNAGHAN, F. D. and WRENCH, J. W.
  1959   *The determination of the Chebyshev approximating polynomial for a differentiable function.* MTAC, **13**, pp. 185–193.

NEWMAN, D. J.
  1964   *Rational approximation to* $|x|$. Mich. Math. J., **11**, pp. 11–14.

NEWMAN, D. J. and SHAPIRO, H. S.
  1963   *Some theorems on Chebychev approximation.* Duke Math. J., **30**, pp. 673–682.
  1964   *Jackson's theorem in higher dimensions.* ISNM, **5**, Birkhauser Verlag, Basel, pp. 208–219.
  1964a   *Approximation by generalized rational functions.* ISNM, **5**, Birkhauser Verlag, Basel, pp. 245–251.

NILSON, E. N.   *See* WALSH, J. L.   *See* AHLBERG, J. H.

NOVODWORSKII, E. N. and PINSKER, I. SH.
  1951   *On a process of equalization of maxima.* Usp. Mat. Nauk, **6**, pp. 174–181.

OBERWOLFACH CONFERENCE "ON APPROXIMATION THEORY", 1963
  1964   Proceedings in ISNM, volume 5. Basel: Birkhauser Verlag.

PASZKOWSKI, S.
  1962   *The theory of uniform approximation I: Non-asymptotic theoretical problems.* Rozprawy Mat., Warsaw, **26**.

PAUC, C.
  1939   *Sur la relation entre un point et une de ses projections sur un ensemble.* Rev. Sci. (Rev. Rose Illustr.), **77**, pp. 657–658.

PEANO, G.
  1913   *Resto nelle formule di quadratura espresso con un integrale definito.* Rend. Accad. Lincei, 5a, **22**, pp. 562–569. Also in Opere Scelte I, Roma (1957), pp. 410–418.
  1914   *Residuo in formulas de quadratura.* In Opere Scelte I, Roma (1957), pp. 419–425.

PHELPS, R. R.
  1957   *Convex sets and nearest points.* Proc. Amer. Math. Soc., **8**, pp. 790–797.
  1958   *Convex sets and nearest points II.* Proc. Amer. Math. Soc., **9**, pp. 867–873.
  1960   *Uniqueness of Hahn–Banach extensions and unique best approximation.* Trans. Amer. Math. Soc., **95**, 238–255.

PINSKER, I. SH.   *See* NOVODWORSKII, E. N.

POLJAK, R. A.   *See* ZUHOVICKII, S. I.

POLYA, G.
  1913   *Sur un algorithm toujours convergent pour obtenir les polynomes de meilleure approximation de Tchebychef pour une fonction continue quelconque.* C. R. Acad. Sci. Paris, **157**, pp. 840–843.

POLYA, G. and SZEGÖ, G.
  1925   *Aufgaben und Lehrsätze aus der Analysis.* Springer, Berlin.

POUSSIN, CH. DE LA VALLÉE

1911   *Sur les polynomes d'approximation à une variable complexe.* Bull. Acad. Roy, Belg. Cl. Sci., pp. 199–211.

1911a  *Sur la méthode de l'approximation minimum.* Ann. Soc. Sci. Bruxelles, ser. 1, **35**, pp. 1–16.

1919   *Leçons sur l'approximation des fonctions d'une variable réele.* Paris: Gauthier-Villars.

POWELL, M. J. D. *See* CURTIS, A. R.

PRASAD, B.

1964   *An Index of Approximations of Functions.* UCSD-64-02, Computer Center, San Diego: University of California.

PRIMAK, M. E. *See* ZUHOVICKII, S. I.

PTAK, V.

1958   *On approximation of continuous functions in the metric* $\int |x(t)| dt$. Czechoslovak Math. J., **8**, pp. 267–273.

QUADE, W. *See* COLLATZ, L.

RABINOWITZ, P. *See* DAVIS, P. J.

RALSTON, A.

1963   *On economization of rational functions.* J. Assoc. Comp. Mach., **10**, pp. 278–283.

1965   *Rational Chebyshev approximation by Remes algorithms.* Numer. Math., **7**, pp. 322–330.

REAM, N.

1959   *Approximation errors in diode function-generators.* J. Electronics Control, **7**, pp. 83–96.

1961   *Note on "Approximation of curves by line segments".* Math. Comp., **15**, pp. 418–419.

REMES, E.

1934   *Sur le calcul effectif des polynomes d'approximation de Tchebichef.* C. R. Acad. Sci. Paris, **199**, pp. 337–340.

1957   *General computational methods of Chebyshev approximation.* Izdat. Akad. Nauk Ukrainsk, SSR, Kiev. English translation: Off. Tech. Ser., Dept. Commerce, AEC-tr-4491, Books 1 and 2.

RICE, J. R.

1960   *The characterization of best nonlinear Tchebycheff approximations.* Trans. Amer. Math. Soc., **96**, pp. 322–340.

1960a  *Chebyshev approximation by* $ab^x + c$. J. Soc. Indust. Appl. Math., **8**, pp. 691–702.

1961   *Tchebycheff approximation by functions unisolvent of variable degree.* Trans. Amer. Math. Soc., **99**, pp. 298–302.

1961a  *Best approximations and interpolating functions.* Trans. Amer. Math. Soc., **101**, pp. 477–498.

1961b  *Algorithms for Chebyshev approximation by* $ax^x + c$. J. Soc. Indust. Appl. Math., **9**, pp. 571–583.

1962    *Chebyshev approximation by exponentials.* J. Soc. Indust. Appl. Math., **10**, pp. 149–161.

1962a   *Tchebycheff approximation in a compact metric space.* Bull Amer. Math., Soc., **68**, pp. 405–410.

1963    *Tchebycheff approximation in several variables.* Trans. Amer. Math. Soc., **109**, pp. 444–466.

1963a   *Approximation with convex constraints.* SIAM J. Appl. Math., **11**, pp. 15–32.

1964    *The Approximation of Functions: Vol. I.* Reading, Mass: Addison Wesley.

1964a   *On the computation of $L_1$ approximations by exponentials, rationals, and other functions.* Math. Comp., **18**, pp. 390–396.

1964b   *On the $L_\infty$ Walsh arrays for $\Gamma(x)$ and $Erfc(x)$.* Math. Comp., **18**, pp. 617–626.

1964c   *On the existence and characterization of best nonlinear Tchebycheff approximations.* Trans. Amer. Math. Soc., **110**, pp. 88–97.

1965    *Nonlinear approximation.* From "Approximation of functions", edited by H. L. Garabedian, Elsevier, Amsterdam, pp. 111–133.

1966    *Experiments on Gram-Schmidt orthogonalization.* Math. Comp., **20**, pp. 325–328.

1967    *Characterization of Chebyshev approximations by splines.* SIAM J. Num. Anal., **4**, pp. 557–565.

1967a   *Nonlinear approximation II: Curvature in Minkowski geometry and local uniqueness.* Trans. Amer. Math. Soc., **128**, pp. 437–459.

*See* DE BOOR, C.

*See* HOBBY, C. R.

RICE, J. R. and USOW, K. H.

1968    *Lawson's algorithm and extensions.* Math. Comp., **22**, pp. 118–127.

RICE, J. R. and WHITE, J. S.

1964    *Norms for smoothing and estimation.* SIAM Review, **6**, pp. 243–256.

RIVLIN, T. J.

1964    *A property of the ratio of trigonometric polynomials.* SIAM J. Numer. Anal., **1**, pp. 131–132.

*See* KRIPKE, B. R.

RIVLIN, T. J. and SHAPIRO, H. S.

1960    *Some uniqueness problems in approximation theory.* Comm. Pure Appl. Math., **13**, pp. 35–47.

1961    *A unified approach to certain problems of approximation and minimization.* SIAM J. Appl. Math., **9**, pp. 670–699.

ROSEN, J. B.

1960    *The gradient projection method for nonlinear programming: Linear constraints.* SIAM J. Appl. Math., **8**, pp. 181–217.

1961    *The gradient projection method for nonlinear programming: Nonlinear constraints.* SIAM J. Appl. Math., **9**, pp. 514–532.

RUDIN, B. D.
1965   *Convex Polynomial Approximation.* Thesis, Stanford.

SALZER, H. E.
1959   *Best approximation of mixed type.* SIAM J. Appl. Math., 7, pp. 345–360.

SANKAR, R. and MALINI, V.
1963   *A note on the relative merits of Padé and Maehly's diagonal convergents.*
Math. Comp., 17, pp. 414–418.

SARD, A.
1949   *Best approximate integration formulas; best approximation formulas.*
Amer. J. Math., 71, pp. 352–357.
1963   *Linear Approximation.* Math. Surveys, 9, Amer. Math. Soc.
*See* MEYERS, L. F.

SCHOENBERG, I. J.
1946   *Contributions to the problem of approximation of equidistant data by
analytic functions.* Quart. Appl. Math., 4, Part A pp. 45–99, Part B
pp. 112–141.
1958   *Spline functions, convex curves and mechanical quadrature.* Bull. Amer.
Math. Soc., 64, pp. 352–357.
1960   *On the question of unicity in the theory of best approximations.* Ann.
New York Acad. Sci., 86, pp. 682–691.
1964   *On interpolation by spline functions and its minimal properties.* ISNM
5, Birkhauser Verlag, Basel, pp. 109–129.
1964a  *On trigonometric spline interpolation.* J. Math. Mech., 13, pp. 795–826.
1964b  *Spline interpolation and best quadrature formulas.* Bull. Amer. Math.
Soc., 70, pp. 143–148.
1964c  *Spline functions and the problem of graduation.* Proc. Nat. Acad. Sci.
USA, 52, pp. 947–950.
1964d  *Spline interpolation and the higher derivatives.* Proc. Nat. Acad.
Sci. USA, 51, pp. 24–28.
1964e  *On best approximation of linear operators.* Kon. Nederl. Akad. Wet. A.,
67, pp. 155–163.
1965   *On monosplines of least deviation and best quadrature formulae.* SIAM
J. Num. Anal., 2, pp. 144–170.
1966   *On monosplines of least square deviation and best quadrature formulae.*
II, SIAM J. Numer. Anal., 3, pp. 321–328.

SCHOENBERG, I. J. and WHITNEY, ANNE
1953   *On Polya frequency functions III: The positivity of translation deter-
minants with an application to the interpolation problem by spline curves.*
Trans. Amer. Math. Soc., 74, pp. 246–259.
SCHUMAKER, L. *See* KARLIN, S.

SCHWEDT, D. *See* MEINARDUS, G.

SECREST, D.
1965   *Error bounds for interpolation and differentiation by the use of spline
functions.* SIAM J. Numer. Anal., 2, pp. 440–447.

SHANKS, D.

    1955   *Nonlinear transformations of divergent and slowly convergent sequences.*
           J. Math. Phys., **35**, pp. 1–42.

SHAPIRO, H. S. *See* NEWMAN, D. J. *See* RIVLIN, T. J.

SHARMA, A. *See* MEIR, A.

SINGER, I.

    1956   *Caractérization des éléments de meilleure approximation dan un éspace*
           *de Banach quelconque.* Acta Sci. Math. Szeged, **17**, pp. 181–189.

    1957   *On uniqueness of the element of best approximation in arbitrary Banach*
           *spaces.* Acad. Rom. Inst. Mat., **8**, pp. 235–244.

    1960   *On best approximation of continuous functions.* Math. Ann., **140**, pp.
           165–168.

    1964   *Some remarks on approximative compactness.* R. Roumaine Math.
           Pures Appl., **9**, pp. 167–177.

SLOSS, J. M.

    1965   *Chebyshev approximation to zero.* Pac. J. Math., **15**, pp. 305–313.

SOUTHARD, T. H. *See* CHENEY, E. W.

SPIELBERG, K.

    1961   *Efficient continued fraction approximations to elementary functions.*
           Math. Comp., **15**, pp. 409–417.

SPRANG, H. A.

    1962   *A review of minimization techniques for nonlinear functions.* SIAM
           J. Appl. Math., **10**, pp. 343–365.

STANCU, D. D.

    1964   *The remainder of certain linear approximation formulas in two variables.*
           SIAM J. Numer. Anal., **1**, pp. 137–163.

STARKWEATHER, W. *See* THEILHEIMER, F.

STECKIN, S. B. *See* EFIMOV, N. V.

STEEN, L. A.

    1965   *Uniform Approximation by Rational Functions.* Thesis, M.I.T.

STESIN, I. M.

    1957   *Conversion of orthogonal expansions into a sequence of convergents.*
           Vyz. Mat., **1**, pp. 116–119.

STIEFEL, E. L.

    1959   *Über diskrete und lineare Tchebycheff-Approximationen.* Numer. Math.,
           **1**, pp. 1–28.

    1960   *Note on Jordan elimination, linear programming and Tchebycheff approxi-*
           *mation.* Numer. Math., **2**, pp. 1–17.

    1964   *Methods—old and new—for solving the Tchebycheff approximation*
           *problem.* SIAM J. Num. Anal., **1**, pp. 164–176.

    1965   *Phase methods for polynomial approximation.* From "Approximation of
           Functions", edited by H. L. Garabedian, Elsevier, Amsterdam, pp.
           68–82.

STOER, J.
1961  *Über zwei Algorithmen zur Interpolation mit rationalen Funktionen.*
Numer. Math., **3**, pp. 285–304.
1964  *A direct method for Chebyshev approximation by rational functions.*
J. Assoc. Comp. Mach., **11**, pp. 59–69.
*See* CODY, W. T.

STONE, H.
1961  *Approximation of curves by line segments.* Math. Comp., **15**, pp. 40–47.

STRAUER, H. D.  *See* MEINARDUS, G.

STRAUSS, E. G.  *See* MOTZKIN, T. S.

STUDDEN, W. J.  *See* KARLIN, S.

SZEGÖ, G.  *See* POLYA, G.

THACHER, H. C.
1965  *Independent variable transformations in approximation.* Proc. IFIP 65
Congress.
*See* CODY, W. J.

THEILHEIMER, F. and STARKWEATHER, W.
1961  *The fairing of ship lines on a high-speed computer.* Math. Comp., **13**,
pp. 338–355.

TIMAN, A. F.
1963  *The Theory of the Approximation of Functions of a Real Variable.*
New York: Macmillan.

TONELLI, M.
1908  *I polinomi d'approsimazione di Tchebychev.* Ann. Mat., Ser. III, **15**,
pp. 47–119.

TORNHEIM, L.
1950  *On n-parameter families of functions and associated convex functions.*
Trans. Amer. Math. Soc., **69**, pp. 457–467.

USOW, K. H.
1968  *Computational Aspects of Approximation in the $L_1$ Metric.* SIAM J.
Num. Anal., **4**, pp. 70–88
*See* RICE, J. R.

VALENTINE, F. A.
1964  *Convex sets.* New York: McGraw-Hill.
*See* MOTZKIN, T. S.

VLASOV, L. P.
1961  *Chebyshev sets in Banach spaces.* Dokl. Akad. Nauk SSSR, **141**, pp.
19–20.
VON NEUMAN, J.  *See* FEKETE, M.

WALSH, J. L.
1931  *The existence of rational functions of best approximation.* Trans. Amer.
Math. Soc., **33**, pp. 668–689.

1935   *Interpolation and Approximation.* Amer. Math. Soc. Colloquium
       Pub., **20**.
1964   *The convergence of sequences of rational functions of best approximation.*
       Math. Ann., **153**, pp. 252–264.
1965   *The convergence of sequences of rational functions of best approximation
       with some free poles.* From "Approximation of functions", edited by
       H. L. Garabedian, Elsevier, Amsterdam, pp. 1–16.
1965a  *The convergence of sequences of rational functions of best approximation,
       II.* Trans. Amer. Math. Soc., **116**, pp. 227–237.

*See* AHLBERG, J. H.

*See* FEKETE, M.

*See* MOTZKIN, T. S.

WALSH, J. L., AHLBERG, J. H. and NILSON, E. N.
1962   *Best approximation properties of the spline fit.* J. Math. Mech., **11**,
       pp. 225–234.

WEINBERGER, H. F.
1961   *Optimal approximation for functions prescribed at equally spaced points.*
       J. Res. Nat. Bur. Stand., **65B**, pp. 99–104.

*See* GOLOMB, M.

WERNER, H.
1962   *Tschebyscheff-Approximation im Bereich der rationalen Funktionen
       bei Vorliegen einer guten Ausgangsnaherung.* Arch. Rat. Mech. Anal.,
       **10**, pp. 205–219.
1962a  *Ein Satz über diskrete Tschebyscheff-Approximation bei gebrochen
       linearen Funktionen.* Numer. Math., **4**, pp. 154–157.
1962b  *Die konstruktive Ermittlung der Tschebyscheff-Approximierenden im
       Bereich der rationalen Funktionen.* Arch. Rat. Mech. Anal., **11**, pp.
       368–384.
1963   *Rationale Tschebyscheff-Approximation, Eigenwert-theorie und Dif-
       ferenzenrechnung.* Arch. Rat. Mech. Anal., **13**, pp. 330–347.
1964   *On the local behavior of the rational Tschebyscheff operator.* Bull. Amer.
       Math. Soc., **70**, pp. 554–555.
1964a  *On the rational Tschebyscheff operator.* Math. Zeit., **86**, pp. 317–326.

WETTERLING, W.
1963   *Ein Interpolationsverfahren zur Losung der lineare Gleichungssysteme,
       die bei der rationalen Tschebyscheff-Approximation auftreten.* Arch.
       Rat. Mech. Anal., **12**, pp. 403–408.

WHITE, J. S. *See* RICE, J. R.

WHITNEY, ANNE. *See* SCHOENBERG, I. J.

WITZGALL, CH. *See* MAEHLY, H.

WOLFE, P.
1963   *A technique for resolving degeneracy in linear programming.* SIAM J.
       Appl. Math., **11**, pp. 205–211.

WRENCH, J. W. *See* MURNAGHAN, F. D.

WULBERT, D. E.
1966 *Continuity of Metric Projections.* Thesis, Univ. of Texas.

WYNN, P.
1960 *The rational approximation of functions which are formally defined by a power series expansion.* Math. Comp., **14**, pp. 147–186.
1960a *Über einen Interpolationsalgorithmus und gewisse andere Formeln, die in der Theorie der Interpolation durch rationale Funktionen bestehen.* Numer. Math., **2**, pp. 151–182.
1964 *On some recent developments in the theory and application of continued fractions.* SIAM J. Num. Anal., **1**, pp. 177–197.

YOUNG, A. *See* BARRONDALE, I.

YOUNG, J. W.
1907 *General theory of approximation by functions involving a given number of arbitrary parameters.* Trans. Amer. Math. Soc., **8**, pp. 331–344.

ZIEGLER, Z. *See* KARLIN, S.

ZUHOVICKII, S. I.
1951 *An algorithm for the solution of the Tchebychef approximation problem in the case of a finite system of incompatible linear equations.* Dokl. Akad. Nauk SSSR, **79**, pp. 561–564.
1961 *On a new numerical scheme of the algorithm for the Chebyshev approximation of an incompatible system of linear equations and a system of linear inequalities.* Dokl. Akad. Nauk SSSR, **139**, pp. 534–537.

ZUHOVICKII, S. I., POLJACK, R. A., and PRIMAK, M. E.
1963 *An algorithm for solving the convex Chebysheff approximation problem.* Dokl. Akad. Nauk SSSR, **151**, pp. 27–30.

# Index